A Level Geography
Independent Investigation
Andy Owen

iNSIGHT &
PERSPECTIVE

Contents

How to use this book

Successfully completing an Independent Investigation for your Geography A level is a huge task. It is complex too – requiring you to demonstrate lots of different skills and abilities. You also need to make tricky decisions at key points in the process. Don't worry – this book is here to help by providing you with a practical step-by-step route through your investigation as well as giving you support with your four days of A level fieldwork. Use these pages to help you get the most out of each of the key features of the book.

Structure of the book

The book takes you through the steps you need to take in order to complete a successful Independent Investigation. Each step is broken down into Action Points so, at any given moment, you know exactly what you should be doing next.

This book will help you with one of the key challenges of the Independent Investigation – making the right choices when you are faced with difficult decisions about your research.

▶ Exploring a focus for your investigation (Step 1).
▶ Choosing the most suitable data collection methods (Step 3).
▶ Selecting the most appropriate chart, graph, or map to draw (Step 11).
▶ Selecting suitable methods of analysis for your data (Step 12).

On each occasion, you will be able to read about a range of methods or approaches so you can select the ones that are most appropriate for your investigation.

Key features

There are key features in the book to help you make sense of the complex task that is an independent Investigation. Each one is signposted as shown below.

Independent or collaborative working icons

You may be surprised to know that not all the steps in the Independent Investigation have to be undertaken completely on your own and without help. You are allowed to work collaboratively with other students at key steps in the investigation. At other times, you must work independently of other students although you can use this book as much as you like at any time during the investigation. The book uses these icons to indicate when you can work with others and when you must work on your own.

 This icon means that, at this step of the investigation, you must work independently.

 This icon means you may work on your own, with another student, or as part of a small team.

Action points

Each of the Steps is divided into a series of Action Points. You need to work your way methodically through these points if you want to access top marks for your Independent Investigation.

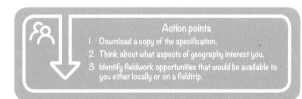

Action points
1 Download a copy of the specification.
2 Think about what aspects of geography interest you.
3 Identify fieldwork opportunities that would be available to you either locally or on a fieldtrip.

Action Point 1
Download a copy of the specification

Web links

Useful weblinks are shown like this. Each link was correct at the time the book went to print. However, websites constantly change so if you find the link is broken then google the website, for example, for this link google textfixer random number generator.

Weblink
http://www.textfixer.com/numbers/random-number-generator.php

Glossary

Key terms are highlighted in the main text in **bold green type** throughout the book. The definitions appear in the margin close by.

Suitable for

In Step 11 Data Presentation you will make decisions about the presentation techniques (graphs, charts, maps) that are appropriate for the data you have collected. This feature reminds you when to use a specific graph, diagram, or chart and what it is suitable for.

Evaluation

Evaluation is an important part of your investigation and plays a key role in the mark scheme and therefore how your investigation will be awarded marks.

You will probably write an evaluation at the very end of the process – which may be several weeks after you started. Therefore, we have used this icon throughout the book to remind you that evaluation is important. Whenever you see this icon make some notes about what is going well with your fieldwork and what has worked out differently from the way you anticipated. You should refer back to these icons and your notes when you get to Step 13 towards the end of your investigation.

Moderator advice

These tips and advice are the kinds of comment that often appear in reports written by moderators. These are experienced geographers who check that Independent Investigations have been marked accurately.

You must have a sampling strategy. You should be able to describe and justify the sampling strategy in your report.

Questions and Answers

You've read the chapter but you're still not 100% sure about something. Questions and Answers have been used to clarify some of the important points made in each chapter.

QUESTION Do I have to do a pilot survey or a control survey?

ANSWER No, these are useful strategies for some kinds of investigations but they are not appropriate for all investigations. The important thing is to design a method of data collection that is appropriate for the needs of *your* investigation. This will include deciding when and where to collect the data and deciding which sampling strategy to use. It is important to be able to **justify** each of these decisions.

Review points

Each of the Steps ends with review points. Tick these off to check that you have covered everything that needs to be done.

Review Points of Style

Tick off each point on the following list before you move on to the next chapter.
I have thought about:
- areas of geography that interest me ☐
- aspects of geography that I am good at ☐
- whether I am confident in using numbers ☐

The Independent Investigation

You are about to begin a rather complex process. To avoid getting bogged down this introduction will help you keep your eye on the big picture. It introduces a few key terms and ensures you understand the basics before you get started.

What do we mean by investigation?

Investigation (or enquiry) means being inquisitive. It involves posing questions, then collecting and analysing evidence to find the answer to your questions. Here are the key elements that every A level Geography Independent Investigation should contain.

Literature research	A review of some of the geographical articles that have been published on the topic of your investigation.
Aim	The overarching purpose of your investigation – what it is you are hoping to achieve or prove.
Research questions*	A small number (probably three or four) enquiry questions that can be used to focus your mind on what answers need to be found.
Fieldwork	The process of collecting evidence from the real-world.
Primary data	Real-world evidence that has been collected first-hand by you.
Presentation	The use of charts, graphs, and maps to represent the evidence.
Analysis	The process of making sense of the evidence to tell a story.
Conclusions	Pulling the analysis together to meet the requirements of the aim.
Evaluation	The process of critical reflection in which you identify strengths and weaknesses in your investigation.

> * It is possible to organise your investigation around hypotheses instead of research questions. These are statements that you attempt to prove or disprove through your research.

What do we mean by data?

In order to conduct your independent investigation you will need to collect data. This data will then be processed and used as evidence to support the conclusions of your enquiry. **Data** comes in many forms and your own investigation may rely on data collected from a number of different sources.

Qualitative data are words and pictures. They include spoken evidence and text in the form of interviews, questionnaires, audio recordings, or blogs. Qualitative data also includes images such as field sketches, photographs, videos, or artwork.

> **Data**
>
> Data means evidence. The word data is a noun which can be singular or plural – like the word sheep.

Quantitative data are numerical. Quantitative data can be divided into three main types.

▶ **Categorical data that can be counted and measured** on the *nominal scale*. The value is always a whole number, such as the number of pedestrians in a street.

▶ **Categorical data that can be placed in rank order** and measured on the *ordinal scale*. In an ordinal scale, the order of the values is significant but the difference between the points on the scale cannot be given a precise meaning. For example, in a perception study, very happy, happy, unhappy, and very unhappy, would be an ordinal scale with four values.

▶ **Continuous scale data** that can be measured on the *ratio scale* or *interval scale*. Because the data is continuous, such as depth of soil (in centimetres) or temperature (in Celsius), the value can be recorded to a decimal point.

Your independent investigation must include the collection and processing of **primary** data. This is data that you have captured and recorded by counting, measuring, or observing something in the field. It is primary because you are the first person to capture it.

There is another type of data that is often useful when conducting an independent investigation and that is **secondary** data. This is data that has already been collected and published by someone else in newspapers, journals, books, or on websites. Just like primary data, secondary data can be quantitative or qualitative. It is not essential to use secondary data in your Independent Investigation.

Assessment

In A level Geography, fieldwork is assessed through an Independent Investigation. You will need to produce a written report of between 3,000 and 4,000 words on a fieldwork investigation of your own choice and design. The report will be marked by your teacher and moderated by the exam board – a type of assessment known as non-examination assessment (**NEA**). The Independent Investigation is worth 20% of the overall mark of your A level.

Step by step

The independent investigation is worth 20% of the marks for your A level geography so it's a big commitment. This book breaks the process down into a series of manageable Steps – shown in the flow diagram Figure 2. Each of the Steps is covered in a separate chapter and broken down into Action Points.

> The 3,000-4,000 word count is a guide rather than a limit. Try to stick to it. Longer reports are often descriptive and lack analysis and can be repetitive.

The process of collecting data during fieldwork is likely to take place over a very short period of time – a few days at most. By comparison, the entire investigation will take a considerable amount of time. Some students compress all of the work into a period of just two or three weeks but, for most students, an investigation needs to be carefully managed over a much longer period of time – perhaps three or four months. This work will be carrying on while you are doing other things, including studying for your other A levels, so you need to have a plan.

Study the roadmap in Figure 2. In addition to setting milestones at Step 7 and Step 14 you might want to set milestones after Step 2 and Step 11. There is no official guidance on how much time to spend on an investigation but between 25 and 40 hours would be a realistic expectation.

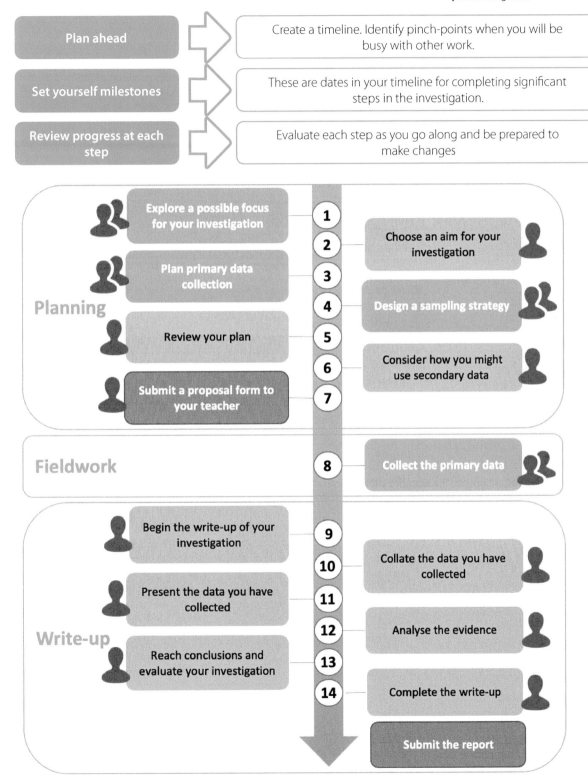

Figure 1 Have an overall plan for your investigation.

Plan ahead → Create a timeline. Identify pinch-points when you will be busy with other work.

Set yourself milestones → These are dates in your timeline for completing significant steps in the investigation.

Review progress at each step → Evaluate each step as you go along and be prepared to make changes

Planning

1. Explore a possible focus for your investigation
2. Choose an aim for your investigation
3. Plan primary data collection
4. Design a sampling strategy
5. Review your plan
6. Consider how you might use secondary data
7. Submit a proposal form to your teacher

Fieldwork

8. Collect the primary data

Write-up

9. Begin the write-up of your investigation
10. Collate the data you have collected
11. Present the data you have collected
12. Analyse the evidence
13. Reach conclusions and evaluate your investigation
14. Complete the write-up

Submit the report

Figure 2 Independent investigation roadmap.

Exploring a focus

Action points

1 Download a copy of the specification.

2 Think about what aspects of geography interest you.

3 Identify fieldwork opportunities that would be available to you either locally or on a fieldtrip.

4 Reflect on your experience of A level fieldwork.

This chapter will help you take the first step in your investigation. You need to:

▷ complete action points 1-4 described in Part 1.1.

▷ read Part 1.2 which describes different styles of investigation. You may want to adopt one of these approaches for your own investigation.

1.1 Getting started

Choosing an investigation that is right for you is a really important decision. However, how do you know if you are choosing a suitable investigation when you have so much choice? This is a decision that a lot of students find very difficult. Don't worry. You don't need to choose just yet. This step is about narrowing down your options rather than making a final decision.

Action Point 1

Download a copy of the specification which will include the mark scheme for the investigation.

Figure 1.1 Possible areas of geographical investigation.

You can investigate anything related to the content of your A level Geography specification. Figure 1.1 gives an idea of the breadth of content that can be investigated. Download the A level Geography specification from the website of your exam board. The reference numbers for these specifications are shown in Figure 1.2.

Some things you might think of are not permitted. For example, the Bradshaw model of river development is not part of the A level specification.

Popular choices	Other possibilities – check your specification
Coastal landforms and processes. Coastal management. Mitigating risk (e.g. flood hazards). Changing Places / Shaping Places (e.g. regeneration or rebranding). Quality of the urban environment. Identity / diversity. Movement of water through the drainage basin. Perception studies (e.g. perception of crime or perception of flood risk).	Glaciated landscapes. Carbon cycle. Soils. Zonation and succession (e.g. in a sand dune ecosystem or salt marsh). Population change / migration. Woodland management. Globalisation. Urban microclimates.

Exam Board	Reference number
AQA	7037
Edexcel (Pearson)	9GEO
Eduqas	601/8847/9 Qualification Accreditation Number (page 2)
OCR	H481
WJEC/CBAC	601/8455/3 Ofqual Qualification Number (page 3)

Figure 1.2 Reference numbers for the current A level Geography specifications.

Action Point 2

Think about what aspects of geography interest you.

You can investigate any geography that is described in your A level specification. That's a big starting point – *so, how do you narrow down your options?* One good way of developing a focus is to rule out the things that wouldn't be suitable. You can do this by asking yourself some questions – just make sure you are honest with yourself. Figure 1.3 provides some questions and also explains why these are important.

Be curious! Choose an investigation that interests you. You are going to spend a lot of time working on it!

Figure 1.3 Ask yourself these questions to narrow down your choices.

1 *What kind of geography do I enjoy?*

It's better to investigate an aspect of geography that you understand and find interesting.

▶ Do I find physical geography more interesting than human geography, or vice versa?

▶ Which geographical themes do I like?

▶ Do I want to investigate the interaction between people and the environment?

Think about broad themes in geography such as coastal landforms, or regeneration of urban places, and jot down 3 that interest you most.

2 *Do I enjoy talking to people, including strangers?*

Some people are very outgoing while others are shy. That's normal. So, if you know that you find it difficult to approach people you don't know then choosing an investigation that will rely on you asking lots of people to answer a questionnaire may not be a good thing. Tick the box that describes you best.

I would enjoy asking people questions and conducting interviews. ☐

I don't mind doing a few interviews with people I don't know. ☐

I would prefer to only interview people I know. ☐

I don't want to talk to people as part of my investigation. ☐

3 *Am I scientific – good with measurements and maths?*

Some investigations, especially those that investigate physical geography, will involve a lot of measurements and create a lot of numerical data. That data will have to be processed. Other investigations rely on 'softer' forms of evidence, such as articles, interviews, and images. You will need to know how to analyse any data that you have collected. Mark a point on the line below that represents how confident you feel about each statement that follows:

1 I am good with measuring and numbers.

2 I am good at drawing graphs and processing numerical data.

3 I am good with words and interviews.

4 I am good at interpreting visual evidence.

not confident at all ———————————————————————— very confident

Action Point 3

Identify fieldwork opportunities that would be available to you either locally or on a fieldtrip.

Primary data

Primary data are forms of evidence collected first-hand by you.

Whatever kind of investigation you do, you will have to visit somewhere to collect some **primary data**. If you live in a city you might be quite mobile – able to use public transport perhaps to visit the site where you will be collecting your data. However, if you don't drive and you don't have access to public transport then you will have to collect data from your local environment. It makes good sense to conduct your fieldwork close to home.

▶ You are familiar with the area and its geographical features.

▶ It's on your doorstep so it's convenient.

▶ If the data collection takes more than one day you can go back to collect more.

Start off by thinking about opportunities for geographical investigation in your local area. So, do you live near a city centre, coastline, or ecosystem that you could investigate?

Alternatively, your school may be organising a residential fieldtrip. If so, find out where you are going and research what sorts of geographical environments are available nearby. Think about the statements in Figure 1.4.

Figure 1.4 Consider the fieldwork opportunities that are available to you.

My school is organising a residential fieldtrip so I must research what is available in that place. ☐

I have no transport so I must research opportunities for fieldwork local to home or school/college. ☐

I am mobile so I can research a wider range of places to collect my data. ☐

Action Point 4

Reflect on your experience of A level fieldwork.

Use your experience of the four days of fieldwork you have already experienced at A level to think about:

▶ the kinds of fieldwork you enjoyed and found interesting;

▶ what you learned about:
  - data collection methods;
  - how data can be presented (in maps and graphs);
  - how data can be analysed – including the use of statistical tests.

Analysis

Analysis requires you to examine the individual pieces of evidence before explaining connections to reveal your overall conclusion.

Think about the purpose of fieldwork for a moment. Your independent investigation isn't an excuse to 'Write everything I know about ...'. It must be an investigation which means that you need to uncover evidence to make connections or test an idea. The mark scheme rewards **analysis** of the data you have collected so it's important to think, even at this very early stage, about whether the investigation you are exploring will provide you with opportunities for analysis.

Your investigation must be manageable and achievable. Don't try to do too much.

Finally, think about this. The difference between a weak investigation and a successful investigation may be traced back to decisions made during this very first step of exploring a focus – see Figure 1.5.

Weaker investigations	Successful investigations
Are largely descriptive.	Analyse and explain the evidence.
Are based on a very narrow range of data.	Analyse a wide range of data.
Prove a known fact, for example, well-being in neighbourhood x is higher than in neighbourhood y.	Investigate patterns and try to find explanations for these patterns, for example, 'how and why does well-being vary within the inner urban area of town x?'.
Are too ambitious in scale, attempting to cover a huge geographical area.	Investigate a small, well-defined geographical area.
Start with a data collection technique and only think of the reason for the investigation later.	Start with a clear focus for the investigation and then select appropriate data collection techniques.

Figure 1.5 Moderator observations about weaker and successful investigations

Before moving on to Step 2 read Part 1.2 of this chapter. This describes examples of different styles of investigation that could be successful and approaches that you could adopt.

QUESTION Can I use my experiences of one of my four days of A level fieldwork to help me choose an area of research for my independent investigation?

ANSWER Yes, you can use it for inspiration. Hopefully, you can evaluate this experience and use it to narrow down your choices. However, you now have the opportunity to do something that really inspires you – so keep an open mind when considering what it is you really want to do.

QUESTION For one of my four days of A level fieldwork we studied regeneration in Liverpool. Can I create an independent investigation where I collect some data about regeneration in my home town and then compare it to the data we all collected in Liverpool?

ANSWER Yes, in theory you can. However, an investigation like this, where you replicate an idea you tried out on a fieldtrip and then make a comparison with somewhere local is full of potential pitfalls. Consider the following.

1 The two places must have some things in common to make a comparison sensible. If the two places are very different in size, for example, it won't work.
2 There is a danger this type of fieldwork is very descriptive.
3 What if you discover you don't have enough data from the first place? Can you go back and collect more?

To make this idea work, the two places must have a lot in common and you must be sure that you can analyse the data to explain any similarities or differences.

1.2 Styles of investigation

Pages 10-17 describe different ways of approaching a geographical investigation. Use these pages to think about the style of Independent Investigation that you want to do.

Remember, you may work on your own, with another student, or as part of a small team when you are exploring a focus for your investigation.

Dynamic

Beaches are part of a dynamic coastal system. Wave and tides generate forces that create constant change.

Investigating a geographical process

Geographical processes create change in the environment. Changes can be constant, like the movement of sediment on a beach by the waves and action of longshore drift. These marine processes create a **dynamic** environment on the beach – sorting pebbles by size and shape and also shifting the shape of the beach profile – changes that can be easily investigated.

Figure 1.6 Dynamic change on a beach. The second photo was taken after a few waves had swept across the sediment.

Other processes are more gradual. Nevertheless, they create dramatic change after a period of time. Think about some of the processes that impact on urban and rural environments such as deindustrialisation or regeneration. These processes are caused by economic change. They can take years or even decades to create massive changes in the built environment as factories close and are replaced by tertiary sector industries.

▶ How has deindustrialisation affected the sense of local identity?
▶ Have there been benefits socially or environmentally?

Figure 1.7 The impact of deindustrialisation and regeneration.

Secondary data sources such as old photos, artwork, historic maps, or archived newspaper reports will provide evidence of past conditions while your primary data collection will reveal how places have changed. Figure 1.7 provides an example.

A Ink sketch shows Shelton Bar, a steel works, in 1963.

B Photo showing the same location in 2018.

Processes in the physical environment include:	These processes can be investigated through the measurement or observation of:
Marine erosion, sediment transportation, and deposition	• beach profiles • size and shape of beach deposits and thickness of beach sediment • frequency and wavelength of waves
Aeolian erosion, transportation, and deposition	• sand dune profiles • wind speed and direction
Fluvio-glacial deposition	• shape, size, and orientation of fluvio-glacial deposits
Sea level change	• profiles of emergent coastal features such as raised beaches, marine terraces, and fossil cliffs • size and shape of fossil beach deposits
Succession and zonation in sand dunes or salt marshes	• percentage cover, plant abundance, diversity, frequency, and height
Water cycle processes that explain movement of water through the drainage basin	• **antecedent** weather • interception, infiltration rates, and overland flow • soil profiles and moisture content

Processes in the human environment include:	These processes can be investigated through the measurement or observation of:
Regeneration and rural diversification	• property values • socio-economic indicators • questionnaires
Deindustrialisation	• quality of the built environment • art and literature • re-photography • attitudinal surveys
Rebranding and re-imaging	• perception studies • advertising materials • interviews • blogs
Migration	• demographic data • interviews / personal histories / literature • mental mapping
Gentrification	• property values • quality of the built environment • re-photography • questionnaires

Figure 1.8 Processes that can be investigated in the physical and human environments. Check that they are described in the specification you are following before starting any investigation.

Antecedent

Antecedent weather conditions are those that have already happened. Yesterday's rainfall will have an effect on flood risk today.

Test your understanding

Some geographical processes are described in Figure 1.8.

a) Think about which of these processes occur in your own local environment.

b) Check that they are described in your A level Geography specification.

How to investigate a process

Geographical processes create change over time but you can still collect all of your data at a single point in time – usually during one day. You just need to think about what it is you are aiming to discover. For example, you could investigate:

▶ **factors that control the process**. For example, in a coastal location you might investigate the factors that affect the rate of cliff recession – how do geology, fetch, and management strategies affect the rate of change?

> ▶ **effects of the process**, such as the effects of swash and backwash on movement and sorting of beach sediment by size and shape;
> ▶ **how much change has been created** by the process over a longer period of time using secondary data, like the ink sketch in Figure 1.7;
> ▶ **whether a geographical process has had similar or different impacts in two locations**. For example, by comparing how the process of counter-urbanisation has affected two rural communities.

When making comparisons in fieldwork always compare like with like. In this case, compare two rural communities of a similar size at different distances from the urban centre.

Longitudinal surveys of a process

It may be possible to collect data over a period of time to assess the impacts of a geographical process. For example, you could collect data on traffic and pedestrian flows at different times of the day, or throughout the week, to identify busy and quiet periods. You could collect weather data over a period of days or weeks to assess the impact on movement of water though a drainage basin. If so, this type of study is known as a **longitudinal survey**.

Longitudinal survey

A longitudinal survey takes place over a longer period of time – at least a week, usually much longer.

Investigating perceptions

Our **perceptions** are informed by our senses - what we can see, hear, smell, or feel. People create perceptions of a place directly – by experiencing it first-hand. So, for example, someone living close to a river will have a perception about the risk of flooding that is informed by their own experience of flood events. Someone who is visiting the area, or someone who has only just moved into the area, may have a different perception of the flood risk. You might investigate how and why different groups of people perceive the same place in different ways.

Perceptions

Perception studies are those that investigate the attitudes and points of view held by one or more groups of people.

> ▶ Is the perception of local people different from the perceptions of visitors?
> ▶ How and why do the perceptions of long-term residents of a community vary from those of newcomers?

Figure 1.9 The Elephant and Castle Shopping centre, London.

When the Elephant and Castle Shopping Centre (seen in the centre of Figure 1.9) opened in 1965, the concrete and glass architecture was criticised by many. In 2018, it was announced that the controversial building would be demolished.
However, many local people protested. They feared that the regeneration would not include enough affordable housing.

Change can be controversial. Perceptions of different groups of people could be investigated.

Rebranding and perceptions

We also create perceptions of a place through our experience of how it is represented in books, websites, film, or any other media, including social media. This phenomenon allows **players** who want to change perceptions of a place to use the media to rebrand or re-imagine what a place is like.

An alternative approach is to investigate how places are represented in the media. Art, adverts, music, film, TV, and literature all contain representations of places.

- What images are used?
- Why were these images chosen?
- How accurate are these representations?
- How do local people feel about them?

Figure 1.10 A lively and colourful mural in Derby ironically suggests that nothing ever happens in the city. This gives one perception of Derby. You could investigate whether locals and/or visitors agree.

Test your understanding

Study Figure 1.10 and think about the inner urban areas of your local town or city.

- What processes are changing this place? How quickly is change happening? How might you collect evidence about change?
- Who are the key players in the decisions about regeneration? How might you collect evidence about the attitudes of local people to that change?

Investigating a geographical concept

Specialised geographical concepts such as identity, inequality, and risk help us bring meaning and order to complex patterns we observe in the real world. What is more, many of the specialised concepts help us understand aspects of both human and physical geography (see Figure 1.11 below). Consequently, thinking about concepts can help you to explore a focus for your fieldwork wherever you intend to collect your data, whether it is on the coast, in a rural environment, or in a city.

Causality	Inequality	Risk
Equilibrium	Interdependence	Sustainability
Feedback	Mitigation and adaptation	Systems
Globalisation	Representation	Thresholds
Identity	Resilience	

Figure 1.11 Specialised concepts

Systems

A way of breaking down complex environments into a more manageable set of interrelated components and processes.

Risk

Uncertainties that can pose a threat or hazard.

Threshold

The level at which a process causes new and significant effects.

Figures 1.12 - 1.14 show how concepts could help us investigate two contrasting fieldwork locations.

> **Systems** What processes occur in the coastal **system** here? What part does this beach play in the local sediment cell? Is the coastline stable, accreting, or being eroded over time?

> **Risk** How do the artificial reefs help manage the **risk** of coastal erosion? Are the current coastal management strategies working effectively?

> **Threshold** How effective are these coastal defences against rising sea levels? Is there a **threshold** beyond which the risk of coastal flooding would become too great and the coastline would have to be realigned?

Figure 1.12 The artificial reefs and beach at Sea Palling, Norfolk.

Mitigation and adaptation

Risk can be reduced by managing the hazard, or by adapting the behaviour of people who are affected by the hazard.

Resilience

The ability of people or a place to return to normal after a period of difficulty or traumatic event.

Inequality

Inequality occurs where one place, or one group of people, has a disproportionate share of something.

> **Mitigation and adaptation** How can social and economic issues be reduced? What adaptations could be made to transport links or public services in order to reduce the risks caused by inequality?

> **Resilience** What do people think of initiatives that attempt to make the local economy more resilient such as mobile libraries, car-share schemes, community shops, or the sale of local produce and services? How much is the local community engaged in these initiatives? How can the voluntary sector and businesses contribute?

> **Risk** Coastal flooding and erosion are two physical risks to this community. How do people perceive the risk of future coastal flooding?

> **Inequality** in rural and coastal communities may be recognised in health issues of an ageing population, poverty due to lack of well-paid jobs and full-time employment, or the lack of services.

Figure 1.13 The community of Sea Palling, Norfolk.

Risk Are local independent businesses threatened by competition from chain stores?

Representation
The way that places (or environments) are described in the media.

Representation How does Cardiff City Council manage the image of the city? What promotional materials and advertising do they use?

Mitigation How can the local council and businesses ensure that the city centre remains economically vibrant in the face of competition from other regional shopping centres?

Figure 1.14 The Hayes. A pedestrian area of shops and bars in central Cardiff.

Test your understanding

1 Consider Figure 1.14 and the research questions below. Identify the specialised concept that is at the heart of each research question.
   ▶ Is there a direct link between online sales and the decline of the high street?
   ▶ What do local people love about their city? Is it related to social, cultural, historical, or other factors?
   ▶ Has migration contributed to an ethnically mixed and cohesive society?
   ▶ Has technology and the introduction of global brands and images diluted Cardiff's sense of place?
2 Think about the specialised concepts described in Figures 1.12 – 1.14. Explore the idea of investigating one of these specialised concepts in a location that is accessible to you. What research questions come to mind?

Break bigger concepts down

Some of the specialised concepts are particularly big and complex. The concepts of sustainability and globalisation are good examples. Each of these concepts can be broken down to make them easier to use in an investigation. For example, if you wanted to investigate the impact of globalisation on a small neighbourhood of Bristol, London, or Liverpool you should choose just one or two of the aspects shown in Figure 1.15.

Sustainability is a complex concept so be careful not to over-simplify such an investigation. You could use some or all of the criteria in Egan's Wheel (Figure 1.16) to find similarities and differences between your chosen two places. Remember, description alone is not sufficient for an independent investigation. You will need to consider why one neighbourhood is more sustainable than another, or focus on how sustainability could be improved.

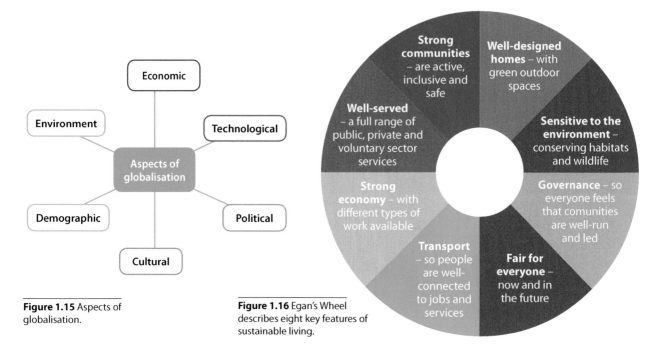

Figure 1.15 Aspects of globalisation.

Figure 1.16 Egan's Wheel describes eight key features of sustainable living.

Investigating a local issue

One common approach to fieldwork is to investigate a geographical issue that affects your local area. There are two basic types of issue:

▶ controversial issues that create disagreement (or conflict) between different groups of people. An example would be when local residents object to the proposed building of new homes;

▶ geographical problems that require a decision to be made. An example would be to decide on the best route for a new cycle path in an urban environment.

Issues that have created conflict in the local community provide a popular option for geography investigations. You might, for example, investigate a development that significantly alters the identity of an urban or rural community. It may be a proposed new development such as the building of a new housing estate, bypass, or supermarket. Alternatively, it may be an issue that threatens the sustainability of a community, for example, the threatened closure of a service such as a local shop, post office, or primary school.

Such issues often create strong local feelings with some people in favour of change while others oppose it. One aspect of such an investigation would be to identify the different players and interview them. These players may be individual local residents, businesses, employees of the local authority, or local voluntary groups. The attitudes and viewpoints of these players are likely to vary greatly.

You could investigate the reasons why local attitudes to the issue vary so much.

▷ What influences these attitudes?

▷ Can you identify political, religious, economic, social, or environmental influences on the arguments that people use?

You may be able to identify a suitable issue by reading your local newspaper, reading a blog, or by talking to local council members.

Text analysis

Text analysis (also known as discourse analysis) covers a wide variety of techniques that attempt to understand the meaning given by individuals to what they say or write.

Figure 1.17 Local residents protest about the development of housing on a greenfield site, Staffordshire.

The development of housing on a greenfield site on the urban fringe is a controversial issue. You could investigate a local issue such as this by:

▷ interviewing decision-makers such as members of the council or planners;

▷ using a questionnaire, Likert Scale survey, or Guttman Scale survey to collect qualitative data about the attitudes of local residents;

▷ collecting quantitative data on traffic and noise, as one major objection to new housing developments in rural locations is about the increased amount of traffic;

▷ collecting secondary evidence from online sources such as local newspapers, blogs, and Facebook accounts of the development. Use **text analysis** to identify viewpoints and opinions.

Review Points

Tick off each review point before moving on to Step 2.

I have downloaded a copy of the specification. ☐

I have thought about:

  ▷ areas of geography that interest me; ☐

  ▷ aspects of geography that I am good at; ☐

  ▷ whether I am confident in using numbers. ☐

I have identified local fieldwork opportunities that would be available to me. ☐

I have thought about my previous experiences of fieldwork and how these might influence my own investigation. ☐

I have read about different kinds of investigation and have identified an approach (for example, investigating a concept) that could provide a focus for my own investigation. ☐

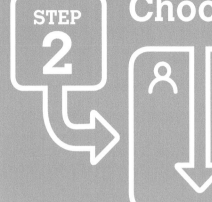

STEP 2 Choosing an aim

Action points

1 Read geographical literature to help you develop your aim.
2 Be clear about the scope and scale of your investigation so that it is manageable.
3 Break down your overall aim into manageable chunks using a small number of research questions or hypotheses.
4 Write a title for the investigation.

You must work independently when choosing your title, deciding on research questions/hypotheses, and planning other details of your investigation.

By the end of this Step you should be able to propose a title for your investigation – a short statement or research question that conveys the aims of what it is you hope to achieve.

Action Point 1
Read geographical literature to help you develop your aim.

Hopefully, during Step 1, you were able to find an aspect of theoretical geography that interests you and that you think you could investigate first-hand. The mark scheme makes it clear that each investigation needs a theoretical context. This means that your aim should be linked to something you've read about in the **geographical literature** – usually a process, concept, model, or theory, or possibly a case study that you are going to make comparisons with. Spending a little time researching relevant geographical literature in the areas of geography that interest you most will help you:

> develop a clear aim for your investigation;

> identify specific research questions or hypotheses that will sharpen the focus of your investigation.

Later, when you are writing up your report, an understanding of the literature will help you:

> explain why you decided to conduct the investigation;

> interpret and explain the evidence you found;

> reach conclusions about whether your first-hand observations support or contradict the literature.

Geographical literature

Research of geographical literature is reading about geography's concepts, processes, theories, models, or case studies.

Double check that the geography you are interested in is described in your A level specification.

Types of literature

A good investigation will refer to a range of different sources. You might research the following types.

> Academic journals and publications. Academics (researchers often employed by universities) report the findings of their own research in short articles. These articles are reviewed by other academics (a process called peer-review) so they should be accurate and unbiased but they can be technical and difficult to read.

Use a search engine such as Google Scholar or refseek.com to find academic articles that match your interests.

- Reports published by statistical and scientific organisations such as the Office for National Statistics (ONS) or the Environment Agency. These organisations publish reports that are considered to be accurate and unbiased.
- Professional organisations such as the Royal Town Planning Institute publish research and case studies online.
- Government and local government websites contain reports on issues such as business, crime, environment, housing, and transport.
- Reports published by non-government organisations such as charities and think-tanks. Think-tanks employ researchers to write reports on contemporary issues in a style that is easier to read than an academic report. They often describe themselves as being non-political. However, one of the aims of their research is to provide evidence that can be used to lobby politicians to try to influence government decision-making. Many think-tanks are funded by big business – and their research is sometimes used to try to change policies that would work in favour of their funders. For these two reasons, the evidence that is published by think-tanks needs to be treated with a certain amount of caution as their reports may present a one-sided account of the issue.
- News items online or in newspapers. Journalists frequently discuss contemporary geographical issues. These articles are based on research but sometimes present a **partisan** point of view because of the political leaning of the news organisation.

> **Evaluation**
>
> Consider whether you have a range of sources and opinions.

> **Partisan**
>
> A one-sided or prejudiced point of view can be described as partisan or biased.

Figure 2.1 Sources of up-to-date research, reports, and case studies that could help your literature research.

Source	Type of literature
Office for National Statistics https://www.ons.gov.uk/	The UK's largest independent producer of official statistics. Reports include employment, the economy, cultural identity, well-being, housing, population, and migration.
Environment Agency https://www.gov.uk/government/organisations/environment-agency	Government organisation with responsibility for environmental issues in England. Research articles and case studies on river floods, river management, coastal flooding and erosion, and coastal management.
Natural Resources Wales https://naturalresourceswales/	Government organisation with responsibility for environmental issues in Wales. Research articles on flooding, landscapes, waste, and forestry.
Scottish Environment Protection Agency https://www.sepa.org.uk	Government organisation with responsibility for environmental issues in Scotland. Research articles, tools, techniques, data, and case studies on air quality, flooding, climate change, environment, energy, land, waste, water.
Northern Ireland Environment Agency https://www.daera-ni.gov.uk/	Executive agency within the Department of Agriculture, Environment and Rural Affairs. It is responsible for conservation of Northern Ireland's environment and natural heritage.
National Housing Federation https://www.housing.org.uk/	Represents the views of housing associations in England. News items, reports, podcasts on topics such as rural housing, social housing, regeneration, brownfield sites.
Centre for Cities https://www.centreforcities.org/	Non-partisan think tank. Research, blogs, podcasts, and data on topics relating to UK cities including housing, migration, and the high street.
Campaign to Protect Rural England https://www.cpre.org.uk/	Pressure group founded in the 1920s to campaign for a sustainable future for the UK countryside. Reports include topics such as green belts, housing, transport, climate change, and landscapes.
Joseph Rowntree Foundation https://www.jrf.org.uk/	Left-leaning think tank that focuses on poverty in the UK. Research articles, blogs, and data on poverty-related issues such as social housing, affordable rent, and homelessness.
The Progressive Policy Think Tank https://www.ippr.org/	Left-leaning think tank. Research articles on topics such as the economy, the environment (including air quality in UK cities), housing, infrastructure, jobs, skills, society, and migration.
Migration Watch https://www.migrationwatchuk.org/	Right-leaning think tank that focuses on the 'problem' of immigration. Research articles and blogs on migration-related topics such as housing, the economy, and population.
Royal Town Planning Institute https://www.rtpi.org.uk/	A professional organisation for town planners. Projects include research into place, poverty, and inequality, or the spatial implications of new housing.
The Design Council https://www.designcouncil.org.uk/	Independent charity with an interest in the quality of the built environment. Resources include an archive of reports on issues such as cities, diversity, housing, places, and spaces.

Keep an accurate record of sources

Keep an accurate record of where you found each source of information. You will refer back to this literature research when you are writing the report of your investigation. Each source needs to be accurately cited (see pages 233-235).

Bookmark useful pages in the literature as you come across them – using post-it notes if you are reading printed materials. Record the URL of useful websites and also, because websites change, the date that you accessed the site.

Action Point 2

Be clear about the scope and scale of your investigation so that it is manageable.

Figure 2.2 Deciding the scope and scale of your investigation.

Having decided on a likely aim for the investigation you need to carefully consider its proposed scope and scale. Keep it manageable. Don't try to do too much – in terms of the amount of geography you want to cover (scope) or the size of the fieldwork area (scale).

| **Your aim should have a realistic scope.** | | Break larger concepts or issues into smaller chunks. | | For example, don't aim to investigate climate change. Aim to investigate perceptions of a recent extreme weather event. |
| **Your aim should have a manageable scale.** | | Focus your aim on a small geographical area. | | For example, don't aim to investigate the impacts of regeneration in London. Aim to investigate the impacts of regeneration on a small neighbourhood of a few streets. |

How to investigate the local scale

Most students investigate at the local scale. This doesn't necessarily mean a place that is local to your home – you can do your investigation at a field study centre many miles away – it means your fieldwork site is small. Your choice of fieldwork site will depend on several factors.

▶ Accessibility – does the site have public access? If not, can you get permission to work there?
▶ Suitability – does the site have the features you want to investigate?
▶ Safety – will the site provide a safe working environment? (There is more on this aspect on page 109.)
▶ Scale – have you chosen a site that is an appropriate size for your investigation?

Consider the scope and scale of the proposed aims described below. Only the fourth title has been proposed at a suitable scope and scale.

Aim 1

To assess the impacts and responses to weather and climate whilst making links to global warming and climate change.

Primary data will be collected in Birmingham. This will be compared to secondary data for the whole of the UK.

1 The scope of this proposal is far too ambitious. There are numerous, complex impacts of climate change and people's responses are also extremely varied.

2 The scale of the fieldwork (Birmingham) is far too large. Birmingham has a population of over 1 million – an independent investigation cannot collect enough evidence of people's responses to climate change that will reflect the views of such a large area.

3 The scale of the secondary data does not match the scale of the primary data – both need to be from the same small area at a local scale.

Aim 2

To identify the factors that affect infiltration rates across the Shropshire Hills Area of Outstanding Natural Beauty.

Infiltration rate experiments will be conducted at 12 different sites across the AONB to test the influence of altitude, slope angle, soil type, geology, and land use.

The proposed site for this investigation is unnecessarily large. The Shropshire Hills AONB covers over 800km² and includes a large number of small hills and a very wide variety of rock types. It would be impractical and time-consuming to travel to 12 sites across such a large area. Furthermore, the wide variety of terrains and geology would create too many variables. See pages 31-32.

Aim 3

To answer the following research question. To what extent has the regeneration of London Docklands been successful?

This aim is much too ambitious in its scope and scale. The regeneration of London Docklands was a huge project which took almost 20 years; impacted on two London Boroughs; reclaimed about 750 hectares of land; and created 22,000 new homes. Collecting enough data to assess the success of this massive project would take years of full-time research!

Aim 4

To assess the relative importance of factors that affect the perception of the risk of river flooding in the village of Clun in Shropshire.

This aim is focused, manageable, and has selected an appropriate local scale. The population of Clun is less than 700 people so it should be possible to conduct an attitudinal survey with local residents that would reflect the views of the wider population of the village in a reasonable amount of time.

Test your understanding

Study the aims on this page. Choose Aim 1, Aim 2, or Aim 3. Suggest how the scope and scale of each of these investigations could be improved.

So you have now decided on an overall aim for your investigation. You will need to break this aim down into objectives – separate elements which, when taken as a whole, enable you to answer your aim. Imagine you have decided to investigate the concept of risk and that you have access to a location that has experienced a number of floods. Figure 2.3 shows such a location. To keep the scope and scale manageable you have decided that your aim will be:

To investigate perceptions of flooding in Clun.

Figure 2.3 Useful question starters. The photo shows Clun, South Shropshire. The area was affected by floods in 2014, 2017, 2018, and 2019.

How?
Why?
What ought?
Where?
What might?
Who?
When?
Which?

The use of research questions

The ability to pose and then answer research questions is at the heart of any geographical investigation. You can use three or four tightly focused research questions to break the aim down into manageable chunks. The research questions should form a logical sequence, creating a logical route through your enquiry from beginning to end.

The use of research questions is helpful because it will encourage you to be analytical – forcing you to make connections and offer explanations. Analysis is essential. It will give your report clarity and focus. Without research questions there is a danger that your fieldwork report will lack analysis and be overly descriptive. You will be able to measure your progress through the investigation as you find the answers to these questions.

> You must use research questions and/or hypotheses to give your investigation a clear purpose.

An aim can be broken down using a sequence of research questions. See how this has been done with the Aim on the next page. By collecting evidence to answer each of these questions, the overall aim of the investigation can be met.

Aim

To assess the relative importance of factors that affect the perception of the risk of river flooding in the village of Clun in Shropshire.

> The aim has a manageable scope and the fieldwork site is of an appropriate scale.

Research questions

1 How great is the risk of flooding in Clun?
2 How might length of residence in Clun influence perceptions?
3 How might distance of the resident's home from the river influence perceptions?

> The first research question is appropriate because, if there is no history of flooding, then residents will not perceive any risk.

> The second and third research questions identify factors that may influence perception. Each can be measured using a simple survey of residents. The data could be represented using isoline or choropleth maps of the village – leading to analysis, interpretation, and explanation of the evidence rather than simple description.

Validity of research questions

A valid research question is one that is actually testing what it is the researcher intended to test. You must consider the validity of any potential research questions. Will the question actually help you achieve part of your aim or not? If a question is sending you off on a tangent, then it is probably invalid and should be scrapped. For example, imagine an investigation about the use of public transport. Questions about bus routes and the cost of a bus ticket would be valid because each of these factors affects how public transport is used. Questions about favourite vehicle colour would be invalid. This seems obvious – however, it's quite common for geography students to use invalid research questions.

Another pitfall is to fail to ask valid questions that are fundamental to the research. For example, an investigation about change over time – such as the impacts of regeneration – needs to use at least one research question about what the place was like before regeneration.

Evaluation

You should use hindsight, at the end of your investigation, to evaluate the validity and usefulness of your research questions.

Test your understanding

Study the proposed investigations (one below and the second on page 24) . Assess the validity of the research questions.

Aim 1

To what extent has the regeneration of Cardiff Bay been successful?

Research questions

1 Is Cardiff Bay more economically vibrant than other parts of Cardiff?
2 The environment in Cardiff Bay is sustainable.
3 Are perceptions of Cardiff Bay positive?

What makes a good research question?

Study Figure 2.4. It shows the type of traffic congestion that is typical in many UK cities. The research questions use some of the starters from Figure 2.3. Let's analyse how useful these research questions might be.

Question 1 is invalid in the context of a geographical investigation about traffic congestion or traffic management.

Question 2 is not very precise – surely the answer would depend on time of day. You could improve the question's precision by asking 'How do flows of traffic vary throughout the day?' Then it might be a useful research question.

Question 3 is another simple question. It would require measurement using a noise meter. The answer would provide a useful fact but **Question 4** provides a much more interesting question because it investigates a possible link or explanation between two variables.

The scope of **Question 5** is much more ambitious than questions 2-4. The answer is likely to be complex. It is possible to imagine various lines of investigation that could be taken to break this big question down into smaller, more manageable chunks. This might make a good overall aim for an investigation.

Figure 2.4 How useful are these research questions?

1 How many cars are silver?

2 How much traffic is there?

3 How noisy is the traffic?

4 How are local house prices affected by noise from this busy road?

5 What ought to be done to make this environment safer for local residents?

Review your research questions

Before finalising your draft research questions you should review their usefulness. So, what can we learn from Figure 2.4?

1 Invalid questions should be identified and scrapped.
2 Imprecise questions need to be rephrased to make them useful.
3 Some questions are very straightforward. A little research would provide the answer quite easily. If all of your research questions are like this, your investigation may not be sufficiently demanding.
4 Other questions are more open-ended. Such questions would require more complex research and take longer to answer. A good investigation will probably need to combine a small number of straightforward questions with others that are more open-ended.

Figure 2.5 summarises the differences between styles of question.

▶ Questions on the left are useful but not very demanding because the answers are probably very straightforward.
▶ The questions in the middle are better. They are more useful and interesting as research questions because they are about the relationship between two variables.
▶ The questions on the right are more interesting again and could provide excellent research questions because you may find a variety of potential answers. However, this type of question needs to be phrased very carefully to make them valid. You may need to gather a great deal of evidence to answer them fully so they may give you a useful way to express your overall aim.

Figure 2.5 Styles of question.

	⟶ Increasing complexity of question ⟶		
	Simple questions that have a straightforward answer	**Research questions about connections**	**Research questions that have a complex answer**
Question starters	When? Where? How many? Which?	How does? What effect would? Why? What factors?	Who benefits? What might? What ought? Who might?
Example questions	Which is the busiest shopping street? When is the busiest time of day? How many cars pass in 5 minutes?	How does wind speed vary with altitude? What effect would traffic noise have on house prices? Why does the diversity of plants increase away from the sea in a sand dune? What factors have the greatest impact on resilience?	Who would benefit most if flood protection was improved? What might be the consequence of regeneration? What ought to be done to make this community more sustainable? Who might benefit most from improved flood defences?

Using a hypothesis

While most students use research questions to structure their investigation, some successfully use hypotheses instead. A hypothesis is a statement rather than a question. It is a provisional idea which can be proven to be correct or incorrect, based on the factual evidence collected in your fieldwork. Just like in a science experiment, a hypothesis is appropriate if you want to test an assumption that can be made about quantitative data – in other words, evidence that can be counted or measured. In an A level geography investigation you could use a hypothesis to scientifically test a geographical theory, for example, that water moves through some soils more rapidly than others because of varying permeability.

Infiltration rates will be faster in sandy soils than in clay soils.

Once you have chosen a suitable hypothesis for your fieldwork you should state the null hypothesis. This is what you would discover if the hypothesis was incorrect. For the hypothesis above, the null hypothesis would be:

There is no significant difference in infiltration rates between sandy soils and clay soils.

Note that the statement made in the null hypothesis is that there is no difference between the infiltration rates. A null hypothesis is not the opposite of the original statement.

A hypothesis is particularly useful to test an assumption that one variable may be linked to another. For example:

Wind speeds decrease with distance from the sea along the transect through the dunes.

Distance, height, and time are all variables that can be measured in geography fieldwork and each of these variables may be linked to other variables. So, hypotheses are particularly useful to test an assumption about:

▶ how things change over time;
▶ how the distribution of a feature varies over space.

For example, each of the following is an appropriate use of hypothesis.

More traffic travels into the city during the morning rush hour than at any other time of the day.

Independent retailers are less concentrated in the part of the city that has experienced regeneration than elsewhere.

When not to use a hypothesis

A hypothesis should not be used to test a statement that is so ambitious in its scope that you cannot collect enough evidence to either prove or disprove it. For example, it would be beyond the scope of an A level geography investigation to test this hypothesis.

Recent extreme weather in Manchester is due to climate change.

Another common error is where a hypothesis is used to make a simple statement about something which requires qualitative evidence. For example:

Harrogate is a good example of a sustainable community.

This isn't an appropriate way to use a hypothesis. 'Good' and 'sustainable' are both qualitative concepts that will mean different things to different people. It is difficult, therefore, to prove or disprove this hypothesis without relying on your own judgement. This means that any conclusion you reach will lack credibility. It is possible to construct testable hypotheses in qualitative investigations but the wording can be tricky. Instead, it is wiser to stick to using research questions such as:

In what ways could Harrogate be made more sustainable?

Write a title for the investigation.

Having completed Action Points 1-3 you are now ready to write a title for the investigation. The title:

▶ should convey what it is you are aiming to achieve;

▶ can be written as a statement or as a research question.

If you are using a research question, then it needs to be relatively complex in style – like those in the right-hand column of Figure 2.5.

Test your understanding

Study each of the following proposed investigation titles. Imagine that you are giving feedback to the students who have proposed each of these. Identify three titles that should be rejected. Explain why each is not suitable.

1 The regeneration of London Docklands since the mid-1980s has had mainly positive impacts for the economy and people of East London.

2 How can neighbourhood X be made safer for local residents?

3 River X conforms to Bradshaw's model.

4 The proposed housing development at place X is likely to make flooding more likely at place Y.

5 In a transect through a sand dune, the variety of plants increases with distance from the beach.

6 Residents who have lived in X for more than 10 years have a more positive perception of flood defences than residents who have recently moved in to the area.

7 Place X is a perfect example of a modern sustainable residential community.

8 How might coastal town X rebrand itself to improve the local economy?

QUESTION Can I ask my teacher to give me a list of investigation titles that have been used successfully before?

ANSWER No, that isn't allowed. You can collaborate with others when you are choosing a broad aim for your investigation but you must develop your own title, research questions, and/or hypotheses.

QUESTION My friend and I want to do similar investigations in the same place. Is that allowed?

ANSWER Yes, there is no problem if you do an investigation in the same place or one that investigates the same issue, or concept/theory, or model. However, you must each develop your own aim, research questions, and/or hypotheses and title. You must do this independently of each other.

Review Points

Tick off each point on the action planning list before you move on to Step 3.

I have done my literature research and bookmarked and made a note of useful sources and urls. ☐

I've checked that my proposed investigation relates to part of the specification. ☐

I have defined an appropriate scale and scope for my investigation. ☐

I have identified a small number of research questions or hypotheses. ☐

I have considered the validity of my research questions. ☐

I have drafted a title which provides a clear aim for the investigation. ☐

STEP 3

Planning primary data collection

Action points

1　Decide what kind of primary data you will need to collect.
2　Research the methods you could use to collect the data.
3　Identify any specialist equipment that might be needed.

3.1 Developing a plan

During Steps 3, 4, and 5 you will design a strategy for collecting the primary data you need to meet the aims of your investigation. This process will require some research to identify suitable methods of data collection – you can do this by reading part 3.2 and selecting the techniques that are most appropriate. You may collaborate with other students when planning suitable strategies for collecting primary data.

Action Point 1

Decide what kind of primary data (quantitative and/or qualitative) you will need to collect in order to answer your research questions or hypotheses.

Careful planning is the key to a successful investigation.

Your independent investigation must include the collection and processing of primary data. This is data that you have captured and recorded yourself by counting, measuring, or observing something in the field. It is primary because you are the first person to capture it.

This first Action Point requires some thought.

1　What sort of primary data do I need to collect to answer my research questions?
   ▶ Is the data likely to be affected by several different variables? if so, will I need to limit the number of variables that affect my data so that meaningful comparisons can be made?
   ▶ Is the data likely to provide evidence that is relevant to my investigation?

2　How could I collect the data?
   ▶ Do I understand the specific methods that can be used?
   ▶ Will I need specialised equipment?

What is data?

Data comes in many forms. Don't be confused by the 'data' part of primary data. We often think of data as numbers. Geography students collect numerical data such as:

- slope angles;
- sediment size and shape;
- traffic and pedestrian flows;
- wind speeds;
- infiltration rates.

All of this is quantitative data that can be number-crunched later. However, the term 'primary data' covers a very broad range of different kinds of evidence.

Geography students can collect evidence by taking their own photographs, making video or audio recordings. They can also conduct questionnaires as well as longer, more detailed interviews. These are all examples of qualitative data. To summarise:

- Quantitative data can be counted or measured. It can be sub-divided into different scales of measurement: nominal, ordinal, ratio, and interval (see below). Quantitative data are objective forms of evidence.
- Qualitative data can be observed and recorded as words, sounds, or pictures. Qualitative data are subjective forms of evidence so are essential where the researcher is interested in understanding values and attitudes, for example, in a perception survey.

Quantitative and qualitative data can each provide useful and reliable forms of evidence to support an investigation. Whether you rely on one form of evidence more than another will depend on the context of your investigation.

Using a wide variety of data rather than one data source has clear advantages.

- Using data from only one source could provide misleading results if the source is unreliable. By using data from different sources your investigation is more likely to produce reliable results.
- Each type of data has a small range of suitable techniques that may be used to present and analyse it. By collecting a range of data types you will increase the opportunities for presentation and analysis.

Types of data and measurement scales

Many geographical investigations use a great deal of quantitative data. In order to present and then analyse this data using the most appropriate methods you really need to have some understanding of how quantitative data is measured. Figure 3.2 summarises the four levels of measurement that are used in research and statistics. Each of these is then described in a little more detail.

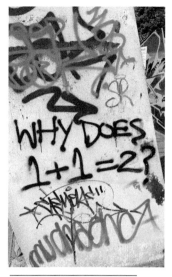

Figure 3.1 What is data? Data doesn't have to be numerical.

Do not dismiss the idea of collecting qualitative data. Qualitative data provides valid evidence in many investigations.

A simple understanding of measurement scales is essential if you are going to select suitable methods to present and analyse quantitative data.

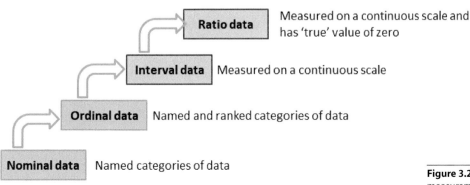

Ratio data — Measured on a continuous scale and has 'true' value of zero

Interval data — Measured on a continuous scale

Ordinal data — Named and ranked categories of data

Nominal data — Named categories of data

Figure 3.2 Types of data and measurement scales.

The nominal scale

In the nominal scale data are allocated to discrete categories and counted. This data is often described as being **discrete** or categorical. Nominal data is useful in both human and physical geography, for example:

▶ types of land use or categories of shops in a city centre;

▶ categories of agricultural land use;

▶ species of plant in an ecosystem;

▶ categories of traffic such as cycles, cars, vans, and lorries.

As researchers we are interested in the **frequency** of the data – the number of individual examples that fall into each category such as the number of independently owned shops compared with the number of chain stores in a regenerated city centre. Nominal data are always whole numbers – never percentages or fractions.

It is worth noting that much of the data in the census (a secondary source) is on the nominal scale – people are put into categories depending on their ethnicity, type of home, or educational attainment.

The ordinal scale

The ordinal scale of measurement also places data into discrete data categories. However, unlike the nominal scale, the ordinal scale uses categories that can be arranged in sequence or rank order. Imagine a situation where you are asked to rate an experience, perhaps a new film or TV show, as very poor, poor, satisfactory, good, or very good. You would be using an ordinal scale. An everyday example is shown in Figure 3.3. The ordinal data scale is used when we have a sense that data can be put into rank order but where we cannot precisely measure how much better/larger/higher one category is than another.

Figure 3.3 Food hygiene ratings are an everyday example of ordinal data.

The **ordinal scale** is commonly used in investigations of perception. For example, respondents could be asked whether they strongly agree, agree, disagree, or strongly disagree with a statement. This is an example of a Likert (pronounced 'lick it') scale (see page 64). However, ordinal scales can also be useful in some physical geography investigations, for example, you can use Power's scale (page 75) in a sediment survey or the ACFOR scale (page 87) in a vegetation survey.

Discrete

Data that is counted in separate categories on the nominal or ordinal scale.

Frequency

Frequency describes the number of items of data that fall into each category.

Evaluation

Think about whether you have sufficient variety of different data types. If not, your options for processing, presenting, and analysis could be limited.

Ordinal scale

The ordinal scale allocates data into categories that can be put into rank order.

Using the ordinal scale has some big advantages.

1   The ordinal scale is particularly useful in human geography research where we can use it to 'measure' views and perceptions such as satisfaction, happiness, or agreement.
2   Use of the ordinal scale can save time. For example, if you are conducting a questionnaire you can include some questions that gather ordinal data by using bipolar or Likert surveys. This will speed up the process of collecting the data. Ordinal data is also significantly quicker to analyse than qualitative data.

The interval and ratio scales

The interval scale is a numeric scale used to measure intervals along a **continuous scale**. This means that data on these scales can be measured (rather than counted) and given a value along the scale. It is often described as continuous data. So data collected on the interval scale can be measured to fractions of a unit, such as a temperature of 10.6°C.

The ratio scale is also a continuous scale. Time, distance, and velocity are all examples of the ratio scale. Examples in geography fieldwork might include:

▶   height and wave length of waves on a beach;
▶   wind speed and infiltration rate in an investigation of a sand dune ecosystem;
▶   noise levels beside a busy urban road.

Data collected on the interval and ratio scales are particularly useful in geographical investigations because they open up the options for data processing, presentation, and analysis. Because data on these scales can be quantified, the analysis of patterns, trends, and correlations can be more sophisticated than for data on nominal or ordinal scales.

Continuous scale
Data that can be measured on the interval or ratio scale.

Figure 3.4 Summary of how data on each scale can be presented and analysed.

Suitable methods	Nominal scale	Ordinal scale	Interval/ratio scale
Data presentation (charts and graphs)	Bar charts, pie charts	Bar charts or radial charts	Bar charts, rose diagrams, line charts, dispersion graphs, and scatter graphs.
Data presentation (maps)	Dot maps, located pie charts	Located bar charts, located radial charts	Isolines, choropleths, and proportional symbol maps
Measures of central tendency	Mode (or median if there is only one category)	Mode or median	Mean, median, or mode
Other forms of analysis			Interquartile range, Nearest Neighbour Analysis, Zingg Analysis
Statistical tests	Chi square test	Mann-Whitney statistical test	Spearman's Rank Correlation Coefficient

Limit the number of variables

Some geographical investigations are affected by a large number of variables in the data. Infiltration rates depend on variables such as antecedent weather, geology, soil type, and slope angle. For example, if you want to investigate the impact of slope angle on infiltration, you could limit the effect of geology on infiltration rates by making sure that all sample points are chosen from sites that have the same geology. Public perception of a geographical issue (such as risk, identity, or globalisation) depends on socio-economic variables such as age, education, ethnicity, or health and well-being.

Property values depend on the variables shown in Figure 3.5. As a geographer
you are mostly interested in the impact of location variables. You could
investigate how house prices or rental values vary with distance from a feature in
the local environment such as a busy road or a green space. You should control
the other variables.

▶ Economic variables tend to vary over time so the way to rule out the effects
of these variables is to collect data over as short a period as possible. If you
were collecting secondary data on house prices from a website you would
need to restrict your search to very recent sales.

▶ You can control property variables by collecting house price data for
properties that are all of a very similar type, size, and age.

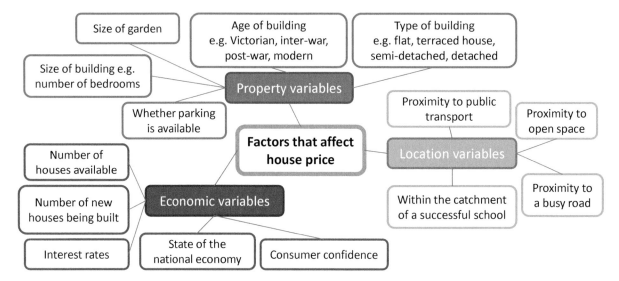

Figure 3.5 A number of variables
influence property values. The
number of variables that are
investigated needs to be carefully
limited within the investigation.

Figure 3.6 How are property values
affected by their location?

We could investigate the impact of urban green spaces on changing places by:

▶ using attitudinal surveys or questionnaires to assess the value of green spaces
to the well-being of local residents;

▶ using a transect to investigate how property prices are affected by distance
from the green space.

Control groups

When your investigation contains a wide variety of different variables it is a good idea to use a **control group**. This allows you to make comparisons between data where the variables are controlled (or limited) and data where one particular variable may be playing a significant role. For example, in our theoretical investigation of property values, we may suspect that proximity to a successful school or public transport hub (like the underground station in Figure 3.7) is responsible for higher property prices. To investigate this idea:

▶ identify a control group – in this case a location that is unaffected by either the school or the transport hub;

▶ compare property values in the control group to property values in locations close to:
  - the school;
  - the underground station;
  - the bus station.

> **Control group**
>
> A control group provides a standard to which data collected in fieldwork can be compared.

Figure 3.7 In larger cities such as London, property values tend to be higher in neighbourhoods close to public transport hubs.

Now that you have thought about the data that is needed it is time to select suitable methods for collecting this data. Pages 34-94 describe a number of different methods. Use these pages to research suitable methods.

Selecting suitable methods

In selecting the methods that you intend to use, the keys to success are:

▶ choosing **suitable** methods that are appropriate to the **aims** of your investigation;

▶ selecting a **range** of methods rather than relying on one. By selecting a range of valid methods you are more likely to collect data that is accurate and reliable;

▶ avoiding methods that are **irrelevant.** You should avoid using every possible method you can think of for the sake of it. Doing this will generate more data than you can handle – some of which may be irrelevant or repetitious;

▶ demonstrating that you can **personalise** the method to make it effective for your own needs. For example, having chosen to use a bipolar survey (page 39) you should develop your own bipolar statements rather than using examples copied directly from this book or elsewhere.

Think critically about potential methods

At this stage your research will initially focus on 'How?' In other words: how can I collect the data that I need? However, you also need to consider two other important questions.

▶ Why is this method the best one for me to use?

▶ What are the potential strengths and/or limitations of using this method? How can any limitations be minimised?

These are important considerations because a well-written report will justify the selection of your methods. It will also evaluate their success.

Figure 3.8 summarises some of the things that you should consider when you are selecting methods for collecting primary data.

Evaluation

Your finished report must evaluate your data collection methods so make a note of any limitations and how you tried to minimise these.

Remember that, in a great report, you will justify why you selected your methods of primary data collection.

A poor investigation	A great investigation
Relies very heavily on just one method of primary data collection. For example, relying only on the use of an Environmental Quality Index (EQI) in an investigation of regeneration.	Uses a variety of suitable methods of data collections. For example, in an investigation of regeneration you might use an EQI, re-photography, a Likert survey, and collect data on footfall.
Uses an 'off-the-shelf' survey sheet such as an EQI that has been found online. However, some of the criteria in the EQI are not relevant to the aims of your investigation.	Personalises 'off-the-shelf' survey sheets so that they have specific relevance to the aims of your investigation.
Relies very heavily on secondary data with hardly any primary data collection.	Uses a mixture of appropriate methods to collect valid primary data and supplements this with some relevant secondary data.

Figure 3.8 Select your methods of primary data collection carefully.

Action Point 3

Identify any specialist equipment (for example, clinometers or quadrats) that might be
needed and make sure you can borrow it.

At this point you need to consider the following questions.

▶ Will I need specialist equipment to collect the data? If so…
- is this equipment available?
- will I be able to borrow it?
- do I know how to use the equipment correctly?

Don't underestimate the time it takes to design your primary data collection methodology.

Data that needs specialist equipment

Quantitative data that is continuous will need to be measured. Wind speed, slope angles, soil moisture, infiltration rate, and noise levels are examples and some of these will need specialist fieldwork equipment. Thankfully, you can download apps onto a smart phone to collect some of this data. For example, you can use a smart phone as:

▶ a compass;
▶ a noise meter;
▶ a clinometer;
▶ a lightmeter.

A clinometer is used to measure angles. It can be used to measure the angle of a slope such as a beach profile or sand dune profile. With some simple trigonometry you can use a clinometer to calculate the height of a geographical feature such as a cliff or tree. You may be able to borrow a clinometer. Alternatively, you could download a free clinometer app onto your smartphone, like the one shown in Figure 3.9.

Figure 3.9 You can download an app to use your mobile as a clinometer.

Some investigations, however, may need specialist equipment for which there are no apps. Wind speed, for example, needs to be measured using an anemometer, like the one in Figure 3.10. If you are analysing soils you may need to borrow soil sieves and have access to accurate digital scales to record weight lost after your soil samples have been dried in a soil oven (you can use a domestic oven on a very low heat).

Figure 3.10 An anemometer is used to measure wind speed.

Data that does not need specialist equipment

A lot of data can be collected without the need for any special equipment.

▶ **Quantitative data** on the **nominal scale** can be counted. Examples of this kind of data collection include pedestrian counts, traffic surveys, and sediment surveys. You will need to have designed data collection sheets (see pages 132-135) but you are unlikely to need any sophisticated equipment. You could use your mobile phone as a stopwatch and you can improvise a quadrat with tent pegs and string (see page 85).

▶ **Qualitative data** includes spoken evidence and text in the form of interviews, questionnaires, audio recordings, or blogs as well as images such as field sketches, photographs, videos, or artwork. Spoken evidence can be collected using a well-designed survey sheet such as a bipolar survey, Likert survey, or a questionnaire. Interviews could be recorded on your smartphone and a phone or camera could be used to record images.

QUESTION I will want to collect footfall and traffic data from several locations at the same time. Is it possible to share the task of data collection with other students?

ANSWER Yes, you are allowed to work collaboratively when you are collecting primary data. It will be important that everyone in your team knows what to do and collects the data in the same way.

QUESTION I only want to use qualitative data. Is that ok? I'm worried that it isn't as good as quantitative data.

ANSWER Using only qualitative data is fine. It's not true to say that one type of data is better than another type of data. What is important is that the data is valid and that it answers the thing you have set out to investigate.

QUESTION Do I have to use a control survey?

ANSWER No, a control survey is a useful strategy for many investigations but it is not appropriate for everyone. The important thing is to design a method of data collection that is appropriate for the needs of your investigation. This will include deciding when and where to collect the data and deciding which sampling strategy to use. It is important to be able to **justify** each of these decisions

3.2 Primary data collection methods

This section provides advice on methods for collecting data from primary sources in the field. Your four days of fieldwork give you an ideal opportunity to test some of these methods. As well as learning **how** to collect data you should take the time to consider **why** the methods you use are suitable.

Primary data collection methods

When you are planning your own Independent Investigation use this section to help you select the data collection methods appropriate for your investigation. You should think about the following issues:

▶ how the method could help you investigate your own research questions;
▶ whether quantitative data would be complemented by the collection of qualitative data;
▶ whether secondary data would complement any of this primary data.

Accessibility Index

The concept of accessibility is important, for example, for equal opportunity and disability, because planned environments such as town centres should be designed to enable easy access for everyone. In reality, of course, some urban environments are harder to navigate than others if you are partially sighted, suffer from hearing loss, or rely on the use of a wheelchair.

To investigate accessibility you can plot the location of important features such as disabled parking spaces, ramps, or textured pavements onto a base map. In addition, you can assess features of the built environment using an **Accessibility Index**. This is a set of statements (or criteria) that allow you to make a judgement about features such as:

▶ frequency of public transport and whether it is accessible to all; parking provision;
▶ **circulation spaces** for pedestrians including safe places to cross roads;
▶ entrances to public buildings and shops to include ramps, handrails, and automatic and/or wide entrance doors;
▶ circulation around shopping centres or inside shops.

Two different examples of accessibility surveys are given in Figure 3.13. The first uses a bipolar scale. Rather than using either of these Accessibility Surveys you could conduct a pilot and add or remove criteria. You can also weight the scores to reflect the relative importance of the criteria.

Why investigate accessibility?

You might want to examine contrasting levels of accessibility for named groups of people (for example, young able-bodied people compared to parents with a pushchair, or someone with a visual impairment) as one aspect of:

▶ the quality of the built environment in a recently regenerated area;
▶ an investigation of accessibility in neighbouring urban wards using **Egan's Wheel** to define aspects of sustainable urban living.

> It is a good idea to collect a range of primary data using a variety of techniques rather than relying heavily on only one survey method such as an EQI.

Circulation space

Circulation spaces are those areas (indoors or outdoors) that are left empty so that people can easily move about.

Egan's wheel

Egan's wheel represents 8 key features of sustainable living: Strong communities, Well-designed homes, Sensitive to the environment, Governance (well-run, well-led); Fair for everyone, Good Transport, Strong economy, Well-served (services).

Figure 3.11 Textured (or tactile) paving is designed to aid pedestrians who have a visual impairment. Cathedral Road, Cardiff.

Figure 3.12 Assess obstructions to pavements as part of an accessibility survey. Brick Lane, London.

Location .... Date/time:							
Pavement accessibility		+2	+1	0	-1	-2	
Is the pavement wide enough for a wheelchair?	More than sufficient.						Insufficient.
How steep are gradients?	Flat.						Steep.
Is the pavement obstructed?	No obstructions.						Numerous obstructions.
How even is the pavement?	Even.						Uneven.
Has tactile paving been used?	Numerous examples.						None.
Are the kerbs dropped at crossing points?	Numerous examples.						None.

Figure 3.13 Examples of Accessibility Indices.

Building accessibility	Yes	No
Is there designated blue badge parking?		
Is the front door accessible by ramp?		
Does the entrance have a handrail?		
Does the door open automatically?		
Is there an audible/tactile intercom?		
Is the door wide enough for a wheelchair?		
Is the reception desk at an appropriate height?		
Are corridors / aisles wide enough?		
Can shelves be reached from a wheelchair?		
Do signs use lettering that is large enough?		
Has a hearing loop been installed?		
Is the lift large enough for a wheelchair?		
Does the lift have controls at an appropriate height?		

Evaluation

Did you use 'off the shelf' data collection sheets, like these, or adapt data collection sheets to make them relevant to your investigation?

Test your understanding

Consider how you might use qualitative data such as photos and questionnaires to complement data from an Accessibility Survey.

Attitude surveys

Attitude surveys can be used to investigate people's perceptions and views on a wide range of geographical subjects. The two most commonly used techniques are bipolar surveys and Likert surveys, while the Guttman survey offers a way of investigating the strength of someone's opinion. See the separate entries for each method.

Attitude surveys have some limitations and you should think about how to reduce the possible effects of these limitations when you design your survey. For example, different people may interpret the scales and descriptions in different ways which could compromise the reliability of the survey. One way to address this is to use a pilot survey to ensure that the statements, criteria, and scaling are working effectively. This will take additional time so it should be built in to your work schedule.

Why use attitude surveys?

Attitude surveys are quicker to conduct than traditional questionnaires and generate ordinal data which is simpler to analyse than qualitative data. The traditional way to investigate people's attitudes and perceptions is through questionnaires and interviews. However, these methods take a lot of time and the qualitative data generated can be time-consuming to analyse.

Bipolar surveys

The **bipolar scale** (or bipolar semantic scale) is a method for collecting people's attitudes. It uses pairs of adjectives, or pairs of statements, that are opposite to one another. Respondents have to decide where their opinion fits between pairs of opposing statements that lie at either end of a scale.

The simplest form of bipolar survey uses pairs of adjectives as opposing sides of the bipolar scale. Research suggests that a 7 point scale is best. An example is shown in Figure 3.14.

One limitation of these simple bipolar scales is that the results could be unreliable as adjectives used in a bipolar survey may mean different things to different people. For example, in slang, the meaning of words like sick, bad, and wicked is the opposite of what they usually mean.

	+3	+2	+1	0	-1	-2	-3	
Attractive								Unattractive
Quiet								Noisy
Safe								Unsafe
Clean								Dirty
Friendly								Unfriendly

Figure 3.14 A simple bipolar scale uses pairs of opposing adjectives.

Weblink

http://www.thesaurus.com/ Use the search engine to find synonyms (similar words) and antonyms (opposite words).

An alternative approach is to use opposing descriptions rather than simple adjectives. An example, which could be used in a coastal environment, is shown in Figure 3.15. By using descriptions rather than simple adjectives you should reduce the level of subjectivity of your survey. This should make your data more reliable because respondents will have a clearer idea of what you mean by each statement and respond more consistently.

Criteria	Negative evaluation	-3	-2	-1	0	1	2	3	Positive evaluation
Aesthetic Do the defences add value to the visual quality of the landscape?	Greatly detracts from the visual quality of the landscape.								Greatly enhances the visual quality of the landscape.
Access Do the defences allow access to the beach?	Difficult access to the beach for everyone.								Direct access to the beach for everyone.
Recreational Value Do the defences enhance the recreational use of the beach area?	No additional value added to people's recreational use of the beach.								Greatly enhances people's recreational use of the beach.

Figure 3.15 A bipolar scale that uses opposing descriptions.

Evaluation

You should evaluate the reliability of your bipolar data. Did you use a pilot? If so, that should improve reliability. Did you work as part of a team to collect the data? If so, did everyone use exactly the same method, thereby improving reliability?

Figure 3.16 Traffic in Digbeth, an inner urban area of Birmingham.

Make sure that your statements are focusing on only one idea at a time. For example, in a statement about the safety of the urban environment, shown in Figure 3.16, a description such as *'noisy and dangerous levels of traffic'* would produce unreliable results because people may feel that traffic is noisy but not dangerous, or vice versa.

Positive	+2	+1	0	-1	-2	Negative
Housing is sick.						Housing is in poor condition.
Not much traffic.						There are no safe places to cross the road.
Really wide pavements.						Uneven pavements.
Streets are well lit at night.						Streets seem to be gloomy.
Area feels safe. There is no graffiti.						Area feels unsafe. There is a lot of graffiti and litter.

Figure 3.17 A student's bipolar survey which contains errors.

Test your understanding

A student is investigating the concept of sustainability in an urban environment. Study the bipolar scale that they have designed which is shown in Figure 3.17. How might it be improved?

Carbon content surveys (see also Soil Surveys)

Plants absorb carbon dioxide from the atmosphere during photosynthesis and store it as carbon. Woodlands store huge amounts of carbon in the trees, their roots, and in the soil. It is impossible to accurately measure the amount of carbon stored in any ecosystem but in a woodland you can make some estimates of the amount of carbon stored in the trees themselves. To do this you will need to complete the following steps.

One Estimate the biomass of a sample of trees by measuring their girth – the circumference of the trunk.

Two Get an overview of the density of the woodland – how closely together the trees are planted.

Why investigate woodland carbon stores?

You could investigate the factors that might determine the amount of carbon stored such as:

- tree species;
- density of planting;
- age of trees;
- health of the woodland soil.

You could also compare two areas of woodland to investigate the potential human impact on the store through woodland management such as coppicing, planting, clear felling, mono-culture (like Figure 3.18) or mixed planting (like Figure 3.19).

If a woodland is being managed for wildlife you may find that fallen trees are being allowed to rot – therefore releasing carbon slowly back into the soil. You could investigate the micro-ecosystem of the log - investigating light levels, soil moisture, soil organic content, and invertebrates because these help to transfer carbon from the log to the soil.

You can record the number of earthworms in the soil by making a solution of yellow mustard powder in cold water and pouring this into the soil. The mustard is an irritant so the earthworms come to the surface where you can record their numbers and species.

Figure 3.18 Coniferous plantation. Forestry Commission woodland at Shelve Hill, Shropshire.

Figure 3.19 Mixed deciduous planting. Forestry Commission woodland at Shelve Hill, Shropshire.

Figure 3.20 Download an app for your smartphone that enables you to measure light intensity.

You may want to try to estimate the amount of carbon stored in an area of woodland. If so, you will need to sample a number of trees to calculate the average amount of carbon stored in each tree. The circumference of the tree depends largely on the age of the tree (although it also varies by species). Therefore managed woodlands that have only a single species of tree, all planted at the same time, will have similar sized trees so the sample can be small – say 10-20 trees. However, if the woodland has trees of different species and ages then you will need a much larger sample – at least 50 trees.

Estimating the biomass of a tree

The biomass of a tree must be calculated first in order to estimate the carbon stored within it.

One Measure the circumference (girth) of the tree in centimetres. Take the measurement at 1.3 metres from the ground each time.

Two Convert the circumference of the tree to dry weight of the timber. Use Figure 3.21.

Three Divide the dry weight value by 2. This will give you an approximate value for the weight of carbon stored in the tree.

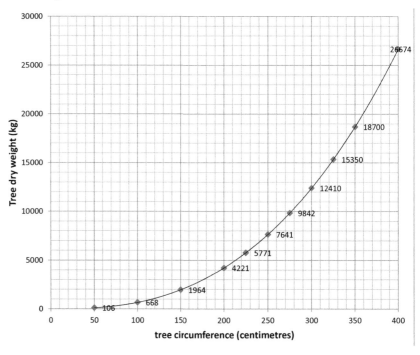

Figure 3.21 Use this graph to convert circumference of your tree to dry weight.

Weblink

https://www.forestresearch.gov.uk/ Forest Research provided the data for Figure 3.21. Use its website to read research papers that could be useful in your Literature Review.

Estimating the density of trees in a woodland

Density of planting is another factor that will affect the amount of carbon that can be stored in a woodland. In a very small woodland it may be possible to count every tree but, in a larger woodland, you will need to sample the distance between trees in order to calculate density. The **Point-quarter method** is the best way to do this.

One Set out a transect through the woodland of at least 150 metres. Start the transect within the woodland rather than at the edge. Trees tend to grow more densely at the edge of a woodland because they receive more light.

Two Choose at least 5 sample locations along your transect using random number tables to select the sites. Mark each site with a stake or peg.

Three Imagine that your first sample location is at the centre of a compass. Divide the area immediately around the sample location into four quadrants. Notionally these are to your NE, SE, SW, and NW.

Four Measure the **distance** from the sample location to the **nearest** tree that has a circumference greater than 40cm (at 1.3 metres from the ground) in **each** quadrant – so four trees in total.

Five For each of the four trees, measure and record the circumference.

Six Repeat actions Four and Five (above) for trees that have a circumference of between 2.5cm and 40cm. This will give you an indication of the density of the smaller trees that form the under-storey. Notice that, in Figure 3.22, the south-west quadrant has two large trees. Each of these is nearer to the sample point than the large tree in the south-east quadrant. However, you should measure the distance to the nearest large tree in each quadrant rather than the four nearest large trees.

Figure 3.22 Use the Point-quarter method to estimate woodland density.

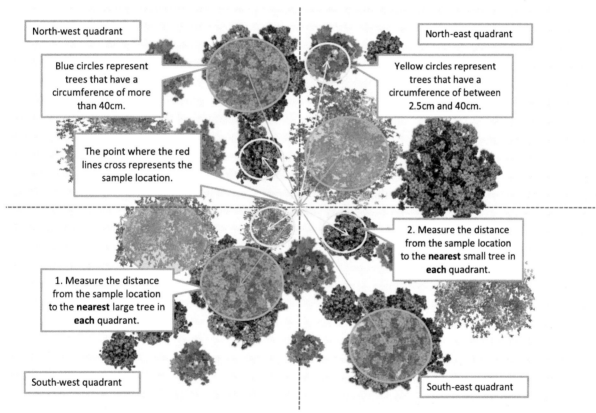

Calculating the density of a woodland

Once you have finished taking measurements between the trees you can calculate the density of the larger trees by following these steps.

One Calculate the mean distance ($\bar{D}$) from the sample locations to the larger trees (with a circumference greater than 40cm).

Two Use the following equation to calculate density. If you have measured in metres, this will give the density of trees per square metre.

$$Density = 1/ (\bar{D})^2$$

Three There are 10,000 square metres in one hectare. So multiply the value obtained in the equation above by 10,000.

Worked example

Total distance (m) for a sample
of 20 trees (5 locations) = 142.7
Mean distance (m) = 7.135

Density per square metre $= \dfrac{1}{7.135^2} = \dfrac{1}{50.908225} = 0.01964$ per square metre

Density per hectare $= 0.01964 \times 10,000 = 193.4$ per hectare

Four Repeat actions Two and Three for trees with a circumference of 2.5 - 40cm to give you the density of the smaller trees that form the under-storey.

Estimating carbon stored per hectare

So far you have seen how to estimate:
▶ the amount of carbon stored in a sample of trees;
▶ the density of trees per hectare

These are two important factors that help determine the carbon store of any woodland. You can use the two values that have been calculated so far to estimate the amount of carbon stored in the trees of an area of woodland.

One Total up the amount of carbon stored in trees you sampled and divide by the number of trees in the sample to calculate the mean amount of carbon stored in each tree.

Two Multiply the mean amount of carbon stored in each tree by the density of trees per hectare.

Cleanliness Index (see also EQI)

A **Cleanliness Index** (also known as a Graffiti Index) is a measure of the amount of litter, graffiti, and fly posting (leaflets that have been glued to buildings, posts, or street furniture). The Local Government Association uses the Cleanliness index to assess whether streets have litter and/or graffiti that fall below 'an acceptable level'. The Cleanliness Index uses detailed criteria (statements) to assess the quality of the environment, so it works in much the same way as an EQI.

Why use a cleanliness index?

You might use a cleanliness index as part of an investigation of:
▶ the success of a regeneration scheme;
▶ the impact of deindustrialisation or dereliction;
▶ perceptions of different groups to the quality of the urban environment;
▶ fear of crime.

You should complement data gathered from a cleanliness index with other quantitative and qualitative data. This will depend on the focus of your investigation but it might include:
▶ **photos** (qualitative data) that record the quality of the urban environment;
▶ **participant observation** (qualitative data) – observing whether people stay for longer in cleaner urban environments;
▶ **rateable values or property values** (quantitative data from a secondary source) to investigate a possible correlation between street cleanliness and land values;
▶ **questionnaires or interviews** (qualitative data) to assess the views of local residents or community groups about graffiti.

How to create a Cleanliness Index

One Develop a set of criteria to define street cleanliness.

Two Choose a sampling strategy.

▶ You could use one or more transects – perhaps radiating out from the town centre.

▶ Alternatively, divide the town up using a grid and sample each grid square so you can map your results.

Three Stop and record the amount of graffiti that is visible on any building, fence, post, pavement, or wall using your criteria.

Figure 3.23 An example of a Cleanliness Index used by the Local Government Association.

Level	Score	Criteria
A	3.0	No litter/detritus/graffiti/fly posting.
B+	2.5	The location is predominantly free of litter/detritus/graffiti/fly posting except for some small items.
B	2.0	
B-	1.5	
C	1.0	A widespread distribution of litter/detritus/graffiti/fly posting with minor accumulations.
C-	0.5	
D	0	The location is heavily covered in detritus with significant accumulations or there is extensive graffiti and/or fly posting which is clearly visible and obtrusive.

Why investigate graffiti?

The cleanliness index (Figure 3.23) assumes that all graffiti is bad – but is it? Some groups of people might see graffiti as a positive and decorative feature of the environment while others might perceive it to be a nuisance. The pedestrians seen in Figure 3.26 were all photographing a large 'piece' (or masterpiece) of graffiti because they appreciate it as street art. You could investigate whether graffiti (or street art) is associated with gentrification. You could investigate whether graffiti attracts visitors and contributes to the local economy.

The cleanliness index assumes that all graffiti is the same but there are all sorts of different types of graffiti, from tags and paste-ups to stencils, throw-ups, and (master) pieces of street art. You could design a graffiti index that differentiates between different types of graffiti and then investigate whether some places have types of graffiti that people generally like whereas other places have types of graffiti that people generally dislike. If you were going to do this then you would have to conduct a qualitative survey first to determine what different groups of people think about different styles of graffiti.

Weblink

https://lginform.local. gov.uk/search Local Government Association website describes how levels of litter and graffiti can be used as a measure of street cleanliness.

Figure 3.24 Types of graffiti.

A Paste-up graffiti (a form of fly posting)
B Stencil graffiti
C Tag graffiti

Figure 3.25 Large (master) pieces of graffiti on the corner of Hanbury Street and Brick Lane, London.

Figure 3.26 Tourists photographing graffiti on the corner of Hanbury Street and Brick Lane, London.

Crime Surveys (see also Mental Mapping)

To investigate crime you can plot the location of crime prevention strategies such as the use of CCTV cameras, shuttered windows, or **alley-gating** (see Figure 3.27) onto a base map of your fieldwork location.

Alternatively, you can assess features of the built environment using a **Crime Index**. This is a set of statements (or criteria) that allow you to make a judgement about the use or absence of crime prevention strategies.

Why use crime surveys?

There are a number of different approaches to investigating evidence of crime in the environment. You can investigate:

▶ **the perception of crime**. You might use emotional mapping and combine this qualitative data with secondary data about actual reported crimes to see whether the fear of crime is justified;

▶ **ways of mitigating (reducing the risk) of crime**. You might use a Crime Index to assess how effectively a community is safeguarding itself and compare this with secondary data about actual reported crimes to see whether crimes are more or less common in areas that are well protected;

▶ **whether there is a correlation between reported crime and another variable** such as footfall, traffic, or rateable values in a city centre.

Be careful not to jump to conclusions about apparent correlations. In a university town, you may find evidence that locations that have a higher crime rate also have a larger than average proportion of students. It would be **wrong** to assume a **causal link** between these variables. In other words, we cannot assume that the students are causing the crime.

Alley-gating

Alley-gating is a crime prevention strategy. It is used in areas of housing that have access to the back of residential properties via an alleyway.

Figure 3.27 Alley-gating, Cardiff.

Causal Link

A causal link occurs where one variable is the direct cause of variation in a second variable.

Test your understanding

Study Figure 3.28. Consider how you might use a pilot survey with local residents to decide on a suitable weighting for each criteria.

Crime Index

Like other indices, such as Cleanliness Index or EQI, a Crime Index relies on you making consistent judgements about evidence in the environment to collect ordinal data. Design a survey sheet similar to Figure 3.28. Use features that you have identified in your study area and give them scores that you think are appropriate. A great way to decide on a scoring system would be to interview local residents or experts such as community police officers then choose scores that reflect the relative importance given by your respondents.

Location .... Date/time ....

	Score
Burglar alarms	+5
External lighting	+5
Security cameras	+10
Neighbourhood watch stickers	+3
Security bars on windows	+10
Security shutters on windows/doors	+12
Anti-climb paint	+5
Easy access to the back of the property (e.g. alley)	-5
Street is badly lit	-8
Adjacent land is derelict	-5

Figure 3.28 An example of a Crime Index.

Emotional mapping
(see also Mental mapping)

Emotional mapping is a data collection strategy that you would use to investigate people's emotional responses to a place. At a simple level we all have places that we feel attached to emotionally – places where we have happy memories or places where we feel relaxed and comfortable. On the other hand, we may have had experiences that give us negative perceptions of certain places – places where we feel uneasy, unhappy, or afraid, perhaps because of the fear of crime, or because of the amount of traffic, noise, or pollution. Emotional mapping is a way of collecting evidence of people's feelings about a place.

One Identify your participants. You may want to work with individuals or with a focus group.

Two Create a base map of your fieldwork location and a series of questions – see Figure 3.29.

Three Ask your participants to respond to the questions by marking locations on the map. You could ask them to use colours or emojis to represent how they feel about places in your study area.

Figure 3.29 An example of an emotional mapping survey.

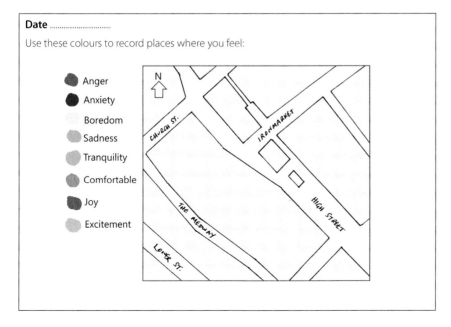

Date ....

Use these colours to record places where you feel:

- Anger
- Anxiety
- Boredom
- Sadness
- Tranquility
- Comfortable
- Joy
- Excitement

Environmental Quality Surveys (or EQI)

An **Environmental Quality Index (EQI)** is a technique which uses detailed criteria (statements) to assess the quality of the environment. An EQI relies on you identifying the elements of the environment and creating criteria which can be used to make judgements objectively about their quality.

Why use an EQI?

An EQI turns qualitative judgements about different elements of the environment into ordinal data that can be easily processed, represented, and analysed. The use of well-defined criteria will enable you to get consistent results. This is especially important if several people are collecting the data.

An EQI can be easily adapted to suit many different contexts or types of investigation. For example:

1 in an **investigation of regeneration**, you might want to judge the quality of green spaces, parking provision, or pedestrian areas;

2 in a **coastal investigation** you might want to judge the quality of coastal defences, or make a judgement about vulnerability of residential areas or access to the beach;

3 in an **investigation of rural deprivation** you could use an EQI to assess the provision of local services;

4 in an investigation of **urban or rural sustainability** use an EQI to make judgements about elements of **Egan's Wheel**.

How to use an EQI

To carry out an environmental audit using an EQI follow these steps.

One Decide on the elements of the environment that you wish to score.

Two Write the criteria. These are descriptions which can be used consistently by you, or members of a team, to judge each element of the environment. Each criterion can be numbered using, for example, a scale of 1 to 5. See Figure 3.30.

Three Carry out pilot surveys to assess the effectiveness of your EQI survey. You can then amend the EQI data collection sheet if necessary before the actual fieldtrip.

Four Use the pilot to take photos of scenes that you think typify each criterion (see page 91). This will make your use of the EQI more consistent and, therefore, the data will be reliable.

Five Remember to add a space on your data collection sheet to record the location and time of each survey.

Feature	Criteria				
	5	4	3	2	1
Vegetation	Plenty of trees. 1+ tree per 20m.	Some trees. 1 tree per 20-40m.	Few trees. 1 tree per 40-80m.	Sporadic trees. 1 tree per 80-100m.	No trees or greenery.
	5	4	3	2	1
Litter	Occasional litter. One item every 50m+.	Hardly any litter. One item every 11-50m.	Some litter. One item every 6-10m.	Lots of litter. One item every 1-5m.	Abundant litter. More than one item per metre.

Figure 3.30 Use precise criteria to assess each feature in an EQI survey.

Combine an EQI with other quantitative and qualitative data

Consider using an EQI in combination with other quantitative data such as the amount of traffic, pedestrian crossings, or CCTV cameras (nominal/discrete data), and noise levels (ratio/continuous data). You could also combine an EQI with qualitative data such as interviews or images. The images could be your own photos (primary evidence) or old photos and artwork from secondary sources. For example, you could use an EQI and complement this with data by:

▷ **using re-photography** (a qualitative method where you compare your own photos to older images from secondary sources – see page 92) to analyse whether urban change has had a positive or negative impact on environmental quality;

▷ **measuring noise levels of traffic** and **plotting the location of features** such as traffic calming to investigate how traffic affects environmental quality.

Adding weightings to an EQI

You may decide that the environmental features included in the survey do not have equal importance. For example, local residents may tell you that they are much more affected by traffic noise and litter than they are by vegetation. If so, you can increase the weighting of the features that are considered to be more important. Do this by multiplying them by a factor, as in Figure 3.31.

> The addition of a weighting is a good idea. Use evidence from your pilot survey to decide on appropriate weightings.

Feature	Criteria				
	5	4	3	2	1
Vegetation	Plenty of trees 1+ tree per 20m	Some trees 1 tree per 20-40m	Few trees 1 tree per 40-80m	Sporadic trees 1 tree per 80-100m	No trees or greenery 0 trees
Litter	5x2=10	4x2=8	3x2=6	2x2=4	1x2=2
	Occasional litter One item every 50m+	Hardly any litter One item every 11-50m	Some litter One item every 6-10m	Lots of litter One item every 1-5m.	Abundant litter More than one item per metre
Traffic	5x3=15	4x3=12	3x3=9	2x3=6	1x3=3
	Occasional traffic Less than 5 cars per minute	Hardly any traffic 5-9 vehicles per minute	Some traffic 10-15 vehicles per minute. All cars	Lots of traffic 16-20 vehicles per minute. Lorries and cars	Traffic is a nuisance More than 20 vehicles per minute. Lorries and cars

Figure 3.31 Use weightings to reflect the view that some features of the environment are more important than others.

> Scores will be inconsistent if groups of students use an EQI without understanding the criteria. Precise wording for criteria and photos to represent each criterion will increase reliability and comparability of results.

Using an EQI to assess sustainability

You can use EQIs to investigate sustainability of key features of the rural or urban environment. However, sustainability is a huge concept that needs unpacking. To focus your investigation choose two or three aspects of Egan's wheel as a focus for your criteria, as in Figure 3.32.

You could use an EQI in combination with a questionnaire or Likert Scale survey (page 64) to investigate the link between improving the sustainability of urban environments and improving **well-being** of local residents.

Well-being

Well-being is a measure of our mental health – how happy and healthy we feel.

Feature	Criteria				
	5	4	3	2	1
Sensitive to the environment	A wide range of different habitats are available to the public.	Private gardens and communal areas have trees/shrubs as well as grass.	Private gardens have trees/ shrubs but communal areas are grass.	Some areas of grass, e.g. lawns, verges, or sports fields.	No green spaces.
	5	4	3	2	1
Well-served	A wide range of groups are actively involved in providing local community projects.	A wide range of services are available for different community groups.	Services are available for some different groups in the community.	Some services for local residents.	Very few services for any local residents.

Field sketches and sketch maps (see also Visual Evidence)

A **field sketch**, like Figure 3.34, is an alternative method for collecting visual evidence. When you are drawing a field sketch concentrate on only the relevant geographical features. Leave out any unnecessary detail or clutter. You should add notes to the sketch straightaway while you are still in the field, for example:

▶ labels for the main features;
▶ more detailed notes (annotations) that help to make sense of the features in your sketch.

Why use a field sketch?

The act of making a field sketch is not about trying to create an artistic image. You don't even need to be very good at drawing. The process of field sketching makes you observe the landscape much more carefully than normal.

Use a field sketch to focus on specific aspects of the landscape that you perceive to be important. One tip is to cut a rectangular hole (about 15cm by 10cm) in a piece of card. Use the hole like the viewfinder of a camera. Hold it up and observe the landscape through the hole. This technique helps you to observe smaller details that you might otherwise miss if you glance quickly at the wider landscape.

Why bother drawing a sketch? Because in some situations, a field sketch is more useful than a photo. Field sketches are a useful option when:

▶ **the environment is visually cluttered**. A field sketch allows you to make a visual record of only the most important geographical features of a fieldwork location;
▶ **you cannot get into an optimum position to take a photo**. Study Figure 3.33. The artificial reefs have led to the deposition of sand in sweeping bays between each reef. This pattern is not clear in the photo because (without a drone) it was impossible to get the camera high enough to see the features properly. The field sketch allows you to show what the coastline would look like from a slightly higher viewpoint.

Remember to geo-locate your sketch – Figure 3.34 includes a two letter OS tile reference and six figure grid reference.

Figure 3.33 Photo of the artificial reefs at Sea Palling.

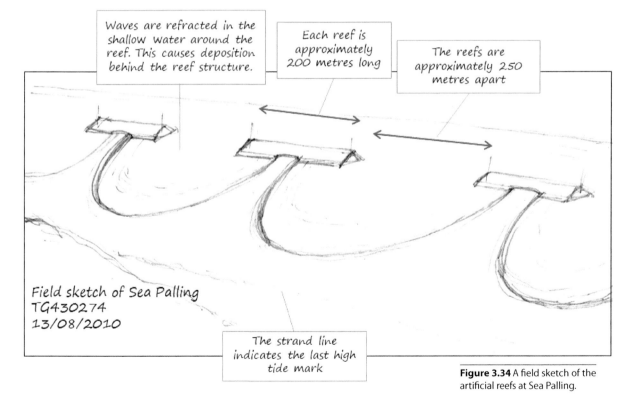

Waves are refracted in the shallow water around the reef. This causes deposition behind the reef structure.

Each reef is approximately 200 metres long

The reefs are approximately 250 metres apart

Field sketch of Sea Palling
TG430274
13/08/2010

The strand line indicates the last high tide mark

Figure 3.34 A field sketch of the artificial reefs at Sea Palling.

Test your understanding

Study Figures 3.33 and 3.34. Identify the main advantages of using a field sketch rather than a photo to represent a fieldwork location.

Sketch maps

Your finished report should contain a map that highlights the main features of the fieldwork location. You may be able to download a suitable map of your fieldwork area from a website. However, online maps are often too busy and cluttered which makes them difficult to use. By drawing a sketch map instead you can:

▶ leave out unnecessary details;
▶ just include the main features;
▶ label the features that are important to your fieldwork.

Remember to give your map a heading, a north arrow, and an approximate scale line. Make a key to match any colours or symbols on your map.

This is a geographical investigation so the moderator will expect to see an annotated map that represents the fieldwork location.

Figure 3.35 A sketch map of a fieldwork location should focus on just the essential features.

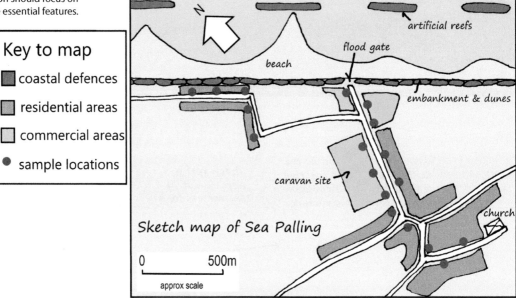

Flood Risk Index

Flood risk can be investigated at coastal locations and in locations that are adjacent to rivers. You may want to use a questionnaire or attitude survey (such as a Likert Scale Survey on page 64) to assess people's perceptions of the flood risk. You might also want to use a land use survey (page 62) to identify which buildings, businesses, or open spaces are at risk of flooding. Take photos of these locations and compare them with photos from secondary sources that show evidence of flooding (see re-photography on page 92).

Why use a Flood Risk Index?

A **Flood Risk Index** takes the idea of a land use survey one step further by attempting to identify which land uses are at the greatest potential risk of flood damage. A Flood Risk Index assigns a score to each land use – the greater the potential damage, the higher the score. Public parks and car parks lie at the bottom of the scale – flood damage here would have minimal social or economic consequences. At the other end of the scale are land uses such as a hospital or large factory where a flood event could cause serious social, economic, or financial losses. You then survey the areas that are at risk, recording the multiple land uses at each location, and calculating a total score for each location.

Weblink

https://floodassist.co.uk/resources/flood-risk
Use this website (or others like it) to identify the locations in your study area that are at low, medium, or high risk.

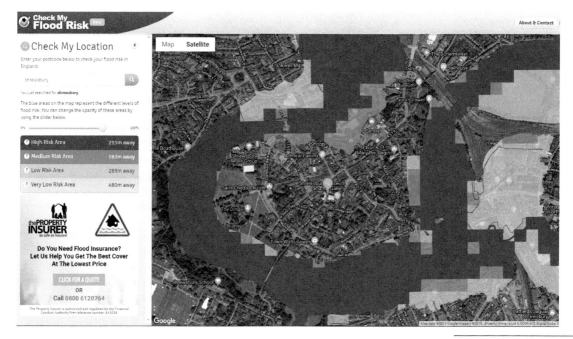

Figure 3.36 A screen shot from
Check My Flood Risk of Shrewsbury
town centre.

How to create a Flood Risk index

One Identify areas that are at risk of flooding - by using a secondary source such
as Check My Flood Risk. See Figure 3.36.

Two Create a scale of land uses such as Figure 3.37. Think about how you will
group the land uses and how you will score them. For example:

▶ Is the risk of damage to a historic building more serious than damage to a
modern one?

▶ Is the risk of economic loss during a flood more important than potential
social impacts? You might justify putting an old people's home and a hospital
in the same high risk category because each would be difficult to evacuate
quickly and a serious flood event could lead to injury or a fatality.

Three Collect the data by recording the land uses you can see at each sample
point. Make one tally mark for each land use and count up the number of tally
marks for each land use. The land use with the most tally marks is your mode.

Four Multiply the value of the mode by the land use score to give a Flood Risk
Index for that location. The higher the index, the greater the impact a flood
would have.

Use a pilot survey to ask
local people what they
think about the potential
social or economic
impacts of floods for
different land uses. Use
this feedback to inform
the scores in your Flood
Risk Index.

Figure 3.37 An example of a Flood
Risk Index.

Location ....

Land use type	Tally	Score
Large shops, high tech industry, large offices, warehouses, hospitals, secondary schools.		10
Major infrastructure, e.g. railways, dual carriageways, medium-sized businesses, independent shops, residential care homes.		9
Smaller offices, elderly people's homes, sheltered housing.		7
Blocks of flats.		6
Housing, corner shops.		5
Garages.		3
Car parks, public parks, playing fields.		2
Derelict land.		1

Record evidence of past floods

In addition to creating a Flood Risk Index you can record evidence of past flood events.

▶ **Look for physical evidence that the river has flooded recently.** This will take the form of rubbish – often plastics – caught in the branches of trees close to the river. Figure 3.39 shows an example. The height of this rubbish above the river bank can be measured with a tape to give an idea of the level of the flood water.

▶ **Record features of the built environment that indicate that the river has flooded in the past.** These features can be photographed, annotated, and their position located on a base map. For example:

- buildings with steps up to the front door so that the ground floor is above flood height;
- place or street names that indicate a history of flooding;
- flood defences such as embankments, floodgates, or fixings in the pavement for demountable defences to be slotted in.

Figure 3.39 Rubbish in the branches of a tree next to the River Severn (Shrewsbury) in March 2016 indicates the height of flood water from previous flood events.

Think about which score you would give to each of the following land uses in a Flood Risk Index.

- Buildings of historic value.
- Primary schools.
- Petrol stations.

- Electricity sub-stations.
- Allotments.
- Crèches.

If you were to use this technique you would need to be able to justify these choices so think carefully about the social, environmental, and economic impacts of floods and why flooding might cause more serious impacts to some land uses than others.

Footfall surveys

Footfall is a measure of how many pedestrians are visiting a place. It is usually simple to count people walking past over a period of, for example, 5 minutes. If you divide into teams and spread systematically through the town you can count footfall at different locations at the same time. This will give you the data you need to draw a map (like the one on page 169). It is important that each group counts for the same length of time and at the same time. Otherwise your results will not be reliable.

Measuring footfall in a public open space, like a park or pedestrian area, can be tricky because of the number of people and the complexity of their movement. For example, they may change direction, or walk in groups with few gaps between them. One strategy to improve the accuracy of the count is for three people to count at the same location for five minutes. Then, calculate the median value.

Why collect data on footfall?

You can use footfall data to investigate the ways that a place changes over time – counting footfall at regular times throughout the day, or during the week, to identify peaks and troughs.

The amount of footfall in a town centre can be regarded as a measure of the health and vibrancy of the high street. Typically, the most successful high street businesses locate in the busiest streets so you could investigate the correlation between footfall and rateable value.

Footfall can be age-related by counting the number of pedestrians who fit into broad age categories (e.g. 0-19, 20-39, 40-59, and 60+). You might then investigate whether some places attract younger or older pedestrians – perhaps investigating the land uses or features that have attracted these different groups through a questionnaire.

You could also use footfall as an indicator of the success of an urban regeneration project. Regeneration should make town centres more attractive so that more people, of different ages, continue to use our high streets. Consequently, you may want to investigate whether there is a correlation between footfall and:

- **features that are introduced to mitigate risk** such as wider pavements, traffic calming, or CCTV;
- **the attractiveness of the urban environment** – whether larger crowds are attracted to green urban spaces, improved signage, or the addition of public seating;
- **economic regeneration** – whether areas that have new shops and places to eat are more vibrant and have greater footfall.

Glacial and peri-glacial surveys (see also sediment analysis)

Glaciated uplands contain clues to the processes of glaciation that have helped shape them. These include landscape features such as corries (or cirques), U-shaped valleys, roche-mountonnees, drumlins, and eskers. Smaller features such as **striations** scored into the rock by the process of abrasion can also be seen. The **orientation** of these features can be investigated to help determine the direction of ice movement.

Why use glacial surveys?

Landscapes are complex. Some prominent features were largely created by processes that were at their most active thousands of years ago. Current landscape processes are, perhaps, only modifying these features. By measuring the orientation of features you can understand how past processes impact on today's landscape.

You can measure the orientation of features such as corries, drumlins, or striations. For example, you could investigate:

▶ whether aspect is an important factor in the formation of corries;
▶ whether striations align with the axis of U-shaped valleys.

Striations	

Striations are the lines which are scored into a rock by the process of glacial abrasion. Striations in bedrock indicate the direction of ice movement.

Orientation

Orientation is a description of the angle which a geographical feature makes in relation to magnetic North.

Figure 3.40 Striations in a polished rock. Sólheimajökull Glacier, South Iceland.

The Stiperstones is a ridge in Shropshire. The ridge is formed of tough Ordovician quartzite and is topped by a series of tors. Angular blocks of quartzite lie in distinct stripes on the upper slopes of the ridge – one of the tors and several stone stripes can be seen in Figure 3.41.

Figure 3.41 Stone stripes at the Stiperstones, Shropshire. SO367991.

The tors and stone stripes probably developed by freeze-thaw weathering of the rock during peri-glacial conditions at the end of the ice age. The angular blocks are not orientated randomly. This may suggest that they have aligned themselves down the slope as they slipped downhill due to the action of **solifluction**. You could use a compass to investigate their orientation and then use a rose diagram to present the data (see page 161).

How to measure orientation

To measure orientation you will need a compass.

One Align the base plate of the compass with the feature.

Two Turn the bezel (outer ring) of the compass to align the needle with North.

Three Read the bearing on the compass. Orientation will always have two values that are 180^0 apart. For example, if the feature is aligned on a west-east axis, the bearing will read 90^0 and 270^0. At this stage it doesn't matter whether you record 90° or 270° on your data collection sheet.

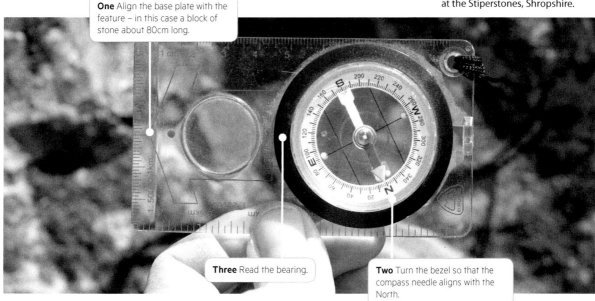

Figure 3.42 Using a compass to measure the orientation of stones at the Stiperstones, Shropshire.

One Align the base plate with the feature – in this case a block of stone about 80cm long.

Three Read the bearing.

Two Turn the bezel so that the compass needle aligns with the North.

Test your understanding
Consider why it is that the orientation of striations should be measured in bedrock.

Guttman Scale Surveys

The Guttman Scale is a type of attitude survey (see page 39) which is used **to assess strength of opinion**. Respondents are given an ordered series of statements (items) to which they must answer yes/no or agree/disagree. Each group of items focuses on attitudes about a single geographical issue. The items gradually increase in how specifically people feel about that issue. The aim of the survey is to discover at what point in the scale each respondent will switch from answering with '*yes*' to '*no*'. People who switch early will be taking one extreme position on the issue, while people who continue to answer with '*yes*' until the end of the scale will take the opposite extreme. An example of a Guttman Scale is shown in Figure 3.43.

Figure 3.43 Examples of Guttman Scale surveys.

The UK needs nuclear power.	YES / NO
New nuclear power stations should be built in the UK.	YES / NO
I would be happy to have a new nuclear power station built within my county.	YES / NO
I would be happy to have a new nuclear power station built within 20km of my home.	YES / NO
I would be happy to have a new nuclear power station built within 5km of my home.	YES / NO

Plastic packaging on all fresh fruit and veg is a useful convenience.	YES / NO
Plastic packaging on fresh fruit and veg is necessary for some produce.	YES / NO
I would prefer to buy fresh fruit and veg without plastic packaging.	YES / NO
I would be prepared to pay a little more for fresh fruit and veg if it did not have plastic packaging.	YES / NO
I refuse to buy fresh fruit and veg in plastic packaging.	YES / NO

Creating a Guttman Scale

You will need to conduct a pilot survey to test that the items make a progressive scale. To do this, you need to follow these steps.

One Generate a list of potential items.

Two Conduct a pilot. Ask a small number of people to answer yes/no. You could use other students for this.

Three Create a table with rows for the respondents and columns for the questions. If you use a spreadsheet such as Excel the next steps will be very quick.

Four Sort the columns with items that most frequently have 'yes' on the left.

Five Sort the rows with the respondents that most frequently answered 'yes' at the top.

Six Select the items that show a natural progression by deleting items that generate 'no' responses in the middle of a series of 'yes' responses.

One limitation of Guttman scale surveys is that some respondents may feel that they are being drawn into an extreme position and therefore do not answer as honestly as you might like. One way to reduce this effect is to mix some other items into the survey that appear to be related but are actually only used to conceal the increasing strength of opinion in the items that interest you. An example is shown in Figure 3.44.

> **Evaluation**
>
> Respondents may not feel comfortable if they think they are presenting themselves in an unfavourable manner. Did you consider this when you designed your questions?

Figure 3.44 An example of a concealed Guttman Scale survey.

Immigration is necessary.	YES / NO
Immigration from Europe has some benefits for the UK.	YES / NO
Emigration for UK citizens to other parts of Europe is a right.	YES / NO
Immigration from Europe has many benefits for the UK.	YES / NO
European migrants should take a UK citizenship test.	YES / NO
Immigration from Europe should be allowed to continue with few restrictions.	YES / NO
European migrants contribute to the UK economy by doing a lot of very useful jobs.	YES / NO
Immigration from Europe should be allowed to continue with no restrictions.	YES / NO

Index of decay

An **index of decay** is another way of collecting ordinal data on the quality of the environment. It could be used in conjunction with an EQI (see page 48) and other measures of environmental quality such as the amount of traffic or noise levels (see page 70) or Cleanliness index (see page 44).

As the name suggests, an index of decay is used to record the features of an urban environment that are in need of repair. It is most commonly used to assess residential districts but could also be used in industrial areas.

Figure 3.45 provides a typical example. You can vary the criteria and the scores. In this example, the negative features have been given negative scores but you could devise your own system.

Creating an Index of decay

One Use a pilot survey to identify examples of decay.

Two Design your data collection sheet. Decide on a scoring system. The scores can be weighted so that the most serious problems get the largest scores.

Three Select your sampling locations – aim to generate enough data to be able to draw a map.

Four Select a sample of buildings at each location using a systematic or random sampling strategy. Assess 3-5 buildings at each location and tick the scores for each building. Then tally up the total score for the location.

Structural damage (roof missing) (-20).

Broken glass (-10).

Windows bricked up (-12).

Figure 3.45 Use photos to record typical examples of each score.

> ## Evaluation
>
> Use photos to record typical examples of each score in your index. This will help you to make consistent assessments and, therefore, provide you with more reliable data.

Location .... Date/time:				
	None	**Little**	**Some**	**Much**
Broken glass in windows	0	-3	-5	-10
Paint peeling	0	-1	-2	-3
Rotting timbers	0	-2	-4	-8
Windows boarded up	0	-3	-6	-12
Slipped tiles/slates on roof	0	-1	-2	-3
Settlement cracks in walls	0	-3	-6	-12

Figure 3.46 An example of an Index of decay survey sheet.

Antecedent

Something is antecedent when it precedes something else. So, antecedent weather describes the weather conditions of the past few hours or days.

Evaluation

Remember that results are difficult to analyse unless you limit the number of variables that you investigate at any one location. See pages 31-32.

Figure 3.47 An infiltration ring.

Infiltration rate surveys (see also Soil surveys)

Infiltration is the process by which water enters the soil. **Infiltration rate** is the speed at which this process occurs. Infiltration rate is calculated by measuring the time it takes for water to sink into the ground from a suitable receptacle (see Figure 3.47). Initially the water infiltrates quickly. Then, as the pore spaces become saturated, the rate of infiltration slows and stops.

Why measure infiltration?

Infiltration rates vary depending on a range of factors. These include **antecedent** weather, vegetation cover, gradient, geology, soil type, land use, and soil compaction. Infiltration rate surveys can be used to investigate the relative importance of some of these factors. For example, infiltration rates could provide useful evidence in the investigation of:

▶ the development of a soil catena on a slope;
▶ whether soils have been compacted by visitors after an event such as a festival;
▶ whether some soils are more likely than others to lead to flash flooding of a local river.

Conducting an Infiltration rate survey

You will need quite a large supply of water – something to consider if you need to carry a heavy bucket of water to a sample point at the top of a hill! You will also need a stop watch (you can use your smartphone) and a data recording sheet.

One Find a suitable receptacle to act as the infiltration ring. You need a cylinder about 10cm in diameter and 30 to 40cm long. A large tin (with the bottom cut out) or a length of waste pipe is ideal.

Two Use a sampling strategy to select your sites, for example, at systematic intervals down a slope, or a stratified sample across an area with contrasting types of bedrock.

Three Knock the infiltration ring into the ground at the first site to a depth of about 10cm.

Four Place a ruler inside the infiltration ring so that you can record the water level as it drops.

Five Quickly fill the ring with water to a depth of 15 or 20cm (depending on the height of the ring). Initially the level of the water may drop quickly so record the depth of water every 60 seconds – more frequently if necessary. Then, as infiltration slows, record the level every few minutes.

Six As the water level falls the pressure exerted by water in the ring will reduce and infiltration will slow. This is a potential experimental error rather than a change in infiltration due to pore spaces in the soil becoming saturated. So, top up the water level to the starting level again. Do this every time the water falls more than 10mm. Remember to record that you have added water each time on your data collection sheet.

Seven Continue the experiment until the water stops falling.
Plot the results of your infiltration rate experiments using a line graph (see page 155).

Elapsed time (minutes)	Depth of water (mm) (plus top up)	Amount water level dropped (mm)	Time between readings (minutes)	Infiltration rate (mm per hour)
0	200	-	-	-
1	196	4	1	4 x (60/1) = 240
2	193	3	1	3 x (60/1) = 180
3	191	2	1	2 x (60/1) = 120
5	188 (top up to 201)	3	2	3 x (60/2) = 90
8	198	3	3	3 x (60/3) = 60

Figure 3.48 An example of a data collection sheet for an infiltration rate survey.

Interviews (see questionnaires)

Interviews are different from questionnaires because they only use open questions. This allows respondents to talk freely about their perceptions or experiences. Consequently it is a good idea to make an audio recording of each interview so you can listen to them again. That will help you to focus on the words people use and analyse any differences and similarities between what people say.

Why conduct interviews?

Interviews are a useful source of data for any investigation which involves research into people's perceptions or their values and attitudes. They are flexible forms of survey – you can write questions that are suitable and unique to your own investigation.

How to conduct an interview

The process of interviewing someone, and then analysing the results (see page 184), is much more time-consuming than conducting a questionnaire. To save time you may decide to interview only a small sample of people. For this reason, you should not think of the interview process as a way of recording the views of everyone in the community – your small sample size is unlikely to represent a large and diverse population. However, interviews can be a useful way of gathering the views of a small, homogeneous group. Interviews are often used successfully to record the views of a small 'expert' group who have a stake in an issue such as planners or business leaders.

For advice on ethical issues of interviews see pages 108-109.

For advice on sampling strategies for interviews see pages 100-101.

For advice on analysing interviews see pages 187-188.

Another useful way to collect interviews is by setting up a focus group of between 6 and 12 people.

One Identify your focus group. The participants should have something in common, for example, all members are students, or local residents, or local business people.

Two Write a small number of open questions. Send them to the focus group members so they have time to think about their responses.

Three Meet with the group. Ask the questions and encourage the focus group to discuss the issues that arise. You will need to make an audio recording of the discussion to analyse later so make sure that everyone gives their consent.

Image (photo) elicitation (see also Visual Evidence)

In **image elicitation** participants either respond to visual images or make visual images of their own. This technique works well with a small focus group of people (say 6 to 12 people). In image elicitation you ask participants to either:

▶ **respond to images that you have made.** These will probably be photos or maps of the local environment that you have taken, or found from secondary sources, but you might also include other images such as paintings or video; or

▶ **ask the participants to take photos of elements of the local environment.** For example, you might ask people to take photos that represent a concept such as globalisation or sustainability. Alternatively, you might explore perceptions by asking the participants to take photos of positive or negative aspects of the local environment.

This technique can be especially useful in helping participants express complex or abstract ideas. Instead of trying to find the right words, they use images to express their ideas. Image elicitation is also a good way to get people to respond to emotive subjects such as loneliness.

Why use image elicitation?

Consider this data collection technique if you are interested in perceptions, identity, or representation. For example, you could use this technique if you were investigating urban or rural places and you wanted to know:

▶ **how places create a sense of identity for local residents.** For example, what features of the environment help create a sense of community cohesion?

▶ **how people perceive complex concepts that may have an impact on their local environment:** concepts such as sustainability, risk, diversity, inequality, or globalisation;

▶ **how our experience of the environment influences our perceptions and behaviours.** For example, are there places in the local environment where people feel happy, content, safe, fearful, or sad? If so, why, and how can these places be changed for the better?

Land use surveys

A land use survey is used to identify how buildings and parcels of land are being used. In a restricted area, such as a small town centre, it may be possible to record all land uses. However, for larger areas, you will need a sampling strategy, such as a number of transects radiating out from the town centre.

Why record land use?

Land use surveys can provide useful data in a number of different types of investigation. For example, you might use a land use survey to:

▶ **investigate relationships** between land use, footfall (see page 55), and rateable value (available as a secondary source);

▶ **identify how land use is changing.** This is particularly interesting in urban areas that have experienced recent change as a result of redevelopment or gentrification. Compare your primary data to secondary sources such as the images recorded in Google Street View or artists' recent paintings of street scenes (see page 92);

▶ **assess how land use is influenced by physical factors** of the urban landscape such as the route of major roads – see Figures 3.49 and 3.50. They show how land uses in Birmingham are influenced by the route of the inner ring road. The road was completed in 1960 and had the effect of a 'concrete collar' around the CBD, restricting the outward growth of city centre land uses.

Image elicitation

Image elicitation is a research method that uses visual images to elicit a response from a group of participants.

Evaluation

Be aware that multiple land uses in a taller building can be difficult to record accurately.

Figure 3.49 Land use outside the inner ring road. Birmingham. SP067873.

Figure 3.50 Land use inside the inner ring road. Birmingham. SP068872.

How to record land use

To record the results of a land use survey you will need to design a data collection sheet and, for speed, categorise the land uses using a predetermined system. The best way to record the data is on a large scale map that shows each building. A scale of 1:2500 is suitable.

There are various ways of categorising land uses but the simplest method is to use initial letters in the RICEPOTS system. Figure 3.51 shows how land uses are divided into 8 main categories. You then add a second letter to sub-divide the main categories, for example, Rb – Residential bungalow. Some letters are suggested in Figure 3.51 but you should add your own letters after a pilot survey.

Weblink

https://parallel.co.uk/ This GIS website includes a link to Ordnance Survey OpenData basemaps. Use this free scalable map to print a black and white image of your town centre/investigation locality.

Code	Land use category	Add extra letters to sub-divide the main categories
R	Residential	b = bungalow, d = detached, f = flat, s = semi-detached, t = terraced
I	Industrial	c = chemical, e = electricity generation, h = heavy industry, l = light industry, m = mining, w = warehousing
C	Commercial	b = books, c = chemist, c/s = clothing and shoe, d = department store, g = garage, h = homeware and furniture, j = jewellers, m = market, n = newsagent o = office, s = supermarket, t = travel agent, v = vacant
E	Entertainment	b = bar, c = cinema, g = gym, n = nightclub, r = restaurant or café, s = sports centre, t = theatre
P	Public building	a = ambulance station, b = benefits office, e = education, f = fire station, g = government office, h = hospital, l = library, m = magistrate or law court, p = police station, w = place of worship
O	Open space	a = allotment, c = cemetery, d = derelict, f = farmland, g = green space (small), p = park, s = sports field
T	Transport	b = bus station, c = car park, r = railway station, t = taxi rank, u = underground station/metro
S	Services	b = banks and building societies, d = dental, e = estate agents, i = insurance, m = medical, s = solicitors

Figure 3.51 Use RICEPOTS to categorise land uses.

Likert Scale Surveys

Likert (pronounced *lick-it*) is an attitude survey technique that is used to collect evidence of people's opinions about a geographical issue or their perceptions of the environment.

Why use a Likert Scale Survey?

Likert Scale surveys are useful for any investigation of people's perceptions. For example, you could use a Likert Scale Survey to investigate perceptions of **well-being** and, in particular, how much our well-being is influenced by the environment. It is well-known that people generally feel happier when they are outside, especially if they are in the countryside or at the coast. This means that, if you live in a town, being close to green spaces, like Figure 3.52, can improve our well-being. On the other hand, features of the urban environment such as derelict buildings, vandalism, and traffic congestion can all have negative impacts on our well-being. People can be fearful of crime and their physical health can be affected by poor air quality.

> ### Well-being
>
> Well-being is a measure of how happy and healthy we feel.

Figure 3.52 A public park in the centre of Cardiff, Wales.

We could investigate the impact of an urban green space on local people by:

▶ asking people what they think of the park using a Likert Survey. Use strong statements like 'It would be a great benefit to live close to this park'. Survey people to see if they agree or disagree;

▶ using information from estate agents to find local house prices. If the park really is attractive to people, then we might expect that houses overlooking the park are more expensive than similar houses a few streets away.

How to construct a Likert Survey

The survey should contain a number of statements or questions known as **items**. Respondents are then asked to evaluate their feelings about each item by ticking a box on a scale line. It's normal to give respondents a 5 or 7 point scale. The points on the scale line are often between 'strongly agree' and 'strongly disagree', although these statements can be replaced with a numerical scale or alternative descriptions such as those shown in Figure 3.53.

> ### Items
>
> A Likert Survey uses **items**. Each item is a statement (or question). People respond to each item on a 5 or 7 point scale.

Figure 3.53 Examples of scales for use in a Likert survey.

Never	Occasionally	Sometimes	Mostly	Always
Completely satisfied	Very satisfied	Moderately satisfied	Slightly satisfied	Not satisfied
Not at all important	Unimportant	Neutral	Important	Very important
Strongly agree	Agree	Uncertain	Disagree	Strongly disagree

A well-designed Likert Survey should contain some items that allow people to respond in a positive way and an equal number of items that allow people to take a negative position. Imagine you are investigating perceptions of the coastal flood defences at Sea Palling. Study the items in Figure 3.55. Notice how some of them take a positive view of the defences while others take a negative position. This helps to make the survey unbiased.

Figure 3.55 Likert Survey to investigate attitudes to flooding in a location that is at risk of coastal or river flooding.

To what extent do you agree with each of the following statements?					
Items	Strongly agree	Agree	Neutral	Disagree	Strongly disagree
1 Flood defences at this location are adequate.					
2 Flood defences make me feel more secure in my home.					
3 Information about flood preparation is difficult to access.					
4 There are insufficient sand bags when floods are forecast.					
5 Flood warnings are not needed for this location.					
6 Flood warnings are always accurate.					
7 Flood defences at this location urgently need to be improved.					

Potential limitations of Likert surveys

Likert scale surveys do have some potential limitations.

▶ Some respondents may avoid choosing 'strongly agree' or strongly disagree' because they don't want you to think that they have extreme views.

▶ Some respondents may frequently choose the neutral middle point on a 5 or 7 point scale. You can reduce the impact of this limitation by using a 6 point scale with no neutral position.

▶ Some people do not want to disagree with statements because they want to be seen as reasonable people. That's why it's a good idea to include an equal number of items that will provide positive and negative responses.

Evaluation

Be aware of the limitations of Likert scale surveys when you come to evaluate your data.

Compare the Likert Surveys shown in Figures 3.55 and 3.57. Identify a fault in the design of Figure 3.57 and suggest how this survey could be improved.

Figure 3.56 The redeveloped part of Birmingham Bull Ring shopping centre.

Regeneration of this area has ...	Strongly agree	Agree	Neutral	Disagree	Strongly disagree
Improved access for shoppers.					
Made the city more attractive.					
Given Birmingham a positive image to visitors.					
Benefited local businesses.					
Made the city safer for pedestrians.					

Figure 3.57 A student Likert Survey.

Longshore drift surveys (see also Sediment surveys)

Sediment is transported along the coast by the process of longshore drift. As the waves and currents slow down they lose energy. As they do so they begin to deposit the sediment. The largest, heaviest sediment is dropped first. Smaller and lighter sediment is transported further and deposited later. This process is known as sorting. This means that beaches may have cobbles or pebbles at one end and smaller shingle or sand at the other.

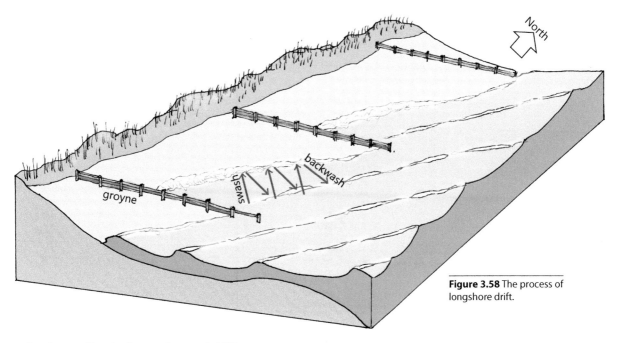

Labels on figure: North, groyne, swash, backwash

Figure 3.58 The process of longshore drift.

Why investigate longshore drift?

Longshore drift is an essential process in moving sediment along the coast within a sediment cell. You could investigate longshore drift in order to:

▶ help explain the formation of landscape features such as coastal spits;
▶ assess the effectiveness of coastal defences such as groynes;
▶ assess the unintended consequence of a harbour wall: does the harbour wall trap sediment and, therefore, interrupt the movement of sediment within the **sediment cell**?

How to investigate longshore drift

You can investigate the direction of longshore drift by:

▶ measuring wind speed (using an anemometer) and wind direction and comparing this to the direction of longshore drift;
▶ using a float to identify the direction and estimate the speed of longshore drift (see Figure 3.59).

You can then go on to investigate the impact of longshore drift on the processes of deposition and sorting by:

▶ using quadrats to sample beach sediment at regular intervals along the beach to assess the degree of sorting (see sediment surveys);
▶ measuring the height of the beach on either side of each groyne to assess the amount of sediment that has accumulated (see Figure 3.60).

Measuring speed of transport of material in the sea

You can use a float such as an orange or a tennis ball to measure the speed and direction of longshore drift. Figure 3.59 shows how to do this. For safety, you should only attempt this technique when the tide is going out.

One Measure a distance of 10 metres along the beach, as close to the water's edge as is safe. Mark each end.

Two Place a float in the sea. Don't throw it as the momentum of your throw might make the result unreliable.

Three Record the length of time it takes for the float to be washed by the swash and backwash along the beach for the 10 metres that you measured out.

Four Repeat the process at least three times. Then calculate the average time it takes for the float to travel 10 metres along the coast.

Five Calculate the velocity of longshore drift. Divide the distance (metres) by the average time (seconds) to get a velocity (metres per second).

Figure 3.59 How to measure the speed and direction of longshore drift.

Investigating depth of the beach

You can investigate depth of the beach by measuring down from the groyne to the surface of the beach. Do this on each side of the groyne. If it is trapping sediment then the beach will be thicker (and the distance smaller) on the side of the groyne that faces into the direction of longshore drift.

Figure 3.60 Investigating the depth of beach by comparing it to the height of the groyne. Borth.

Why measure beach depth?

Groynes are constructed on beaches to interrupt the movement of longshore drift. They trap sand, shingle, and pebbles, making the beach thicker and wider. The beach is then able to act as a buffer – absorbing more wave energy and protecting the coast behind the beach. However, they can also have unintended consequences because they may starve beaches further along the coast from their supply of sediment. So a greater depth of beach in one place may result in a thinner beach elsewhere. This may result in faster rates of erosion elsewhere, something you may be able to investigate using historic maps and photos of the coast from secondary sources.

Mental mapping (see also emotional mapping)

Each of us has a spatial awareness of the world in our mind that is based on our experiences. By asking someone to draw a **mental map** we are able to see how they imagine the world. Mental maps are determined by our experiences:

▶ real experiences of places actually visited;
▶ knowledge of places that is acquired through mass media.

Details that have not been experienced by an individual or are thought to be unimportant will be omitted from a mental map. Consequently, mental maps often show considerable variation with real places.

You can use various strategies to collect mental maps. You can ask participants to:

▶ **draw a map,** like figures 3.61 and 3.62. These maps were drawn by school children. The geographer was investigating whether boys or girls had a more accurate perception of space;
▶ **give an emotional response to places with which they are familiar** – a strategy called emotional mapping.

Why use mental maps?

Mental maps tell us about people's spatial awareness and their perception of scale. They are also useful if you are investigating perceptions of places. For example, you may be interested in how different groups of people perceive a concept such as sustainability, globalisation, identity, or risk. Using mental maps, or a combination of maps, photos, and interviews, can be an effective way of discovering how people feel about issues that affect communities in urban and rural areas such as crime, pollution, vandalism, or traffic congestion.

> **Mental map**
>
> A mental map is a representation of an individual's spatial awareness.

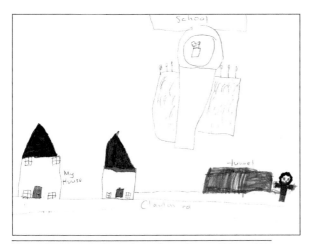

Figure 3.61 A mental map drawn by an 8 year old boy of his neighbourhood.

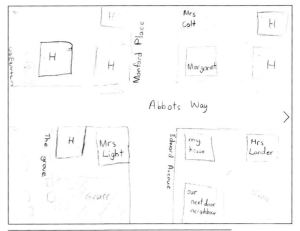

Figure 3.62 A map drawn by an 8 year old girl of her neighbourhood.

> **Test your understanding**
>
> Study Figures 3.61 and 3.62. What are the main differences between these two maps? What might this tell us about each child's spatial awareness?

Figure 3.63 Noise meter apps display instantaneous readouts as well as recording maximum and minimum readings.

Noise surveys

Noise is measured in decibels which is a logarithmic scale. This means that 75 dB is 10 times louder than 65dB and 85dB is 100 times louder than 65dB. Normal conversation is about 65dB. Noise on a busy city street will be between 75dB and 85dB. High noise levels such as busy traffic, or noise from a construction site, can have a negative impact on our experience of an urban environment.

You can use your smart phone to measure noise levels. There are several free apps available - the display from one is shown in Figure 3.63. Noise levels vary quickly over time so you will need to take several readings at each location. This data can be processed later to show average, maximum, and minimum readings.

Noise readings taken at several different locations can be mapped later using an isoline technique (see page 169).

Participant observation

Participant observation is a method of qualitative research in which the researcher observes how individuals or groups of people behave and interact with each other and with the environment. The observations can be recorded using photos, videos, written notes, or an audio recording on your smartphone of what you can see – all of which are qualitative forms of data. You might observe:

▶ what people do;
▶ how long they spend doing each activity;
▶ how they move through the environment.

Why use participant observation?

Participant observation can be useful in a geography investigation because it can tell us something about how people use public spaces:

▶ **how they interact with the space itself**, for example, observing what parts of the environment people look at carefully or how long they spend in particular places, for example, how long they spend sitting on a park bench, studying street signage, or looking at street art (see Figure 3.64);
▶ **how they move around in space**, for example, how they navigate their way through a crowded pedestrian space or how they cross a busy road.

You might use participant observation to investigate whether people adopt different behaviours in different places. For example, in an investigation of an urban environment you might assess whether people behave differently in an area that has undergone economic regeneration compared with a neighbouring area that has not.

Alternatively, you might want to investigate whether different groups of people behave in different ways in the same environment. For example, how do different groups of people (perhaps defined by age, gender, or ethnicity) behave in a busy shopping street or use a recreational space such as an urban park or seaside promenade?

Figure 3.64 You can collect evidence of how people interact with the environment using photos. In this case, the woman on the right spent 3 minutes photographing the graffiti on this derelict building. Brick Lane, London.

Combining participant observation with other data

Participant observation can be combined with other data collection methods to produce a range of qualitative and quantitative data. For example, in an investigation of urban graffiti you could use:

- ▶ **participant observation** - to collect data on how people move through the environment, noting whether they pause to look at graffiti (as in Figure 3.64);
- ▶ **a Graffiti Index** (see page 44) - a form of ordinal data, to assess whether people prefer some types of graffiti to others;
- ▶ **an interview with local business people** (a form of qualitative data) about their perceptions of place and local identity;
- ▶ **secondary data on rateable values or house prices** - to see whether there is a correlation between property values and street cleanliness.

Figure 3.65 Bute Park, Cardiff.

You could collect qualitative data about how people use an urban green space by:

- ▶ **observing how people use the space**: how do people in different groups (such as teenagers, adults, families) use the space? Do these different groups use the space for different amounts of time?
- ▶ **measuring footfall** at different times of the day and week;
- ▶ **photographing any evidence that the park is being managed** such as signs about cycling, ball games, or litter;
- ▶ **interviewing people who use the green space** about the health or well-being benefits;
- ▶ **searching social media** to find people's views about the use of the park, such as attendance at a park run event.

Questionnaires (also see Interviews)

Questionnaires allow people to talk openly and in detail about a geographical issue. The interviewer needs to prepare questions so that the survey has a common structure each time it is used. This will allow you to compare the responses of different people and make the data more reliable. In your analysis you can then look for common patterns and similarities as well as differences between the responses.

Why use questionnaires?

Questionnaires are an extremely useful source of data for any investigation which involves research into people's perceptions or their values and attitudes. They are flexible forms of survey – you can write questions that are suitable and unique to your own investigation. You can combine different types of question into your survey, such as Likert Surveys and Bipolar Surveys (see pages 39) as well as open-ended questions. You don't need any specialist scientific equipment.

For advice on ethical issues of questionnaires see pages 108-109.

For advice on sampling strategies for interviews see pages 100-101.

For advice on analysing interviews see pages 187-188.

Closed question

A closed question has set answers. The respondent has to choose the answer they most agree with.

Open question

An open question allows the participant to respond in any way they want.

Writing questions for a questionnaire

A questionnaire uses a mixture of **closed questions** and **open questions**. The closed questions will allow you to collect a lot of data quite quickly. Later, when you are analysing the data, you can sort respondents into different groups depending on how they answered each closed question. The advantage of using open questions is that people sometimes say things you didn't expect. This means that open questions may allow you to collect some new and surprising evidence. However, it can be time-consuming to analyse the results of open questions so it's a good idea to use only a few open questions within a questionnaire survey of 50 or more people.

If you are relying on a questionnaire to generate a substantial proportion of your primary data then the questions need to be carefully designed and tested, using a pilot survey, before you commit to asking a large number of people. To design a successful questionnaire, follow the golden rules in Figure 3.66. In order for your data to be valid, you will need to conduct your questionnaire with a large enough group of people. You will need at least 30, and ideally 50 or more, completed questionnaires.

Leading question

A leading question is one that encourages the person who is being questioned to respond in a particular way.

Be aware of ethical considerations when designing and using a questionnaire. For example, think about issues such as consent and confidentiality.

Keep it relevant. → Only ask questions that are relevant to answer your research questions or hypothesis.

Keep it simple. → Write questions that are clear. You need your respondents to understand what the question is about so avoid geographical jargon.

Ask one question at a time. → Never combine two ideas in a single question. It will make it impossible to analyse the responses.

Avoid leading questions. → Keep your questions neutral. You must avoid showing how you feel about the topic of the question.

Include an option for open responses. → Include an option for respondents to write their own response if they feel unable to choose one of the options you have offered.

Consider the ethical dimension. → Avoid sensitive questions about gender, age, or income. Make sure respondents know that information will be treated confidentially.

Figure 3.66 The golden rules of a successful questionnaire.

1. How old are you? ......

2. What is your full address?

....

Questions 1 and 2 create ethical issues. Question 1 would be acceptable if you gave respondents options (e.g. 0-19, 20-39). Question 2 raises issues of confidentiality. Rather than a full address you could ask for a postcode district.

3. How far do you travel to do your shopping?

	Tick (✔)
Less than 1 mile	
1-2 miles	
5-10 miles	

Question 3 Only ask questions that are relevant to your research. This question does not appear to be relevant to the theme of regeneration. If the question is relevant then the options need amending because these groups aren't contiguous. It also needs an option for over 10 miles.

4. Isn't it true that regeneration has made the city centre a safer place to spend time in the evening?
Yes / No

Question 4 This is a **leading question**. It could be rephrased as: Do you think that regeneration has made the city centre more or less safe in the evening?

5. How has the regeneration scheme affected traffic congestion and parking locally?

A major improvement on before ☐

Some improvement on before ☐

Slightly worse than before ☐

A lot worse than before ☐

Question 5 This question is asking two things at once. Respondents may feel that traffic congestion has improved but parking has become more difficult. If so, they can't answer the question as it stands so it would be better to create two separate questions.

6. Do you think that the involvement of BITC was pivotal in making regeneration the great success that we see today?
Yes / No

Question 6 This is a **leading question**. It suggests that regeneration was a success (the respondent might not think so) and that the BITC was the main reason for that success. The question also uses jargon that many respondents would not understand. BITC stands for Business in the Community. It's a business-led initiative that helps to support local communities both financially and practically.

7. How would you describe the regeneration of the city centre?

A waste of money ☐

Largely successful ☐

Too early to tell ☐

Question 7 This question is fine but the options are rather limited. The simplest way to resolve this issue would be to allow an open response. Alternatively, a pilot survey could have been used to find the commonest responses and these could be used to generate the closed fields.

Test your understanding

Study Figure 3.67. Redesign this questionnaire to remove the errors.

Figure 3.67 This questionnaire has been badly designed. The errors are explained in the call-outs on the right.

Sediment (pebble) surveys (see also Longshore drift surveys)

A sediment or pebble survey may be used as part of an investigation into landscape processes and the resulting landforms or smaller features of the landscape. You would almost certainly do a sediment survey as part of an investigation of coastal processes on a pebble beach, spit, or tombolo.

Pebble surveys can be used to measure:
▶ pebble size;
▶ shape;
▶ orientation;
▶ degree of roundness;
▶ degree of sorting.

Pebble surveys are not restricted to beaches. They can also be used in glaciated landscapes to provide clues to the depositional environment. An analysis of pebble shape may help to determine whether deposition has occurred in a glacial, peri-glacial, fluvio-glacial, or fluvial environment.

Measuring pebbles – size and shape

Pebbles are 3-dimensional objects with three axes – each axis is at right angles to the others. If you just want to record the size of the pebbles you can:
▶ measure the length of the b-axis only;
▶ measure all three axes for each pebble and then divide by 3 to get a mean value.

However, if you are investigating size **and shape** you will need to measure the length of all three axes. This is because the shape of a pebble is described by the ratio of its axes – a measurement which is described as Zingg Analysis (see page 203).

Figure 3.68 Each pebble needs to be measured in the same way.

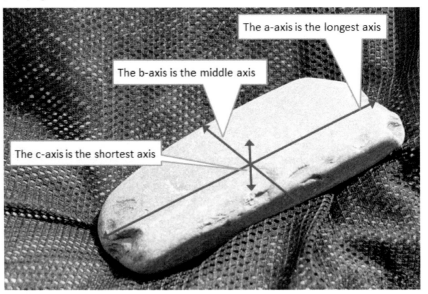

The a-axis is the longest axis

The b-axis is the middle axis

The c-axis is the shortest axis

Why measure pebble size and shape?

Sediment tends to be sorted (by size) by the movement of the waves. Swash can provide a powerful force, moving sand, gravel, and pebbles of all sizes up the slope of the beach profile. The backwash usually has less energy. It drags smaller sediment back down the beach profile but larger pebbles are left behind higher up the slope. These larger pebbles sometimes form distinctive ridges near the top of the beach profile.

Investigating pebble size on a beach profile

To investigate whether pebbles have been sorted by size, by wave action up and down the beach, follow these steps.

One Use a clinometer and tape to measure the gradient of the **beach profile** (see page 80).

Two Collect data from 5 equally spaced sites along the beach profile. This would be a form of systematic sampling.

Three Measure the length of the same number of pebbles at each site.

The most suitable and effective way to represent this data would be to draw a cross section of the beach profile and then locate histograms - one for each sample site - above that line.

You can sample pebbles within the quadrat using the points where the internal wires/strings cross – in other words, at the intersections. Use them systematically, for example, by sampling pebbles at every intersection, like in Figure 3.69, or by using a set of random number tables to generate random grid references.

> **Beach profile**
>
> A beach profile is a cross section of a beach drawn from the low tide mark to above the high tide mark.

Figure 3.69 A quadrat can be used to sample pebbles on a beach.

> Random has a precise meaning in sampling. Don't throw the quadrat over your shoulder. This doesn't make the sampling random, it just makes it dangerous!

> **Evaluation**
>
> Don't select pebbles from within the quadrat at random by just picking some out. Your eye will be drawn to the larger, or more interesting, looking pebbles. This means your sample won't be representative. Use a set of random numbers to select the pebbles.

Power's scale of roundness

Power's scale of roundness is a simple 6-point scale – see Figure 3.70. Use the chart to decide where each pebble in your sample comes on the scale between very angular at one extreme and well-rounded at the other.

Figure 3.70 Powers' scale of roundness chart.

1 Very angular   2 Angular   3 Sub-angular

4 Sub-rounded   5 Rounded   6 Well-rounded

Why use Power's scale of roundness?

Sharp, angular sediments are usually an indication that the process of transport has been short so there has been little time for abrasion. Well-rounded sediments, on the other hand, provide evidence of a much longer period of transportation during which time the pebbles have been worn smooth by abrasion.

Pebble roundness, therefore, can be used as a clue to the depositional environment. Pebbles on a beach, for example, tend to fall on the scale between sub-rounded and well-rounded. Glacial deposits, on the other hand, contain a much wider variety of different degrees of angularity/roundness.

So, if you are examining deposits in a glaciated environment like that shown in Figure 3.71 and 3.72, an analysis of pebble shape may help to determine whether the deposit is glacial till, fluvio-glacial, or fluvial. You don't have to travel to Iceland, of course, to investigate these types of deposits. Your fieldwork could be in a once glaciated upland of the UK and you could use your independent investigation to try to reconstruct the sedimentary processes that occurred at the end of the last glacial period.

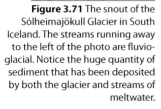

Figure 3.71 The snout of the Sólheimajökull Glacier in South Iceland. The streams running away to the left of the photo are fluvio-glacial. Notice the huge quantity of sediment that has been deposited by both the glacier and streams of meltwater.

Figure 3.72 Examining the roundness of the sediment would help to determine the conditions of transport and deposition. Sólheimajökull Glacier, South Iceland.

Pebble roundness (Cailleux Index)

Another method for describing pebble shape is the Cailleux Index of roundness. The Cailleux Index describes the roundness of a two-dimensional shape. The values of the index range from 0 to 1000, where 1000 is a perfect circle.

The Cailleux Index and Power's Scale of roundness are both useful for telling us about the depositional environment. Environments in which sediment is carried further distances tend to have less angular corners (measured by Power's Scale) and less variability of values on Cailleux Index which is indicated by a smaller interquartile range in values.

To measure pebbles on the Cailleux Index you will need to draw a series of semi-circles on a piece of card. Each semi-circle needs to have a radius that is 1cm larger than the last. To record the data:

One Place each pebble in the sample on the Cailleux chart you have made. Position the sharpest (most acute) corner on the chart. Record the radius of the semi-circle that just encloses this corner of the pebble (see Figure 3.73).

Two Measure the length of the a-axis (the longest axis).

The data you have collected should be analysed by considering the ratio between the radius and the length of the a-axis (see page 74) and presented in a dispersion diagram (see page 196).

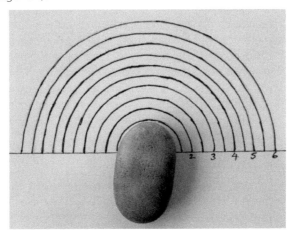

Figure 3.73 Using a Cailleux Scale to measure the radius of a pebble's sharpest corner.

Evaluation

Remember that other factors may also affect pebble roundness – geology especially. Have you considered whether individual pebbles in your sample are all from the same geology?

Sediment orientation (also known as fabric analysis)

Orientation is a description of the angle which a geographical feature makes in relation to magnetic North. In a sediment survey you can measure the orientation of **clasts** (pebbles, cobbles, or boulders) in order to investigate the nature of the sedimentary environment in which they were deposited. Orientation is measured whilst the clast is in situ – do not pick it up to measure it until the orientation has been measured.

To measure the orientation of a clast you will need a compass.

One Using the compass, align the base plate of the compass with the long axis of the clast.

Two Turn the bezel (outer ring) of the compass to align the needle with North.

Three Read the bearing on the compass. Orientation will always have two values that are 180° apart. For example, if the long axis of the clast is aligned on a west-east axis, the bearing will read 90° and 270°. It doesn't matter which of these numbers you record.

> **Clast**
>
> Clast is the geological name for a fragment of rock. A clast can be any size or shape.

Figure 3.74 How to measure the orientation of a clast.

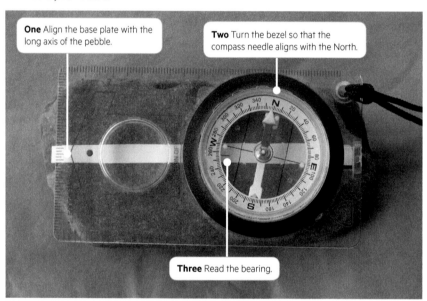

One Align the base plate with the long axis of the pebble.

Two Turn the bezel so that the compass needle aligns with the North.

Three Read the bearing.

Why measure orientation of clasts?

The angle of rest of individual clasts in a sediment can sometimes tell us something about the nature of the sedimentary environment. The long axis of clasts deposited in flowing water tends to be aligned with the direction of flow. By contrast, clasts deposited by stagnating ice will show no alignment. While orientation is a useful clue, it is, in itself, not conclusive evidence of a sedimentary environment. Other evidence, such as an analysis of pebble shape (by measuring all three axes), sediment sorting (see below), and pebble roundness (page 77) should also be collected.

Sediment Sorting Index

Sediment sorting is a measure of how similar all the pebbles are in any one location. Sediment sorting is measured on a simple visual scale from very poorly sorted at one extreme to very well-sorted at the other – see Figure 3.75.

Why use a sediment sorting index?

Sorting is another indication of the sedimentary environment. Sediments that are poorly sorted indicate that deposition has been rapid with little opportunity for sediment to be sorted by the movement of water into clasts of similar sizes. Glacial deposits are usually poorly sorted. Very well-sorted sediments indicate that deposition has taken place over a longer period with plenty of opportunities for flowing water to sort the pebbles by size. Beach deposits tend to be well-sorted or very well-sorted.

 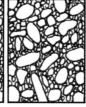 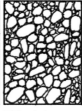 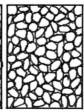

Figure 3.75 An example of a sediment sorting Index.

Very poorly sorted   Poorly sorted   Moderately sorted   Well sorted   Very well sorted

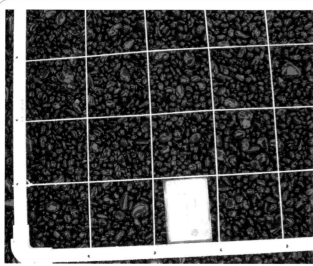

Figure 3.76 A beach deposit.

Figure 3.77 A fluvio-glacial deposit.

Test your understanding
How would you describe the degree of sorting in Figures 3.76 and 3.77?

Slope surveys

Slopes often have complex forms. In order to study a slope you need to break it down into a number of elements which can then be measured. The upper slope often has a convex shape while the lower slope is often concave. In between, these elements are rectilinear (or straight) slopes.

Why investigate slopes?
Slope surveys can be used to investigate:
- whether pebbles have been sorted on a beach profile (see page 80);
- the development of soil catenas (see page 82);
- whether aspect and/or gradient are important factors in the development of glacial or peri-glacial features such as corries or stone stripes (see page 56).

Measuring gradients

Look more carefully at a slope and it is possible to identify **breaks in slope** where there is a distinct change in gradient. The simplest way to survey a slope is to take measurements between these breaks in slope using a tape measure and **clinometer** (an instrument used to measure angles from the horizontal). A traditional clinometer includes a swinging arm or weight. As the clinometer is tipped up to the same angle as the slope, the weight points vertically downwards so that you can measure the angle. Alternatively, you could download a free clinometer app onto your smartphone, like the one shown in Figure 3.79.

Figure 3.78 A complex slope can be broken down into elements at each break in slope.

Investigating beach profiles

Just like the slope seen in Figure 3.78, a beach can be broken down into a number of elements – each gradient separated by a break in slope. It is the action of waves on the beach material that creates a **beach profile.** Swash can provide a powerful force, moving sand, gravel, and pebbles of all sizes up the slope of the beach profile. The backwash usually has less energy. It drags smaller sediment back down the beach profile but larger pebbles are left behind. These larger pebbles sometimes form distinctive ridges near the top of the beach profile.

Figure 3.79 Use your smartphone as a clinometer.

Why investigate beach profiles?

The gradient of a beach depends partly on the size of the beach sediment. Sandy beaches tend to rest at gentle angles – usually less than 10 degrees – whereas pebble beaches usually rest at steeper angles. You could investigate whether the slope of the beach profile is related to pebble size by combining a beach profile survey with one or more of the pebble survey methods described on pages 74-79.

How to measure a beach profile

To measure a beach profile you will need a tape measure, clinometer, and two ranging poles.

One Check the tide timetable. You should do your survey while the tide is going out because that is safest. Start the survey about one to two hours before the tide turns so that most of the beach is exposed.

Two Create a data collection sheet (similar to the one shown in Figure 3.81) to record the cumulative distance along the beach profile. Use it to record the angles and distances between each break in slope.

Three Starting at the lowest part of the beach, work back up the slope. Place the ranging poles at breaks in slope and measure the distance and gradient between each point. The end of your transect should be above the high tide mark as shown by the strand line – the line of detritus washed up by the last high tide.

Four It's a good idea to sketch the slope too – that will make it easier to interpret your data later. An example is shown in Figure 3.82.

Evaluation

You will need to work with a colleague to measure the gradient between the same red/white bands of a pair of ranging poles. If you try to measure the gradient without any poles then the angle will be inaccurate unless you are both the same height.

Figure 3.80 Using a clinometer to measure slope angles on a beach. The dotted black line represents the transect. Notice that the red dashed line is parallel to the slope.

	Angle (degree)	Distance (metres)	Cumulative distance (metres)
Start to break in slope 1.	5	24	24
Break in slope 1 to 2.	16	8	32
Break in slope 2 to 3.	6	14	46
Break in slope 3 to 4.	30	4	50
Break in slope 4 to end.	10	10	60

Figure 3.81 Data collection sheet needed to draw a beach profile.

Figure 3.82 A field sketch with the measurements and angles will help you visualise the slope later.

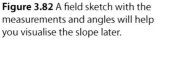
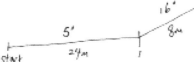

Figure 3.83 Use a protractor and ruler to draw a slope profile.

Use a protractor and ruler to draw the slope profile when you are back at your desk. See Figure 3.83.

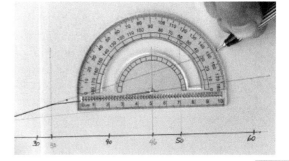

Soil surveys (see also infiltration rate surveys)

Soil is composed of rock particles derived from the parent rock beneath, decayed organic material from plants living above, air, water, and organisms such as beetles and worms. Soils change slowly over time, developing distinctive layers, or horizons. Soil types vary considerably across the UK, influenced by climate, geology, and land use.

Why use soil surveys?

Your investigation may focus largely on local variations in soil type. For example, soils typically develop in sequence from top to bottom of a slope in a **soil catena**. These variations occur due to the movement of water rather than because of any variations in underlying geology (see Figure 3.84).

> ### Soil catena
>
> A soil catena is a sequence of soil types and profiles that develop in different locations on a slope.

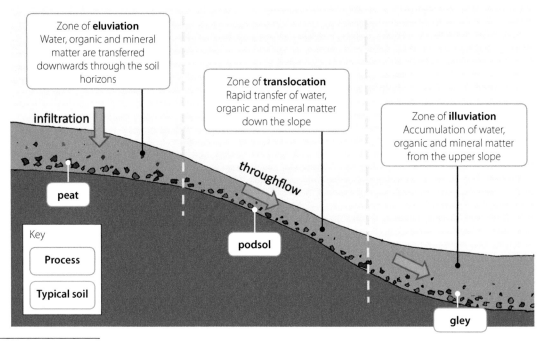

Zone of **eluviation**
Water, organic and mineral matter are transferred downwards through the soil horizons

Zone of **translocation**
Rapid transfer of water, organic and mineral matter down the slope

Zone of **illuviation**
Accumulation of water, organic and mineral matter from the upper slope

infiltration

throughflow

peat

podsol

gley

Key

Process

Typical soil

Figure 3.84 A model soil catena developing on uniform bedrock.

If you want to investigate whether the soils on a slope in your study area have developed in the same way as this model then you must first check a geological map to make sure that the geology is uniform. Choose a slope that is manageable in length, say 150-200 metres long.

Soil is an important store in the water and carbon cycles. For example, **clay soils** are relatively impermeable, resulting in overland flow, whereas **sandy** and **loamy soils** will allow greater infiltration and throughflow so soils can have an influence on lag times – the length of time it takes for a river to go into flood after heavy rain. Consequently, soil surveys may form part of any investigation that focuses on flood risk (see page 52).

The amount of carbon stored in soil depends on its organic content which, in turn, depends on land use. Deciduous trees drop a lot of leaf litter so soils in deciduous woodlands contain large amounts of organic matter and therefore store a lot of carbon. Moorland soils also store large quantities of carbon because organic matter breaks down very slowly in the waterlogged soils. By contrast, arable crops and grasslands create little organic matter so their soils store less carbon. Consequently, a survey of a soil's organic content may form part of an investigation that focuses on carbon stores (see page 41).

Soil profiles

A soil profile is a vertical cross section through the soil that reveals each of the layers, or **soil horizons**, that make up a soil. You will need to dig a soil pit if you want to investigate a soil profile. A soil pit is basically a large hole that is deep enough to reach the **regolith**. You will need permission from the landowner before you start. Soil pits are time-consuming to dig so think carefully about your sampling strategy so that each pit is representative of the population (whether that is determined by land use, slope angle, geology, or another variable).

To investigate soil horizons, you need to follow these steps.

One If the area has vegetation, remove the turf and place it to one side. You should put this back when you refill the hole.

Two Place a large plastic sheet on the ground. Dig soil from your pit and place it on the sheet.

Three Dig down until you reach the regolith.

Four Slice through one face of the hole using the spade or a trowel so that you have a neat, vertical face to study.

Five In an unploughed soil (for example, a woodland or moorland soil) you should be able to see distinct layers. These are the horizons. At this stage you may want to:

▶ sketch or photograph the profile;
▶ measure the depth of each horizon (in centimetres);
▶ record details such as colour and texture of each horizon;
▶ take small samples of soil from each horizon.

Six Fill in the soil and replace the vegetation.

Each soil sample should be stored in a separate sealed and labelled plastic bag. This is because you need to retain any water trapped in the soil for testing later.

Soil texture

Texture is defined by the size of the individual soil particles. It is possible to make qualitative judgements about soil texture by feel, however, if you want quantitative data the easiest method is sedimentation. This method relies on the fact that, when mixed with water, the largest particles in the soil settle out first whilst the clay particles are held in suspension for the longest period of time.

One Add 50-100g of soil to a measuring cylinder and fill with water.

Two Cover and shake the cylinder so that all of the particles are suspended.

Three Allow the liquid to settle. Leave it to stand for at least 8 hours.

Four Measure the depth of each layer of sediment.

The results of a soil texture survey could be presented as either a triangular graph or a histogram.

Humus

Clay 3%

Silt 34%

Sand 73%

Figure 3.85 Measuring soil texture by sedimentation.

Soil water content

Soil water content is determined by a number of factors including soil texture and the amount of pore spaces in the soil. The pore spaces are influenced by the amount of compaction of the soil and the number of invertebrates that have burrowed through the soil. Soil water content can be easily determined from soil samples. To do this, follow these steps.

One Crumble 50-100g of soil into a pre-weighed open oven-proof container.

Two Weigh the soil and container. Record the weight.

Three Place the soil in an oven heated to 105^{0}c for at least 12 hours.

Four Remove the soil from the oven and allow the soil and container to cool. Re-weigh the soil and container.

Five Calculate the weight of the dry soil by subtracting the weight of the container.

Six Calculate the weight of water that has been lost by subtracting the weight of the dry soil from the weight of the wet soil.

Seven Use the following equation to calculate the percentage water (by weight) of the soil. Percentage water (by weight) = (weight lost by drying / weight of wet soil) x 100.

Organic content (see also Carbon surveys)

Investigating the organic content of a soil will help you assess how the soil is acting as a carbon store. The amount of organic matter in the soil will depend largely on land use. For example, woodland soils tend to have more organic matter than a grassland soil because of the large quantity of leaf litter dropped by the trees. However, the percentage of organic matter in a soil will also depend on factors such as relief, rainfall, and drainage. For example, a poorly drained upland soil will become waterlogged. The low oxygen content of this soil will slow down decomposition so the percentage of organic matter will remain very high. That's why moorlands and peatbogs are huge carbon stores.

To investigate the organic content of a soil sample you need a sample of soil that has already been dried in a soil oven at a low temperature (see soil water content, above). To measure the organic content follow these steps.

One Take about 10g of dry soil and grind it with a pestle and mortar.

Two Place the soil sample in a pre-weighed crucible. Weigh the soil and crucible. Record the total weight.

Three Heat the crucible over a Bunsen burner for 30 minutes. This will incinerate the organic matter.

Four Allow the crucible to cool. Wipe off any soot from the bottom of the crucible. Re-weigh the soil and crucible. Subtract the weight of the crucible.

Five Calculate the weight of the organic matter by subtracting the weight of the burnt soil from the original weight of the soil sample.

Six Use the following equation to calculate the percentage organic matter (by weight) of the soil.

Percentage organic matter (by weight) of dry soil = (weight lost by burning / weight of dry soil) x 100.

Test your understanding

Why is it essential to use a dry soil sample when measuring organic content?

Vegetation surveys (see also Carbon surveys)

You should use vegetation surveys if you are interested in identifying the species of plant or tree that are growing in your fieldwork area and their relative abundance or scarcity.

Why use vegetation surveys?

You may be able to investigate plant **succession** and **zonation** – interrelated concepts that relate to how small scale ecosystems change over time. However, you need to check your specification to ensure that this is allowed. You could investigate the interrelationship between people and ecosystems. For example, you could investigate:

▶ whether management of the ecosystem is likely to have an impact on its ability to store water or carbon. For example, you might assess evidence that woodland management can make a contribution to natural flood management;

▶ the use and value of urban green spaces such as recreational fields, cemeteries, allotments, or pocket parks. You could assess the importance of urban green spaces for:
  • wildlife by investigating the biodiversity of vegetation using a quadrat survey;
  • the well-being of local residents by using Likert Surveys or questionnaires;

▶ the effect of trampling on vegetation at a site that is under pressure from visitors.

Using Quadrats

A **quadrat** is a device that helps you to sample from within a small area. It is usually a simple square frame that you place on the ground. It gives you a shape that you can sample inside. The frame is usually quite small – often 50cm by 50cm (which is a quarter of a square metre) – like the one shown in Figure 3.86. However, you can also use tent pegs and string to mark out a larger frame – say 2 metres by 2 metres (4 square metres). The frame is often divided into smaller squares with wire or string to make it easier to identify sample locations within the square.

There are two ways to use a quadrat.

1 **Collect frequency data of plant species**. Use the intersecting lines to identify individual species of plant by counting the number of times (frequency) that each plant species is touched by a crossed-wire in the quadrat. This gives you a frequency for the number of times each plant (or type of pebble) occurs. Remember that some crossed-wires may touch two or more plants.

2 **Estimate percentage cover.** Use the frame of the quadrat to estimate the percentage cover occupied by each plant. Note that this generates a different type of data. Instead of frequency (number of times something is counted) this generates percentage data – indicating how much ground is covered by each species of plant.

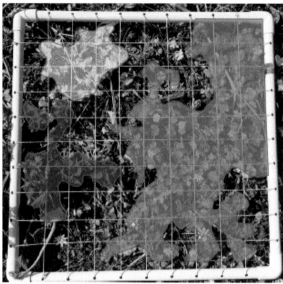

Figure 3.86 Estimating areas within the frame of the quadrat. The percentage of the quadrat occupied by each species of plant was estimated. Three different species of plant can be identified in this quadrat. The second image has been tinted to show the percentage area covered by each plant more clearly.

Evaluation

It is easy to underestimate the area occupied by shorter plants.

To **estimate percentage** cover, follow these steps.

One Conduct a pilot survey to identify the main species of plants in your fieldwork location. Use this information to design a data collection sheet that lists all of the species you are likely to see.

Two Use a sampling strategy to select locations for the quadrat. Vegetation is often sampled along a transect, using either the continuous belt transect or interrupted belt transect technique (see below).

Three Estimate the area covered by each type of plant within a quadrat, as in Figure 3.86. The quadrat in Figure 3.86 is divided into 100 squares so it is easy to estimate the percentage distribution of each plant as each square represents 1%. This style of quadrat works best with low growing plants.

The use of quadrats allows you to record the percentage of ground covered by various plants in each quadrat. You can present this type of data using a kite diagram (see page 162).

One limitation of using a quadrat is that it can be difficult to be accurate about the percentage of vegetation in a quadrat if the plants are of different heights. Taller plants grow over shorter ones so it is possible to underestimate the percentage of the quadrat filled by smaller plants. This is especially true of a quadrat that is sub-divided as the strings/wires flatten the vegetation (see Figure 3.87). To overcome this problem you could use an open quadrat (one without the grid) although this makes the estimation of area more difficult.

Figure 3.87 It can be difficult to estimate the percentage of smaller plants in a wire frame quadrat.

Belt transects

If the transect is short, say 10 metres or less, you should place the quadrats end-to-end. This makes a **continuous belt transect,** as shown in the upper part of Figure 3.88. No variations in the vegetation are missed using this technique but it is time-consuming. Placing the quadrats at regular intervals makes an Interrupted belt transect. This is a quicker technique to use over a longer distance but small variations in vegetation can be missed.

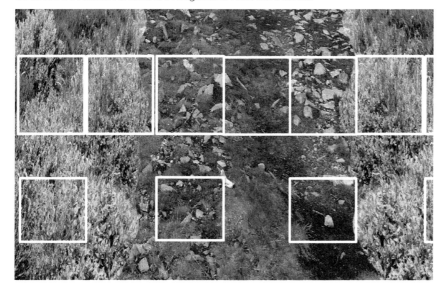

Figure 3.88 Continuous belt transect (top) and interrupted belt transect (bottom).

The ACFOR scale (or Frequency Index)

The **ACFOR scale** is used to measure the abundance of a plant species. Rather than repeated use of a quadrat to estimate the percentage of each species that is present, you can use the scale as an estimate of species abundance across a large sample area – say 10m x 10m. This survey technique is obviously quicker and easier than using several quadrats. It has the advantage of allowing you to record the presence of plants that are 'rare' within your sample area which you would be unlikely to record at all using a quarter metre square quadrat. However, you need to take care - your eye is likely to be drawn to larger and more colourful plants so the abundance of these species can be overestimated.

	Within the sampling area, the plant is …
A	Abundant.
C	Common.
F	Frequent.
O	Occasional.
R	Rare.

Figure 3.89 The ACFOR scale of species abundance.

Zonation and succession

The study of a small scale, local ecosystem, such as a sand dune, woodland, or heath provides an opportunity to investigate the relationship between plants and the **abiotic** (non-living) components of the environment such as soil, water, temperature, and wind. In a sand dune ecosystem it is relatively easy to use measures of species abundance to identify **zonation** – the development, over time, of zones of vegetation that have similar characteristics. However, each A level specification includes a different level of detail about ecosystems so check your own specification before deciding to focus your investigation on zonation or succession in an ecosystem.

Sand dunes are a common feature of coastal landscapes where deposition is occurring – they often form on spits and at the top of sandy beaches beyond the high tide mark. Sand dunes are formed when sand is blown from the beach. The sand is transported up the beach and then deposited around the salt-tolerant plants that grow at the top of the beach.

Embryo dunes A few specialised plants that are tolerant of salt spray live here, like this sea rocket. They take nutrients from decomposing seaweed washed up in the strand line near the top of the beach.

Mobile dunes Marram grass grows here – it has large fibrous roots that hold the sand together. The tall leaves stick up into the air and slow the wind speed so that sand carried in the wind is deposited. Wind easily erodes sand where there are no plants.

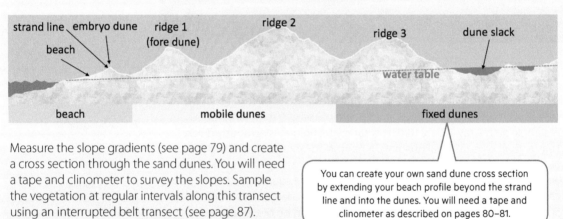

Measure the slope gradients (see page 79) and create a cross section through the sand dunes. You will need a tape and clinometer to survey the slopes. Sample the vegetation at regular intervals along this transect using an interrupted belt transect (see page 87).

You can create your own sand dune cross section by extending your beach profile beyond the strand line and into the dunes. You will need a tape and clinometer as described on pages 80–81.

Fixed dunes This is the oldest part of the dunes. Wind speeds are lower here so erosion is less likely. There are more nutrients in the soil because plants have been dropping leaf litter here for longer than elsewhere in the dunes. Consequently, the fixed dunes have a wide variety of flowering plants, shorter grasses, and shrubs like this bramble.

How to investigate trampling

Some ecosystems are vulnerable to impacts from recreational use. The amount of impact depends partly on the number of visitors and also how well visitors are managed, for example, through the provision of signage or footpaths. However, the level of impact also depends on the fragility of species within the ecosystem with some slow growing plants being particularly susceptible to damage. Salt marsh plants, for example, are particularly vulnerable to damage by trampling.

Moorland ecosystems are also vulnerable to the effects of trampling which can then lead to soil erosion. Trampling kills plants leaving the soil exposed so it is easily eroded by rainwater and by hikers' boots. We can record the amount of footpath erosion by stretching a line across the path and measuring down to the ground as shown in Figure 3.90.

Some plant types are hardier than others. They survive trampling whereas other plants are killed. We could investigate this by using quadrats to sample vegetation across the path in a **belt transect.**

Figure 3.90 How to take data readings to create a cross section across an eroded footpath. Shropshire Hills AONB.

To complete a belt transect follow these steps.

One Measure the width of the path, including at least 2 metres to each side. Divide this by 10 to create 10 evenly spaced sample points.

Two Stretch a line tightly across the path. Make sure it is level.

Three Measure downwards, from the line to the ground, at each sample point. Record the distance from the line to the path or vegetation.

You can present your data in the form of a cross section (see page 156).

The need for control groups

Quadrats are often used to measure how vegetation changes in relation to another variable, for example, how vegetation varies:

▶ across a sand dune with increasing distance from the sea;
▶ across a footpath with variable amounts of trampling.

When you are looking for variations like this it is a good idea to see what the vegetation is like by sampling in an area unaffected by the variable. We call this a **control group**. It allows you to compare the results of the area that you are investigating (for example, the plants that have been trampled on the footpath) with vegetation that is unaffected and therefore 'typical' of the area.

Control group

A control group provides a standard to which data collected in fieldwork can be compared.

Investigating urban green spaces

Green spaces enhance the urban environment by increasing biodiversity, reducing flood risk, and maybe even cleaning the air we breathe. Trees help to reduce traffic noise and provide more surface area for the deposition of dry pollutants (such as brake dust) from traffic, thereby helping to clean the air. Vegetation helps to reduce the risk of flooding by intercepting water and reducing the time it takes for heavy rainfall to reach urban rivers. As a result, planners encourage the creation of urban Pocket Parks – tiny green spaces that benefit the local community by providing a community service and, in their small way, help reduce the risk of flooding. Recreational fields tend to have low biodiversity but gardens and cemeteries provide habitat for urban wildlife such as butterflies, moths, bats, garden birds, and mammals such as foxes.

Figure 3.91 Link Age Plus, Older People's Gardens, is a tiny community allotment on the site of a demolished terraced house. Clinton Road, Bow, London.

You could investigate the impacts of urban green spaces by:
▶ surveying traffic noise to assess whether vegetation is useful in blocking traffic noise;
▶ using a bipolar survey to assess the opinions of local people and determine whether they are aware of the environmental benefits of local green spaces;
▶ conducting a vegetation survey to assess the biodiversity.

Visual evidence (see also Field Sketches and Image elicitation)

Your fieldwork location will be full of visual evidence that may help you answer your research questions. You can collect primary visual evidence of your investigation or the environment you are working in by:
▶ taking photos;
▶ making field sketches (see page 50);
▶ creating sketch maps (see page 52).

You can also use visual evidence as a more fundamental part of your primary data collection by using images (artwork, photos, or maps) to help prompt a conversation with participants. Participants can be asked to respond to images during a questionnaire or interview. Or you can ask participants to create their own drawings, maps, or photos as a way of expressing their opinions and perceptions. These techniques include:
▶ mental mapping (page 69);
▶ image (photo) elicitation (page 62).

Why take photos?
Taking photos is a common way of collecting visual evidence in all sorts of investigations. You might take photos to:

▶ **provide an overview of the main features of the study area.** A panoramic viewpoint is best – perhaps from a multistorey car park, or a hill overlooking the study area;

▶ **illustrate the way that you have used data collection techniques.** For example, if you are using an EQI (page 48), you could take photos that represent each of your criteria. You could take photos that represent EQI scores for litter, graffiti, or the quality of pavements (see Figure 3.92). This should help you to apply the EQI consistently throughout your investigation;

▶ **record geographical features that are relevant to your research questions.** For example, in an investigation of changing places your photos should capture evidence of a concept that is the focus of your investigation such as evidence of risk, identity, diversity, or sustainability in the urban environment. See Figure 3.93.

The ethics of taking photos

If you are taking photos of people as part of your investigation there are some ethical considerations that you should take into account.

1 It is acceptable to take photographs in public spaces – including photos that include strangers. However, show respect to others – don't push your camera in people's faces. Some people do not want to be photographed.

2 Always ask permission if you want to take a close up of someone. Some people do not want to be photographed – you must respect their wishes. Explain that your photos are only for your personal studies and that you won't be sharing them on social media.

3 Don't stand in the way of other pedestrians or block pavements.

4 Don't take photos on private property unless you have permission. This includes shopping centres.

5 Don't take photos of people inside their own homes (through a window) even if you are in a public place because people have a right to privacy.

6 Don't take photos of homeless people without their permission – be respectful.

7 Be aware of how people are reacting when you are taking photos. If they are uncomfortable be respectful and don't photograph them. You can wait until they have moved on or take the photo from a different angle so that you don't include them.

> Don't include photos in your report unless you can analyse them or use them in some way to illustrate a key point.

EQI score = 5	EQI score = -2	EQI score = -5
Pavements are even.	Pavements are uneven.	Pavements are so uneven they could present a trip hazard.

Figure 3.92 Take photos to illustrate criteria in an EQI.

Fixed point photography

Fixed point photography is a technique where photos are taken from exactly the same location over a period of time to record changes in the landscape. The technique is used to analyse landscape change in National Parks over longer periods of time (months or years). You don't have a long period of time to complete your independent investigation but you could still use the technique to record rapidly changing landscapes.

You could investigate:

- ▶ movement of people in a pedestrianised shopping area;
- ▶ the tide rising or falling on a beach;
- ▶ the changing pattern of clouds in the sky as a frontal system rolls over.

Ideally, you should use a tripod so that you can take a number of photos from exactly the same spot.

Participant photography (see also Image elicitation)

Nearly everyone has a camera on their phone. You can use this to your advantage by asking people to take photos of features that matter most to them.

One Set up a focus group of 6 to 12 people. Brief them. Explain the purpose of your investigation and give the participants some criteria for taking the photos. For example, ask them to take at least 10 photos each of features that represent an emotion such as pride or a concept such as risk.

Two Collate (gather) the photos. You will probably do this electronically via email.

Three Display the photos. One effective way to do this is to stick the photos to a large, simple map of the place that is being investigated.

Four Reconvene the focus group so they can view the display. Conduct interviews and record the outcome for further analysis.

Figure 3.93 Architectural details help to create urban identity. New Street station in Birmingham has been clad in a highly reflective material. Rather than seeing the building itself, you see reflections of other buildings. Here you see the iconic Rotunda tower.

Using photos with other data

You may be able to compare your own photos with images from secondary sources in order to investigate:

- ▶ change over time (see Re-photography below);
- ▶ the difference between images that have been taken by others (for example, for branding purposes) and the reality of the environment as you see it.

Re-photography

Re-photography means to take new photos in the same location as an older image. The two images can then be compared to analyse any changes (see pages 189–190 for this type of analysis). The older image may be a photo but it could also be a piece of art such as a drawing or painting. You can find older photos in various secondary sources, postcards provide a useful source, and you can find artwork in galleries or museums (see pages 115–116 on using these sources of secondary visual data).

One Do your secondary research to find interesting images (photos or artwork) of your fieldwork location.

Two Find the location. Take a photo of the same scene so that you can compare the two images later as part of your analysis.

For advice on annotating images as part of your analysis see pages 189–190.

Figure 3.94 Salmon Lane in the Rain, Bow (1987). A painting by the artist Doreen Fletcher.

Figure 3.95 An example of re-photography. Salmon Lane, Bow in 2019.

Comparing media representations to local perceptions

It's easy to find out how a place is represented in the media. Do an online search for *'What is (place name) famous for?'* If you do this you will quickly come up with a list of buildings, landmarks, famous people, or local industries that are connected to your town. You may also find cultural references – search for Birmingham and you will probably find references to Balti (curry), Richard Hammond (TV presenter), and Ozzy Osbourne (rock musician), as well as jewellery and the canal system. You could investigate whether the image represented in the media is similar to or different from the perception of local people.

One Do your online search. Try to find between 10 and 20 landmarks or features that are connected to your place. Print images of each one.

Two Show your images to a group of local people. Ask them to sort the images in order of importance to them. Then select the 5 images that best represent how the group perceives the place.

Three Ask the group to identify any important features of the place that did not appear in your online search. Ask them why these are important. Try to photograph these features and annotate them using phrases used by your participants.

You could extend this investigation by conducting **interviews** with two separate groups of people (see page 61). For example, you could interview one group of elderly local residents and a second group of much younger people. How do the perceptions of each group compare with the media representation of their place? How do their views compare with each other?

Figure 3.96 Ozzy Osbourne is celebrated in Birmingham as a native of the city. His is one of several celebrity stars embedded in the pavement in Broad Street.

> ### Test your understanding
> Use an online search to find famous landmarks or features in your own town. How is this place represented? What proportion of photos show a positive image? Would local people agree with this image?

Review Points

Tick off each review point before moving on to Step 4.

I have considered the use of both qualitative and quantitative data. ☐

I have researched a range of different types of data that would help me with my investigation. ☐

I have identified some appropriate data collection methods and know how and why I would use them. ☐

I have identified any equipment that will be needed to collect the data. ☐

I can justify my choices. ☐

Design a sampling strategy

Action points

1 Research and select suitable methods of data sampling.

2 Design a suitable sampling strategy for your own investigation. Consider the timing and frequency of your sample – how much data to collect, where, and when you will collect it.

Sampling is an important part of any investigation. It is also a critical element of the mark scheme. There are several decisions you need to make in order to design the right **sampling strategy** (also known as a sampling framework) for your investigation. The decisions you need to make when you design your sampling strategy are outlined in Figure 4.1. We will focus on the first two decisions in Action Point 1.

Sampling strategy

A sampling strategy is the plan that you use to collect sufficient data to represent the whole population.

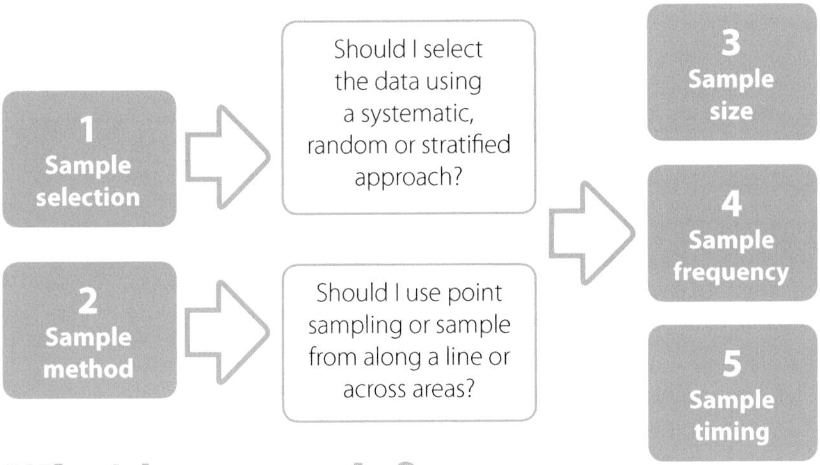

Figure 4.1 Decisions required to design a sampling strategy.

1 Sample selection → Should I select the data using a systematic, random or stratified approach?

2 Sample method → Should I use point sampling or sample from along a line or across areas?

3 Sample size

4 Sample frequency

5 Sample timing

You must have a sampling strategy. The strategy you design depends on the type of data you are collecting. You should be able to describe and justify the sampling strategy in your report.

What is a sample?

It is rarely possible to count or measure everything. Instead of trying to collect every bit of data, you will need to collect a sample of data. The name given to all the data from which you select a sample is the population. This may refer to people, such as all the people in a postcode unit, or other living things such as all the trees in a wood. However, the population can also refer to non-living things, such as all the pebbles on a beach. If collected properly, a **representative sample** will closely match the patterns or trends shown in all the data of your chosen population.

Representative sample

Representative sample reflects the features/characteristics of the whole population.

Action Point 1

Research and select suitable methods of data sampling.

Before you can design a sampling strategy you need to understand the different sampling methods you could use. These are outlined in this Action Point. As you read these think about your own investigation and which methods might be suitable.

Probability sampling

There are three main methods of probability sampling - each is capable of creating a representative sample:

1 You can sample at regular intervals (Systematic sampling).

2 You can sample at random intervals (Random sampling).

3 For populations that are split into sub-groups there is Stratified sampling.

Figure 4.2 The difference between systematic and random sampling.

Methods	How it works	Examples You collect data ...
Systematic	Your sample is chosen at regular intervals. Every *n*th item is sampled.	• at points that are equally spaced (e.g. every 10 metres) along a transect; • at regular intervals throughout the day (e.g. every hour) or at regular intervals throughout the week.
Random	Your data is sampled at random intervals.	• at places that have been chosen by using tables of random numbers to generate grid references; • in streets chosen by putting all street names into a bag and pulling out a sample of names at random.

Weblink

http://www.textfixer.com/numbers/random-number-generator.php
One of many online tools that will generate random numbers for you.

If your data falls into two or more sub-groups you can use a stratified sampling strategy. For example, people can be divided into sub-groups by age and soils could fall into sub-groups by underlying geology. In stratified sampling your sample reflects the proportions that fall in each of these sub-groups of the whole population. For example, imagine you are sampling soils in an area where the geology is 60% chalk and 40% clay. In stratified sampling, 60% of your samples should be collected from the area of chalk geology and 40% from the area of clay.

It is important to realise that stratified sampling only helps you to select the number of samples from each sub-group. You will still need to select data for sampling from each sub-group. To do this you could use either a random or systematic method.

There are three main methods of organising your sample:

▶ you can sample data **along a line** (or transect);

▶ you can sample data from **areas**, for example, by using a quadrat;

▶ you can sample at **points** in space.

You can combine any method of selecting sample data with any method of organising your sample. This gives you twelve options to choose from – they are shown in Figure 4.3. You can think of this as a pick 'n' mix - combining methods of data selection with methods of organising your sample to design a strategy that suits your investigation.

Figure 4.3 The twelve options for selecting and organising your data sampling.

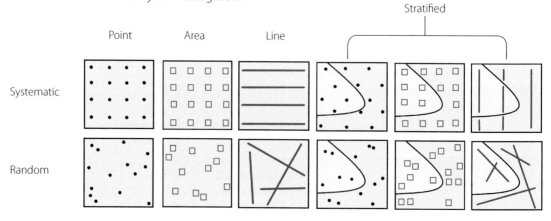

Point sampling

Point sampling is perhaps the simplest way of organising your sampling – it means to sample data from discrete places. For example, you could sample:

▶ noise levels at points located at regular intervals away from a busy road;
▶ footfall at randomly located points in a pedestrianised street;
▶ soil samples from points that have been selected from different land uses.

Sampling along a line

Sample along a line to record change in a variable over distance such as:

▶ a slope or beach profile;
▶ change in environmental quality through an urban area.

Sampling along a line (or transect) is a suitable method if you want to investigate **environmental gradient**. Environmental gradients occur in physical and human environments and can occur in both biotic (living) variables (such as plant species) and abiotic (non-living) variables (such as wind speed, height, temperature, soil moisture content, house prices). The potential relationship between each pair of variables along the gradient could be expressed as a hypothesis, for example:

▶ wind speed increases with height up a hill;
▶ noise levels fall as you get further away from a busy road;
▶ house prices increase as you get closer to an urban park;
▶ plant species are more varied further from areas of trampling;
▶ light levels decrease as you get further into a wood;
▶ in a sand dune, pH becomes more acidic the further from the strandline;
▶ in a salt marsh, salinity of the soil decreases with distance from low tide.

Once you have identified a potential environmental gradient and decided to use a transect, you have further decisions to make – see Figure 4.4.

> **Environmental gradient**
>
> An environmental gradient is a gradual (or continuous) change in values for one or more variables.

Figure 4.4 How to use a transect sampling strategy.

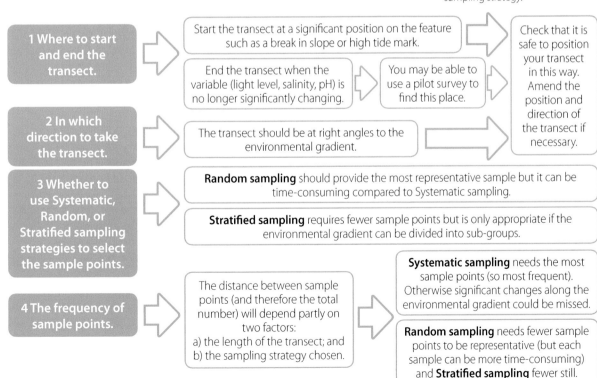

97

Sampling across an area

Sampling across an area allows you to collect data from features that cover space rather than just occur at discrete locations. For example, you might sample:

▶ an area of 50m x 50m in an urban environment and record your impressions of the quality of the environment in that area using a survey technique such as EQI or Cleanliness Index;

▶ an area of vegetation that is 50cm x 50cm using a **quadrat** – However, in some vegetation surveys it is more useful to use tent pegs and string to mark out a much larger area of vegetation (perhaps 5m x 5m).

Quadrat

A quadrat is a square frame that is used as a sampling tool.

Figure 4.5 A quadrat being used to sample vegetation.

Use of a quadrat

A typical quadrat is 50cm x 50cm (one quarter square metre) like the one in Figure 4.5. A quadrat can be used for point sampling or area sampling.

1 **Point sampling**. Use the intersecting lines to identify individuals in your population (usually species of plant but you can also use a quadrat to sample pebbles). This is point sampling within the frame of the quadrat. It gives you a frequency for the number of times each plant (or type of pebble) occurs.

2 **Area sampling**. Use the frame of the quadrat to estimate the percentage cover occupied by each plant. Note that this sampling strategy generates a different type of data. Instead of frequency (number of times something is counted) this generates percentage data – indicating how much ground is covered by each species of plant.

Sampling across larger areas

People say that if you can map it, it's geography! This is because geographers are interested in spatial patterns – in other words, how features are distributed across an area. If you sample along a line you are sampling in one dimension. You will see how a pattern changes with distance but you will not be able to see a spatial pattern. To see a spatial pattern (and then draw a map) you will need to sample in two dimensions. You could do this by:

▶ **sampling along several lines**, for example, four lines radiating out from the town centre towards the suburbs;

▶ **using a base map and overlaying it with a grid pattern**. Then:
  • point sampling at grid intersections or in the centre of each grid square (a Systematic sampling strategy);
  • using random numbers to generate four or six figure grid references and point sampling at these points (a Random sampling strategy).

▶ **using a dérive (drift journey)** to select locations subconsciously or randomly in an urban environment (see the description below).

Having spatial data should give you many more options when you come to presenting your data.

These methods of sampling will generate data across the area. This will enable you to present your data on a map later in the investigation.

Dérive or drift journey

A Dérive is an unplanned journey through a landscape in which the participants (usually a small group) use their senses of sight, sound, and smell to collect qualitative evidence about how they perceive a place. The participants could be given a simple focus, such as to record the things they like and the things they dislike. The participants can use video, audio recordings, drawings, or photos to record their experiences. By working as a small team the participants can cross-reference their observations as they go along to arrive at a common perception of the place.

A Dèrive journey should be aimless and the sampling strategy, used to select places to collect data, should reflect this. The participants can simply wander around and allow subconscious decisions to dictate their route. Alternatively they can use a dice and cards to generate a random set of instructions, like the ones in Figure 4.6. This data collection strategy should allow the participants to observe things that they wouldn't necessarily see if they chose the shortest route through the landscape.

1. Turn left.	2. Follow the loudest sound.	3. Turn right.
4. Pause for a while.	5. Go straight on.	6. Look up.

Figure 4.6 Instruction cards that could be used with a dice to structure a Dèrive journey.

Choosing a suitable sampling method for your investigation

You have seen that there are twelve possible data sampling methods. It is important that you select the sampling methods that are most suitable for your own investigation. For example, you should sample systematically along a line if you are investigating an environmental gradient.

It may be appropriate for you to select a different sampling method for each of your research questions. For example, students are investigating soils on the hill shown in Figure 4.7. Two different sampling strategies are shown in Figure 4.8:

▷ on the left, the student is investigating how geology affects soil type and plant species. She decides to sample percentage cover of each plant type using quadrats (area sampling). The 1km^2 area of the fieldwork location includes two main rock types in a ratio of 60:40. Consequently, she decides to use Stratified sampling with 9 quadrats on the igneous rocks and 6 on the sedimentary rocks;

▷ on the right, the student is investigating soil catenas – how soils vary along a slope. As this is an environmental gradient he decides to select sample sites systematically along a line. He also wants to know whether the soil catenas are affected by aspect so he locates his transects on two contrasting slopes – one that is north facing and one that is south facing.

Figure 4.7 A one kilometre square fieldwork site.

40mm = 1km

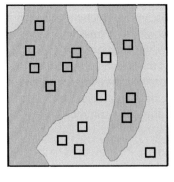

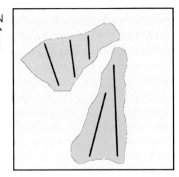

Figure 4.8 Stratified area sampling (left) and Systematic line sampling (right).

In the example shown in Figure 4.8 , the students have demonstrated independence by designing unique sampling strategies. However, it would be advisable for them to collect data together for safety reasons.

| | Lavas and other igneous rocks |
| | Shales and sandstones |

| | Accessible north facing slopes |
| | Accessible south facing slopes |

Opportunistic sampling

Each of the methods of sampling described so far should provide you with a representative sample – one that represents the characteristics of the whole population. However, in some situations, it isn't possible to use any of these methods. For example, you have decided to:

▶ sample points systematically across an urban area but you cannot access some locations because the sample point is in the middle of a building or busy road;

▶ sample systematically along a line up a hillside but some sections of your line are too steep to access safely;

▶ sample every fifth pedestrian for a Likert Survey but some people are too busy to talk to you.

In these circumstances you may need to adapt your sampling strategy so that you can collect data sensibly, safely, and efficiently. This is referred to as non-probability or **Opportunistic sampling**.

Opportunistic sampling is commonly used to:

▶ select locations in an urban environment to take photos or record a bipolar survey (see the description of a Dérive journey on page 99);

▶ select participants in a questionnaire, Likert Survey, or interview (see below).

(see the description of a Dérive journey on page 99);

Opportunistic sampling

Opportunistic sampling means you take the opportunity to collect data whenever or wherever you can. It is sometimes called **Convenience** or **Pragmatic** sampling.

You will need around 50 responses to your questionnaire as a minimum sample size for a homogeneous population.

Sampling people

It can be difficult (although not impossible) to use systematic or random methods of selecting people to question in a survey, questionnaire, or interview so a number of opportunistic methods have been developed. They are easier to use than a systematic or random method because they should allow you to select:

▶ a larger number of participants

▶ your participants more efficiently and, therefore, save you time.

However, opportunistic sampling suffers a limitation – it is unlikely to select a representative sample. That's why the sample size for a questionnaire needs to be relatively large.

There are a number of different ways that you can sample people for a survey, questionnaire, or interview. Four possible methods are described below. Each has its own strengths and weaknesses. Think about which method suits your investigation best and be prepared to justify your decision.

Convenience sampling of a homogeneous population

In Convenience sampling there is no method for choosing participants – you survey anyone who is willing to be involved. However, people are very diverse. To get a representative sample you would need a very large sample size. An alternative and quicker form of Convenience sampling assumes that the population is homogeneous, in other words, everybody in your sample population is pretty much the same as everyone else. In reality, this means you need to select a portion of the population who share a common socio-economic or demographic background such as students at a sixth form college or university. You would be justified in using this strategy if you were researching a geographical issue that affects people aged 16-19 or 19-21. If so, it would be appropriate to use this technique by sampling students from your school or college.

Paper-based surveys can be very time-consuming – even ones of a homogeneous population. Are most of the people in your contact list a similar age to you? If so, you could use an online survey tool to create and distribute your survey to people in your address book.

Weblink

https://www.surveymonkey.co.uk Survey Monkey is a free online survey tool.

Snowball sampling

In **Snowball sampling** you start by questioning a limited number of people. You ask each participant to recommend at least one other person who would be suitable for your survey. You then question the people who have been referred to you. You should use Snowball sampling if you need to survey people with specific characteristics but you cannot find enough people to make a reasonably-sized sample. For example, imagine you want to investigate attitudes of people who have recently moved into a rural location. You know 10 people and start with them. You ask each of them to refer you to other people they know.

Expert sampling

Use **Expert sampling** if you need to collect the views of people who have some specific skill or knowledge that is relevant to your investigation. Before you can question the participants, you will need to define what is meant by 'expert' in the context of your investigation. For example, in an investigation of coastal flood risk you may want to contact the local council to discover which agencies (including the Environment Agency) are involved in local flood management. 'Experts' may have a lot to say so it will probably be appropriate to conduct longer interviews with a few participants rather than a short questionnaire with a large sample. The aim of any interviews may be to identify any significant difference of opinion between the experts.

Proportionate sampling

Proportionate sampling is a type of Stratified sampling (see page 96). You can use Proportionate sampling to ensure that important segments of the population are represented properly in your sample. For example, imagine that you are investigating the rebranding of a rural place. You know from the census that the proportion of people who are retired in your rural location is 25% of the whole population. In Proportionate sampling you would make sure that 25% of your participants are retired. This is important because, without Proportionate sampling, it may be that retired people would be either over-represented or under-represented. For example, if you used Convenience sampling to interview as many residents of a village as possible on a week day between the hours of 10am and 3pm you would probably over-represent the views of retirees because other people might be at school or at work.

So far you have researched various sampling methods and selected those that are suitable for the data that you intend to collect. To create an effective sampling strategy you also need to consider the size, the frequency, and timing of your sample. This is explained in Action Point 2.

Action Point 2

Design a suitable sampling strategy for your own investigation – how much data to collect, where, and when you will collect it.

A sampling strategy (or sampling framework) is used by researchers to collect a representative sample. The whole decision-making process is summarised in Figure 4.9. The top part in the green box is the part you have already completed.

Figure 4.9 Key issues in designing a sampling strategy.

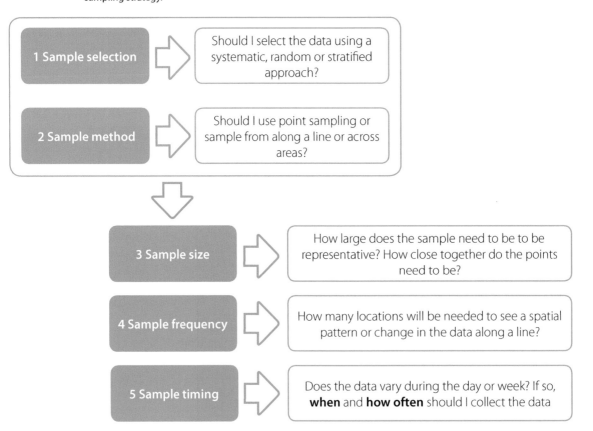

1 Sample selection ⟹ Should I select the data using a systematic, random or stratified approach?

2 Sample method ⟹ Should I use point sampling or sample from along a line or across areas?

3 Sample size ⟹ How large does the sample need to be to be representative? How close together do the points need to be?

4 Sample frequency ⟹ How many locations will be needed to see a spatial pattern or change in the data along a line?

5 Sample timing ⟹ Does the data vary during the day or week? If so, **when** and **how often** should I collect the data

How large a sample?

There isn't an easy answer to this question. You certainly don't need to measure the whole population.

▶ **It would take too long.** In the case of sampling sediment on a beach – it would take forever!
▶ **It isn't necessary.** If the sample is chosen carefully, the sample will represent the whole population quite accurately.
▶ **It may not be possible.** For example, if you want to conduct a questionnaire, some people will refuse to take part.

The main point of sampling is to collect data that is representative of the whole population. If you fail to do this, your sample will be biased. **Bias** can be avoided by considering:

▶ sample size, which is partly dependent on the number of variables;
▶ the frequency and timing of your sample.

Sample size

Sample size is determined by the **number of variables**.

▶ If the number of variables is small, sample size can be small. For example, if pebbles on a beach are all made from the same rock type you are likely to have a small range of pebble shapes – so sample size can be smaller than a beach that has pebbles from a range of different rock types.
▶ If the number of variables is large, then you need a larger sample. For example, people come from a wide range of socio-economic backgrounds so most questionnaires need a large sample size.

If you control the variables (see pages 31-32) then you can reduce the sample size and reduce the likelihood of bias. For example, in an infiltration survey, the variables include antecedent weather, soil type, soil depth, geology, and land use. The sample size needs to be large enough to take all of these variables into account.

How many questionnaires?

If you are planning to use a questionnaire (see page 71) you need a sample of at least 50 people. People are very different – there are multiple socio-economic variables which can affect people's responses. These might include age, ethnicity, education, income, and health. This large number of variables means you could ask questionnaires of over 100 different people before you started to see any kind of pattern in their responses. If you can choose a population that is fairly **homogeneous** then you might only need a sample of 50 before patterns begin to emerge. For example, you might select your sample from:

▶ sixth form students – all a similar age and educational background;
▶ a single **postcode unit** – people are likely to share a similar economic background.

Frequency and timing

The **frequency** and **timing** of your sample are two more factors that will influence whether or not you collect a representative sample. If you fail to consider these factors you are likely to introduce bias in your sample. If the sample is biased you will struggle to reach valid and reliable conclusions.

> ### Homogeneous
> Homogeneous population is one that shares at least one important variable, such as age or income.

> ### Postcode units
> Postcode units are the smallest division of a postcode. They denote a small group of properties – perhaps a single street.

Sample frequency

The **frequency** of your sampling is to do with the number and density of your sample points. The frequency of systematic samples needs careful consideration. If the frequency of sample points is too low then rapid changes in an environmental gradient will be missed. In a sand dune ecosystem, some variations in environmental gradient occur over very short distances. See Figure 4.10. In this example, the systematic sample points are infrequent (too far apart) and the sea rocket, which only grows in the embryo dunes, has been missed completely. In this example, the Systematic sampling needs a higher frequency of sample points.

Figure 4.10 The frequency of sample points needs to be sufficient to represent changes in any environmental gradient.

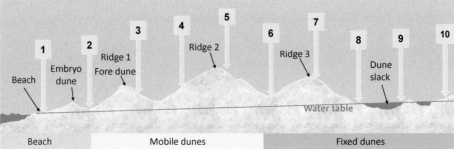

Spatial

A spatial pattern is one that can be seen across an area and that can be plotted on a map.

Identifying spatial patterns

By improving the frequency of your data sampling then you should be able to capture **spatial** variations in data. Remember that it is acceptable to plan your sampling strategy and collect primary data as part of a group. By working as a team you will be able to collect a larger sample of data than if you had worked alone. Furthermore, as a team you could sample data from several points simultaneously, for example, you could count footfall at a number of different locations across a town centre at the same time. This would allow you to create a map from your data.

If you want to use your data to map a spatial pattern then 12 sample points is probably the minimum number. Study Figure 4.11. The map on the left (A) has been drawn using data from 8 sample points. These have been selected using Opportunistic sampling - the sites have been selected because they were at

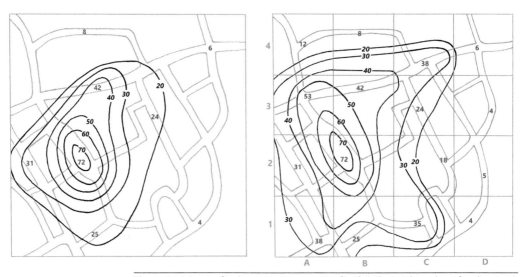

Figure 4.11 A pair of isoline maps representing footfall (the total number of pedestrians). The one on the left (A) has insufficient data to represent the whole population.

convenient locations. The red numbers represent the footfall counted at each sample point. In this example, the frequency of sample points is too small – there are significant gaps between the data points. This problem has been overcome in the map on the right (B) with the addition of a grid. The grid has enabled the researcher to sample data systematically by selecting 16 sample points, each located as close as possible to the centre of each grid square. Notice that the 8 sample points used for the first map are the same but the shape of the isolines is significantly different. The extra sample points provide a greater spatial frequency of data so this sample is more representative of the population as a whole.

Timing of your sample

Finally, you need to consider the timing of your sample to avoid bias. For example, whether you need to sample at different times of the day or week.

▶ A questionnaire conducted between 9am and 5pm will exclude people who are at work so the data collected will not represent the whole population – no matter how large the sample size. If some questionnaires are conducted in the evening, then the sample will become more representative but the sample size needs to increase.

▶ A beach profile survey which is started a few hours after low tide will not be representative of the whole beach because the lower part of the profile will be covered in water.

> Make sure you justify the reasons for your sampling strategy, including the timing and frequency of samples.

Which is the best sampling strategy for me?

Still confused? Here is a quick recap.

1 It's very unlikely that you can collect all of the data so you need a sample.
2 At a basic level, you need a method of selecting and organising your sample. There are twelve options available to you – summarised in Figure 4.12. Select the method(s) that best suits your research questions.
3 At a more advanced level, you need a sampling strategy. This means that you have selected a suitable sample size, sample frequency, and you have considered the timing of your sample.
4 You need to be able to justify and evaluate your sampling strategy. Figure 4.13 gives some help with this.

Figure 4.12 Summary of key sampling methods.

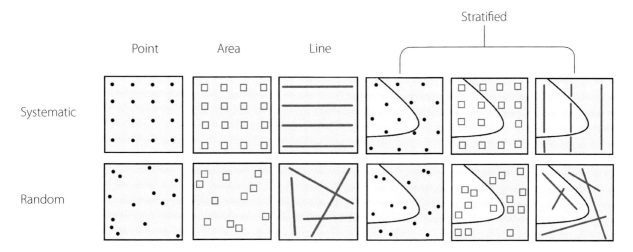

Sampling method	Potential strengths	Potential limitations and mitigations
Random sampling	Every item in the population has an equal chance of being sampled. It therefore provides an unbiased sample.	Using random numbers to generate co-ordinates for sample locations is very time-consuming compared to systematically working along a line and sampling at regular intervals.
Systematic sampling	An effective method if you want to investigate an environmental gradient – in which case you should sample at regular intervals along a transect (for example, up a slope, through the zones of an ecosystem, or through a town).	Systematic samples do not give every item in the population an equal chance of being sampled. For example, in a transect where samples are taken every 10 metres, there is zero chance of a sample at 4 metres or 7 metres. This means you need to sample a higher frequency of data.
Stratified sampling	A very precise form of sampling because the population of each sub-group (or strata) within your population is represented in proportion. This means that no sub-group will be over- or under-represented. It also means that your sample size can be smaller than if you used Random sampling across the whole population.	You will need to do some homework – calculating the proportion of your population that exists in each sub-group before you begin the survey. This may involve using secondary data or a pilot survey.
Opportunistic sampling	A practical solution when other forms of sampling simply don't work, for example, because: • sites chosen at random are inaccessible or too dangerous; • people chosen at random or systematically may refuse to take part in a survey.	Data collected may not be representative of the whole population so you either need to: • choose a homogeneous population to sample from; • have a very large sample size; • adopt one of the specific forms of sampling used for questionnaires such as Snowball sampling, Proportionate sampling, or Expert sampling

Figure 4.13 Summary of the potential strengths and limitations of sampling.

QUESTION I will want to collect footfall and traffic data from several locations at the same time. Is it possible to share the task of data collection with other students?

ANSWER Yes, you are allowed to work collaboratively when you are collecting primary data. It will be important that everyone in your team knows what to do and collects the data in the same way.

Evaluation

Review your sampling strategy carefully when you are writing up your report. With hindsight, are there things you could have done that would have made your sample representative of the whole population?

Review Points

Tick off each review point before moving on to Step 5.

I have researched sampling methods and selected those that are most appropriate for my own investigation. ☐

I have considered:

    frequency of my sample ☐

    the timing of my sample ☐

    what makes an appropriate sample size. ☐

I have now designed my sampling strategy. I can justify my choices. ☐

STEP 5 Review your plan

Action points

1 Consider whether your proposed data collection raises any ethical issues and decide how to manage these.
2 Conduct a risk assessment and decide how you will manage any risks.
3 Review and refine your data collection plan and sampling strategy.

Action Point 1

Consider whether your proposed data collection raises any ethical issues and decide how to manage these.

You should consider the ethical dimension of your research when you are planning and conducting your investigation. Your fieldwork must be carried out with respect for other people and the environment in which you collect data.

Figure 5.1 Ethical considerations.

Access arrangements	⇨	Do you have permission to work at the proposed fieldwork site?	⇨	Review your plans for data collection and sampling. Make amendments to manage any ethical issues you identify.
Respect the integrity of the site	⇨	Conduct fieldwork without causing damage to the environment.	⇨	
Respect the dignity of people	⇨	Be respectful of the place and people who are the focus of your investigation.	⇨	

Access

The first consideration is access.

▶ **Does your site have public access?** Can you use a public footpath or bridleway to access the site? Alternatively, you may be allowed access because the whole site has access such as a beach, public park, or nature reserve.

▶ **If the site is in private ownership, do you have permission to work there?** Most open spaces in town centres have public access but not all do. For example, the car park of a supermarket will belong to the supermarket. If you intend to collect questionnaires from people in shopping malls or retail car parks you must ask for permission – and you may not get it, so be prepared to amend your plan.

> Whatever the investigation, you should consider the ethical dimension. If you have any concerns, this is an issue you can discuss with your teacher.

Respect the integrity of the site

Respecting the integrity site of the site means leaving the site exactly as you found it. A few common sense rules will help you.

▶ Keep to paths wherever possible.

▶ Close gates behind you.

▶ Do not use equipment or techniques that might endanger wildlife.

▶ Follow the country code.

▶ Do not leave litter.

Geographical fieldwork is rarely intrusive but, if poorly managed, it can leave behind damage. Some environments are especially fragile and are easily damaged, in particular:

▶ plants in a sand dune ecosystem can be damaged if too many geography students trample across them;

▶ salt marsh plants are even more fragile and can be easily damaged by even light trampling;

▶ limestone landscapes contain rare plants and unusual geological features that may be easily damaged by clumsy fieldwork. Scrambling across a loose scree slope, for example, could cause damage.

You will need to be particularly careful if you are planning an investigation at a National Nature Reserve or Site of Special Scientific Interest (SSSI). Such sites are managed to conserve wildlife and/or the geology/landscape. Wardens may advise you that you can sample in a particular area of the ecosystem but ask you to avoid working in others. You may need to revise your original data collection plan to comply with their request – that would be the ethical thing to do.

Figure 5.2 Respect the integrity of your fieldwork site. Signage at a National Nature Reserve.

Let's keep it special

The rich variety of habitats here led to this Montgomeryshire Wildlife Trust Reserve being notified as a National Nature Reserve and a Site of Special Scientific Interest (SSSI). Please make sure you keep to the paths, take your litter home and respect the plants and flowers.

Cadwn ni ef yn arbennig!

Oherwydd amrywiaeth eang y cynefinoedd yma mae'r warchodfa wedi ei dynodi'n Warchodfa Natur

Respect the dignity of people

If you are conducting an interview or questionnaire you must respect the dignity of your subject. This means taking care not to cause offence by the way that you behave or the questions that you ask.

When creating an interview or questionnaire you must think about how your questions can be phrased so that they do not cause offence. Asking someone their age is an obvious example that may cause offence. If knowing about age is important to your survey, it is more sensitive to ask people to tick a box to show the age group to which they belong. Gender can be another sensitive subject for those who are transitioning their gender or who have gone through gender reassignment. Ask yourself whether knowing someone's gender is relevant to your investigation. If it isn't relevant then your question is not valid and you shouldn't be asking it.

> Check that your questions only ask people for information that is directly relevant to your investigation and cannot be obtained in any other way.

The 2010 Equality Act identifies nine protected characteristics. This provides a useful checklist for you to consider when designing your questions. You should consider whether your questions could cause offence to anyone because of clumsy wording around one or more of these characteristics.

- Age
- Disability
- Gender reassignment
- Marriage/partnership
- Pregnancy/maternity
- Race
- Religion/belief
- Sex
- Sexual orientation

Raw data

Data that has not yet been processed, presented, or analysed is raw data.

Respecting your subject also means that you need to consider issues of confidentiality and data protection when designing your investigation. This will be an important consideration if you intend to collect information from people during any kind of survey, questionnaire, or interview. Your respondents need to be reassured that the **raw data** they provide will be anonymised so that individuals cannot be recognised and will be treated with confidentiality. Key issues are summarised in the Figure 5.3 below.

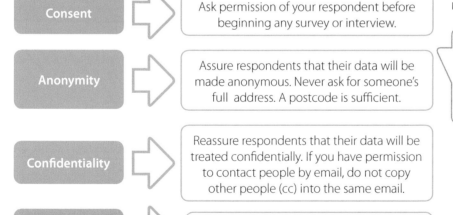

Figure 5.3 Respecting people's data.

Consent ⇒ Ask permission of your respondent before beginning any survey or interview.

Anonymity ⇒ Assure respondents that their data will be made anonymous. Never ask for someone's full address. A postcode is sufficient.

> If spatial patterns are relevant to your investigation, ask for a postcode rather than a full address.

Confidentiality ⇒ Reassure respondents that their data will be treated confidentially. If you have permission to contact people by email, do not copy other people (cc) into the same email.

Secure data storage ⇒ Make sure that you store the raw data from any survey somewhere that is secure.

Action Point 2

Conduct a risk assessment and decide how you will manage any risks.

You need to stay safe during your fieldwork, so it is important to think about any potential risks that you might face. For example, if you are working next to a busy road you must stay on the pavement. If you have to cross the road, then only do so at a safe location – preferably at a crossing point that is controlled by lights. Figure 5.4 lists some potential risks of fieldwork and ways these risks can be reduced.

Potential risk	How this risk can be reduced
Being trapped on a beach by the rising tide. Risk of drowning.	Check the tide table before the visit. Do not work on the beach as the tide is rising.
Strong winds blow sand from the beach. Risk of eye injury.	Check the weather forecast before the visit. Do not work in sand dunes when there are strong onshore winds.
Rocks falling from cliffs above.	Do not work at the top of a beach immediately below a cliff.
Falling on a steep slope and suffering a serious injury to limbs or head.	Do not work close to the top of a cliff. Keep to paths on slopes.
Slipping on wet grass and twisting an ankle.	Wear walking boots rather than trainers.
Falling into a river and suffering an injury or hypothermia. Risk of drowning.	Do not run next to the river. Wear walking boots. Students working in a river must not go in above knees and always work in teams. Check the weather forecast before the visit.
Being hit by a car/cyclist when crossing the road.	Only cross roads where visibility in both directions is good or where there is a pelican or zebra crossing.
Trip hazards when walking through undergrowth.	Wear walking boots. Move slowly and carefully.
Low branches in a woodland. Risk of eye injury.	Keep to paths. Do not run.
Tunnelling in sand dunes. Risk of collapse and suffocation.	Do not play in sand dunes and never dig or tunnel.

Figure 5.4 Potential risks and how to reduce them.

Weblink

https://www.bing.com/maps The Bing search engine has a map view which allows you to switch between aerial images and OS maps at a scale of 1:25,000 – very useful for a virtual visit to your fieldwork site.

Weblink

https://www.geograph.org.uk/ The Geograph® project has collected photos of every grid square of the UK. Use the photos to identify potential risks at your proposed fieldwork site.

Soil catena

Soil catena is the theory that different soil profiles develop on a slope due to the movement of water through the soil.

Conduct a virtual fieldtrip

A virtual visit to your fieldwork site will help you conduct a risk assessment as well as helping you plan some of the details of your primary data collection. Use the internet to view maps of any potential fieldwork sites. You should view aerial images as well as street level photos to help identify any potential risks. A virtual survey will help you to:

▶ plan where you could collect the data;
▶ consider potential risks of the site;
▶ manage the risks so you stay safe.

Review and refine your plans so that you stay safe

Once you have identified the potential risks at your fieldwork site, you can think about specific ways that the danger can be reduced. Use the ideas in Figure 5.4. However, in some cases you may decide that a risk is so great it should be removed or avoided completely. This may occur because your proposed sampling strategy would have you working in dangerous locations, for example:

▶ on a slope that is too steep;
▶ immediately below a cliff face where there is a risk of rockfall.

If this was the case, you would need to review and amend your sampling strategy. Study Figure 5.5 as an example. It shows Roundton Hill National Nature Reserve. As a Nature Reserve public access is not an issue. Although, for ethical reasons, you would want to contact the site manager to get permission before doing any fieldwork that might damage the environment, such as digging a soil profile.

Let's assume you are interested in the theory of **soil catenas**. If so, you would use a transect to sample at locations from the top to the bottom of the hill. Your plan may have been to use two transects, one on a north facing slope and one on a south facing slope. The virtual evidence provided in Figures 5.5 and 5.6 should be enough to decide whether or not this will be possible.

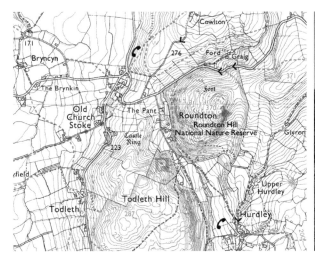

Figure 5.5 An OS map extract at a scale of 1:25,000.

Figure 5.6 The south-east facing slopes of Roundton Hill are too steep to be safely accessible for fieldwork.

Test your understanding

Use evidence from Figures 5.5 and 5.6 to conduct a virtual risk assessment. In your opinion, is it possible to use two transects safely on Roundton Hill? If not, how might you adapt the plan?

Action Point 3

Review and refine your data collection plan and sampling strategy and reflect on whether you will have sufficient data to answer your research questions.

The final Action Point that you need to take in this Step is to review your primary data collection plan and sampling strategy. It may be that your review of the ethical dimension and/or the risk assessment has thrown up a potential problem. If so, it may be necessary to refine your proposed data collection method or sampling strategy to eliminate this issue.

It is also important to try to anticipate how useful your data could be to your investigation. In particular:

▶ Will you be collecting **data** that is **valid** for your investigation?
▶ Will you have a **variety** of different **sources**?
▶ Is your data likely to offer opportunities for a **variety** of different forms of **presentation** (such as maps and graphs)?
▶ is your data likely to offer opportunities for **analysis** rather than simple description?

Consider the bullet points above. They require you to **anticipate** potential pitfalls which would otherwise limit the mark you receive for your report, so take a few minutes to do a thorough review.

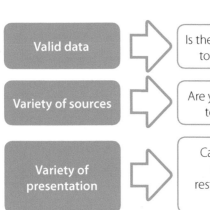

Valid data	Is there a clear link between your research question and the data you propose to collect? If not, you need to consider other methods of data collection.
Variety of sources	Are you relying too heavily on one method of data collection? If so, you need to identify other potential sources of either primary or secondary data.
Variety of presentation	Can you think of at least three different ways to present your data? Think about data types – if you only collect nominal data you will be quite restricted when it comes to drawing maps and graphs. Refer to Step 11 for advice on some more unusual forms of data presentation.
Analysis	Can you imagine digging down into your data to reveal its patterns, trends, and connections. Use your experience of the four days of fieldwork and the analysis techniques you used then. Refer to Step 12 for advice on analysis.

Figure 5.7 Validity of data.

Evaluation

If your review of the proposed data collection method and sampling strategy results in some changes make a careful note. You will want to comment on why and how you changed your plan when you are evaluating your methods in the write-up.

A review of your data collection plan is important. If you can't imagine how your planned data collection will provide you with evidence that will answer the aim of your investigation then you need to think about investigating other sources of information. In this case you have two options.

1 Consider other sources of primary data.
2 Consider whether the use of secondary data could aid your investigation.

Secondary sources may provide data that enables you to widen your choice of presentation techniques or sharpen your analysis. Read Step 6 to help you decide whether or not secondary data may be helpful for your investigation.

QUESTION I am planning to research the distribution of pebbles on a beach. I can't think that this investigation will have any ethical dimension. What should I do?

ANSWER Whatever your proposed investigation, you **must** consider the ethical dimension. However, in some investigations the ethical dimension will be much more significant than others. An investigation that involves a questionnaire, for example, will have a much more significant ethical dimension than a beach investigation. What the examiner is looking for is that you have identified any possible issue and shown how its impact can be minimised. In an investigation of a beach profile, for example, you should place each pebble back on the beach after it has been measured, rather than throwing it into the sea. Throwing it would be unsafe and would show a lack of respect for other people using the beach.

Review Points

Tick off each review point before moving on to Step 6.

I have considered the ethical dimension of my research. ☐

I have conducted a risk assessment. ☐

I have reviewed my plan and made any changes as a result of my ethical and risk assessments. ☐

I have reviewed my plan and thought about how I might be able to analyse my data. ☐

Secondary data

Action points

1 Identify the kind of secondary data that is available and how it might be useful to your investigation.

2 Reflect on whether the use of secondary data might improve your analysis or help answer your research questions.

3 Reflect on whether or not the use of secondary data could influence your primary data methodology. If so, review your design for collecting primary data.

4 Consider the reliability of any sources you use.

5 Carefully record the source of any secondary data for later reference.

You **must work independently** when researching, selecting, and analysing any secondary data.

Action Point 1

Identify the kind of secondary data that is available and how it might be useful to your investigation.

Data that has already been published in newspapers, journals, books, or on websites is secondary data. A wide variety of **secondary data** exists in both quantitative and qualitative forms.

▶ **Images** such as photos, videos, artworks, graffiti, and cartoons.
▶ **Text** in literature, advertisements, and blogs.
▶ **Locational maps** at a wide variety of scales, including large scale historic maps of the location you are investigating.
▶ Tables of **data** that you could process to draw your own maps or graphs.
▶ **Graphs** and **maps** that represent data including interactive maps online.

Big data is widely available

We live in a world where technology is able to capture, collect, and analyse huge volumes of data. This phenomenon is called **big data** and much is freely available online. The velocity at which new data is generated, stored, and analysed is also enormous – it's thought that the amount of data being collected doubles every two years. The nature of big data is very varied. It includes:

▶ quantitative data such as census records containing socio-economic and demographic data, climate records, or real-time data on tides and waves;
▶ qualitative data such as the photos and videos published to sites like Google Street View, Facebook, Instagram, or YouTube.

Google Street View is an example of a source of big data. Images have been collected since around 2008 and many streets have already been photographed at least 5 times – the location shown in Figures 6.1 and 6.2 has

Big data

Big data is a term used to describe any large, complex sets of data. It is characterised by three Vs: Volume, Velocity, and Variety.

been photographed many more times. Use the slide bar in the top left of the screen to view how a street has changed and the magnifying tool to enlarge the thumbnail to full screen.

Figure 6.1 Google Street View images for Centenary Square, Birmingham (2008).

Figure 6.2 Google Street View images for Centenary Square, Birmingham (2014).

Test your understanding

What are the two main differences and similarities between these two images of Centenary Square? How might you use images like this?

Why use secondary data?

Sources of secondary data have a number of benefits which are summarised in the infographic in Figure 6.3. Secondary data may be useful at different steps within the investigation, as shown in Figure 6.4.

If collected by academics or researchers, secondary data provides evidence that is both reliable and accurate.

Figure 6.3 Some benefits of Secondary data.

Some very large sets of data are available online. Known as **big data**, this evidence would take far too long for you to collect it first-hand.

Not only is secondary data easy to find, it sometimes reveals sensitive socio-economic evidence that would probably be impossible to collect first hand.

Step	How to use secondary data
2 Choosing an aim.	Online photos of your fieldwork location can be used at the planning stage to help you pose research questions.
4 Use of secondary data in sampling.	Secondary data such as demographic data can be used to help you design a sampling strategy.
8 Data collection.	Qualitative data can be collected, for example: • blogs can be used to collect evidence of people's viewpoints; • artwork, adverts, and photos can be collected to show how a place is represented; • historical maps and photos can be used to see how a place has changed in recent years. Quantitative data can be collected, for example: • socio-economic variables such as house prices, or data on reported crime, may be collected and compared to variables collected by primary research such as EQIs or traffic surveys; • demographic data such as population pyramids.
12 Analysis.	Many websites include data that has already been represented as graphs and maps that will help you answer your research questions if you analyse the patterns and trends. These include sites that use interactive maps (GIS).

Figure 6.4 How secondary data may be used in the investigation.

Sources of secondary data

Secondary data is available in many different forms from numerous platforms and sources. Photos, videos, audio recordings, blogs, books, journals and statistical documents are all potentially useful sources of secondary data.

Images

Geographical images are a source of qualitative data that you simply cannot ignore. There are literally billions of images available:
▶ images in magazines;
▶ on billboards in the street;
▶ on public transport;
▶ and many more on your smartphone and PC.

Figure 6.5 How Secondary data can be used in an investigation.

With the rapid growth in ownership of mobile phones there has been an explosion of images stored online – a form of big data. Photos, adverts, graffiti, and works of art illustrate how different people represent their view of the world around them so images in secondary sources can be used to investigate **multiple realities.**

Images provide evidence about how people perceive (see) and represent (portray) the environment. When people take photos they select the elements of the landscape that interest them. In this way a photo can tell you something about the way someone else perceives the environment.

The same is true of paintings. Some artists are interested in portraying the ordinary and over-looked features of the urban and industrial landscape such as factories or independent shops – features that help give a place its identity. De-industrialisation and regeneration are causing rapid change so paintings can reveal once common features of the urban landscape that are now rare. Use the Art UK website to find art that represents your local landscape.

A different kind of image is used for marketing a place. Images are chosen carefully to help convey a particular message. For example, images may be used to represent that a place is friendly, fun, vibrant, safe, or a successful place to do business.

There are a number of ways that images from secondary sources could be used in your investigation. Some ideas are summarised in the infographic in Figure 6.5.

 Perception → Photos and works of art can show us how people perceive their surroundings. What has been included in the image? What has been left out? | Photos stored online, e.g. Instagram, paintings in local galleries.

 Branding → Images represent (portray) the real world in a particular way. Why has this image been chosen? What message is being conveyed? | Images in adverts online, in leaflets and magazines.

 Change → Images can provide a baseline against which visual changes in the landscape can be judged. | Old photos, postcards, and paintings in museums.

There are a wide range of sources of geographical images. You could try searching:
- online for contemporary photos;
- in local art galleries for the work of contemporary artists;
- in local museums for paintings by modern artists or photos of local landscapes. Use the Art UK website to help;
- postcards provide a useful source of images of landscapes and towns in the twentieth century.

Test your understanding

1 Study Figure 6.6. Why do you think this image was chosen to represent Derby?
2 Compare Figures 6.6 and 6.7. Why are the two places represented in such different ways?

Figure 6.6 An image used in a public space in Derby to explain a local regeneration scheme.

Figure 6.7 Industrial Ruin I (copper works Swansea) by George Little (1927-2017). Private collection. A painting that represents de-industrialisation.

Don't copy photographs from the internet and include them in your report unless you have analysed them.

Figure 6.8 An image from a postcard – found on an online auction site. The image shows Queen Street in Cardiff (1947). Images like this can be used as a baseline to assess change.

The National Census

You will need to use secondary data if your investigation means you need to know such things as:

- the age structure of the population;
- the health of the population;
- the main occupations that people have;
- how many cars are owned by each household;
- levels of education that people have achieved.

The Office for National Statistics collects and stores this kind of information in the Census. Data for every household in the UK are organised spatially into **wards**. The average population of a ward is around 5,500 people. Rural wards often contain fewer people but cover a larger geographical area than urban wards. The census collects data from the entire UK population every 10 years. No sampling is involved so, unlike primary data, the data represents the whole population accurately.

Using postcodes to search for census data

The official census website can be tricky to use. If you prefer, you can find the same data hosted on other sites that allow you to search by postcode. Figure 6.9 lists some of these sites. A postcode district (like CF5) can have between 8,000 and 85,000 people living in it, depending on whether the area covered by the postcode is rural or urban. The postcode district is then broken down into postcode units (like CF5 2YX). A typical postcode unit has 200-300 people living in it. A ward is usually made up of several postcode units, although the boundaries of postcodes and wards do not always fully match.

Evaluation

The census is a snap-shot in time. Your fieldwork could be located somewhere that has changed significantly since the last census.

Ward

A ward is an administrative district usually with an elected representative.

Weblink

https://www.nomisweb.co.uk/census/2011 The official site of the UK National Census (2011).

Focus your fieldwork enquiry on a small number of postcode units rather than a postcode district which would be much too large.

website	Description
www.ukcensusdata.com	Use the search engine to drill down through the data to ward level and then beyond that to clusters of postcode units. A large variety of demographic and socio-economic data variables from the census are then available for that cluster.
https://streetcheck.co.uk	Search by postcode district to find useful data about housing, people, culture, and employment from the census plus data on crime and broadband from other sources. The data is provided in tables and represented as pie charts.
https://www.getthedata.com	Search by postcode district, or drill down through the postcodes, to find maps, geolocation, and information about deprivation, broadband connectivity, and local schools. The site has a good explanation of postcodes.

Figure 6.9 Websites that allow you to search data from the UK 2011 census.

Test your understanding

Use each of the websites in Figure 6.9 to search for your own postcode district. Make a note about the type of data that is available and whether any of it could be useful in your investigation.

Geographic Information Systems

Some websites use interactive mapping to represent data visually in a **Geographical Information System (GIS)**. The maps are built up from a number of different layers. There is usually a simple base map which shows roads and place names. Then, on top of the base map, there are various layers of data that you can toggle on or off so that you can choose which layer to view. The data is often shown using the colour shading technique used in **choropleth maps**.

Figure 6.10 represents road traffic noise. The blues represent the highest noise levels, in this example, the junction of the M6 and M5 motorways south of Walsall. Notice how large residential areas are affected by lower levels of noise represented by the orange colours. You could, of course, collect primary noise data of your own, perhaps taking readings in one location to see how they vary

Weblink

http://www.extrium.co.uk/noiseviewer.html A GIS that maps noise levels. The site has separate maps for England and Wales.

through the day. This type of map would give you some context for the issue you are investigating but over a much larger area – allowing you, perhaps, to reach some wider conclusions about how the noise levels you have observed in one location might affect people in similar situations in other parts of the UK.

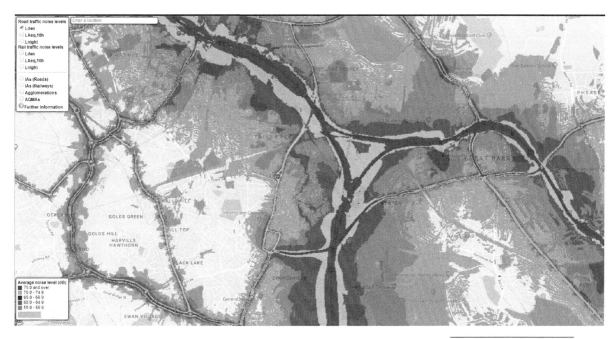

Figure 6.10 Screenshot from the England Noise Map Viewer representing traffic noise in an area to the south of Walsall.

Interactive mapping

Websites that use interactive mapping also provide secondary data that would be difficult to obtain through primary research because of its sensitive nature:

▶ **demographic data** such as population density or age structure;
▶ **indicators of inequality** such as deprivation index or fuel poverty;
▶ **property values;**
▶ **reported incidents of crime.**

Figure 6.11 shows a screenshot from a useful GIS where you can explore crime data. Notice that the data is shown in the form of **proportional circles**. As you zoom in, the circles break up so you can pin-point more accurately where the crimes were reported.

Test your understanding

Suggest three different research questions that could be investigated with analysis of secondary data from one of the GIS sites shown on pages 118-120.

Weblink

https://datashine.org.uk A GIS that uses choropleth maps to represent information from the UK 2011 census.

Weblink

https://zoopla.co.uk/market This property site uses a choropleth to represent average house prices on its 'heat' map.

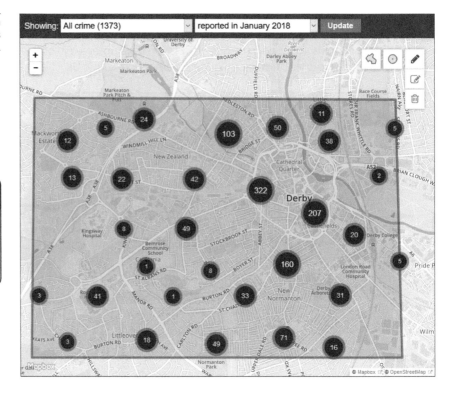

Action Point 2

Reflect on whether the use of secondary data might improve your analysis or help answer your research questions.

It is not essential to use secondary data in an independent investigation and you may decide that you don't need to use any. However, some investigations would be impossible without using some secondary data.

▶ It can be difficult to collect primary data about jobs, income, and health – people don't like talking about these aspects of their personal lives. Instead, we can use secondary sources such as the census or GIS maps to collect data on property values, crime, job types, qualifications, and the age structure of the population.

▶ Investigations which assess change over time need **baseline data** so that you can see how much change has occurred. Historic maps such as OS six inch to the mile maps (published 1842-1952) or older photos (like the ones shown on pages 114 and 117) can be useful when investigating changing places.

Baseline data

Baseline data is data collected in the past which serves as a basis for comparison with primary data collected in the present.

You cannot base your research on secondary data alone. However, you might need to use a combination of primary and secondary data to investigate the connection between two variables. Some examples are given in Figure 6.12.

1 Is traffic busier in areas of higher population density?
2 Is it healthier to live further from busy roads?
3 Are the residents of sustainable communities mainly in professional jobs?
4 Are fewer crimes recorded in areas that have more CCTV cameras?
5 How are house prices affected by the proximity of urban green spaces?

Figure 6.12 Research questions which would require the use of secondary data.

Weblink

https://maps.nls.uk/
The National Library of Scotland hosts 37,000 historic OS maps at a scale of six inches to one mile. Use the side by side viewer to compare the historic map with a modern satellite image.

Use quantitative data to widen your options

We saw in Step 2 that your investigation needs to focus on analysis rather than description. It may be, that having chosen an investigation, you are beginning to realise that you will have fairly limited options for representing and analysing your primary data. Now is the time to consider whether the careful use of some secondary data could provide you with:

▶ data that can be represented using a wider range of map and/or graph styles than is possible with your primary data;
▶ an opportunity to use a map that represents data that is similar to your primary data but which covers a slightly larger geographical area – thereby providing a context for the primary research.

We have seen on pages 117-120 that secondary sources of quantitative data are widely available. This data is often current and covers large spatial areas of the UK. Some other potential sources are shown in Figures 6.13 and 6.14.

Investigations that rely heavily on a questionnaire may offer limited opportunities for data presentation and analysis. Some carefully selected secondary data may widen these opportunities.

Figure 6.13 Other sources of big data for investigations of the human environment.

Website	Description
https://data.london.gov.uk/	The London DataStore is a portal that includes blogs and quantitative data such as 2011 census for London, air quality data, and quality of life indicators.
National Health Service https://digital.nhs.uk/data-and-information	Collects, transports, stores, analyses, and disseminates the UK's health and social care data.
National Records of Scotland https://www.nrscotland.gov.uk/	Collects, analyses, and publishes a wide range of information, statistics, & data about Scotland's people including the 2011 census.
Scottish government www.gov.scot	Provides information and statistics on Scotland for topics such as Arts, culture, and sport; Business, industry, and innovation; Economy, Energy, Environment, and climate change; Farming and rural; Marine and fisheries; Transport.
UK Government www.gov.uk https://www.gov.uk/browse/environment-countryside https://www.gov.uk/government/statistics	Information, regulations, data, statistics, and government consultations. Specific areas such as Statistics, Environment, & countryside.
Welsh government https://gov.wales/statistics-and-research/	Statistical reports and data published by the Welsh Government (available in the Welsh and English languages).

https://www.bgs.ac.uk/home.html	The website of the British Geological Survey contains free geological maps of the UK. You can download a geological map of the UK to your smartphone using the iGeology app.
https://www.channelcoast.org/ or http://wavenet.cefas.co.uk/Map	Real time data on wave height, wind direction, and temperature for coastal locations around the UK. If using the Channel Coast website follow the link to Realtime Data.
https://www.riverlevels.uk/	This website publishes discharge data for rivers in the UK. This website is particularly useful if you are investigating flood risk.
http://www.wetterzentrale.de/en/default.php	This German website has archived European weather charts since 1979. Use it to check antecedent weather or weather prior to a flood event. Use the Archive and follow the link to CFSR before searching for the date that interests you.

Figure 6.14 Sources of big data for investigations of the physical environment.

Action Point 3

Reflect on whether or not the use of secondary data could influence your primary data methodology. If so, review your design for collecting primary data.

> It's easy to rely heavily on secondary data in some investigations. Be careful to include sufficient primary data.

It's a good idea to use secondary data to research your fieldwork location before you visit. It may be that secondary data will influence how you collect primary data or the design of your sampling strategy. For example:

▶ **in an investigation of water movement through a drainage basin** it would be useful to examine a geological map before your visit as this may influence where you conduct infiltration experiments. You could use a stratified sampling technique to collect data from areas of permeable and impermeable rocks;

▶ **in an investigation of regeneration** it would be useful to know what baseline evidence exists before you design your sampling strategy. Photos or surveys conducted before regeneration may influence where you collect primary data or the questions that you ask. If a previous survey has published its results, you might use some of the same questions in your own questionnaire so you can make direct comparisons.

Study Figure 6.15. These contrasting population pyramids represent the age structure of two locations in the same town. It would be very useful to know about these differences before you finalised the design for your primary data collection. This knowledge should inform:

▶ your decision about where to collect data;

▶ what questions to ask – since the needs and perceptions of the two populations are probably quite different.

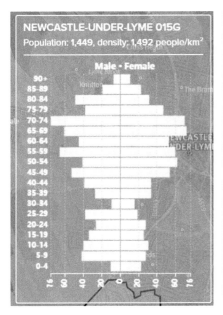

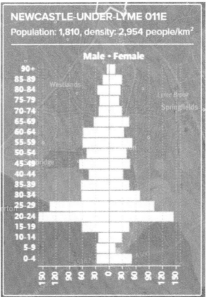

Figure 6.15 Population pyramids for a cluster of postcodes in a suburban location (left) and an inner urban area (right) of Newcastle-under-Lyme.

Weblink

https://parallel.org. uk Interactive maps representing deprivation, population density and age structure, air pollution, fuel poverty, and life expectancy.

Using GIS to plan a transect

Maps representing socio-economic data can be used to plan a sampling strategy. For example, we could use a GIS like the one shown in Figure 6.16 to plan a transect through a district of a town or city – like Birmingham. We could use the GIS to check that our proposed transect goes through districts with different levels of deprivation. On this map, areas coloured blue/green have a better standard of living than the UK average whereas areas coloured red/orange have a lower standard of living than the UK average. The data for each area pops up as the cursor moves over the map. You could use stratified sampling – visiting one place of each colour on the map – and carry out EQI surveys at each sample site.

Figure 6.16 An interactive map representing an index of multiple deprivation. A screenshot from parallel.co.uk.

123

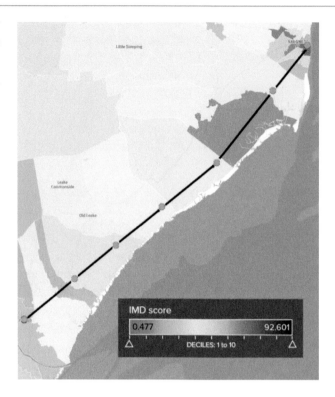

Figure 6.17 A student has used a GIS map showing an index of multiple deprivation to plan this transect through rural Lincolnshire.

IMD score

0.477   92.601

DECILES: 1 to 10

Test your understanding

Study the transect shown in Figure 6.17. What sampling strategy has been used? How could this strategy be improved?

Action Point 4

Consider the reliability of any sources you use.

Evaluation

Consider the reliability of each secondary source you use. Can the evidence be trusted?

Select secondary data carefully. Only present and analyse data that will be useful to answer your aim.

Whenever primary or secondary data is collected you will need to consider whether the data is accurate and reliable. This is especially true of secondary data when you don't necessarily know how the data was collected or who collected it. It's important to realise that some sources of secondary data are more trustworthy than others. Academic reports are peer reviewed, in other words, the validity of the data is rigorously checked by other specialists so academic sources should be trustworthy and reliable. Blogs and newspapers, on the other hand, are less reliable sources of evidence because authors and editors tend to present their own values and attitudes about geographical issues.

Images used in adverts or promotional materials do not necessarily represent places accurately. Images may have been digitally manipulated or cropped. They focus on positive features of the environment and ignore less favourable features. It is the nature of an advert to promote something and therefore represent a partial or partisan point of view – but this is not a reason to ignore adverts as a form of evidence. They should be analysed carefully to assess what <u>is</u> and what <u>is not</u> being represented.

Figure 6.18 An image used in a public space in Birmingham to promote the city.

Test your understanding

Study Figure 6.18. This billboard had been placed on a building site in Birmingham, close to the main train station. Use the internet to research the target demographic of Harvey Nichols. Why do you think the city council chose this combination of fact and image to represent Birmingham?

Action Point 5

Carefully record the source of any secondary data for later reference.

It is essential to keep an accurate record of your sources of secondary data because:
- you may need to visit the source again;
- you must provide a citation for any source when you write up your report.

It is very important to acknowledge any sources of secondary data you use. Providing accurate references is what all good researchers do. Failure to provide a reference could be very serious. You might be accused of copying someone else's ideas and passing them off as your own – something known as plagiarism.

To provide a reference for a book, or an article in a magazine, the normal convention is to:
state the author's name (surname first); then the year of publication; next, give the title of the book or article (in italic font); finally, give the name of the publisher.

You can bookmark the URL of any website that you intend to use as a source of secondary data. You can use post-it notes to mark useful pages in any books or other printed materials. However, websites are constantly changing so you will also need to record the date on which any secondary data is downloaded. This information will be needed when you write up your report because you will have to provide detailed references for any source you have used. It would be a good idea to create a table similar to Figure 6.19 and use it to record your online sources as you go along.

Figure 6.19 Use a table to record your online sources.

URL	Name of author or organisation	Date accessed	How I could use or analyse the data
https://www. doreenfletcherartist.com/ copy-of-fp-026-approaching-storm	Doreen Fletcher	12/02/2019	A blog about change in the East End of London (Tower Hamlets) and the importance of independent businesses. I could use coding to analyse the text in the blog. I could photograph the same street scene and analyse change.
https://data.london.gov.uk/ dataset/equality--diversity-and-inclusion-evidence-base	Greater London Authority (GLA)	12/02/2019	A report which provides quantitative data for London. I could analyse the occupancy rating by ethnic groups in Tower Hamlets.

QUESTION What is the difference between a literature review and the use of secondary data in my investigation?

ANSWER A review of the geographical literature is essential. It provides the theoretical background to your investigation. Secondary data is evidence that can be analysed and used to help answer your research questions. Carefully chosen secondary data can enhance your investigation – especially when it provides data that can be mapped.

Review Points

Tick off each review point before moving on to Step 7.

I have identified some secondary data that will be relevant. ☐

I have thought about how secondary data could help with my analysis and help me answer my research questions. ☐

I have considered whether or not I can use secondary data to help with my sampling strategy. ☐

I have reflected on the reliability of the sources I wish to use. ☐

I am recording the source of any secondary data I wish to use. ☐

STEP 7 Submit your Investigation Proposal

Before you go ahead with your data collection you must complete an Independent Investigation Proposal Form. This form will be reviewed by your teacher and submitted to your exam board. At the end of your investigation the Proposal Form will be attached to your completed investigation when you submit it for marking. It provides evidence of your thinking during the planning phase of the investigation.

Action Point 1

Fill out a Proposal Form with as much detail about your plan as possible.

Each Exam Board has an Independent Investigation Proposal Form which you must complete. You will be able to get one from your teacher. The forms vary slightly from one Exam Board to another but they each contain fields for you to fill in. Figure 7.1 describes these fields and suggests how you should complete them.

The form is quite short – just one side of A4 paper. It includes a space for your teacher to make a comment (the WJEC and Eduqas forms can be sent to the Exam Board **by your teacher** for a comment by a moderator). Despite the fact that the spaces for you to fill in are quite small you should give as much detail as you can.

Your teacher is allowed to comment on your proposal form. They can:

▶ advise on health and safety issues;
▶ point out potential ethical concerns;
▶ advise you about the use of specialist equipment;
▶ comment on whether the proposed research is linked closely enough to the specification;
▶ give **general guidance** on methodology and analytical techniques;
▶ promote good practice such as advising about referencing sources and using a bibliography.

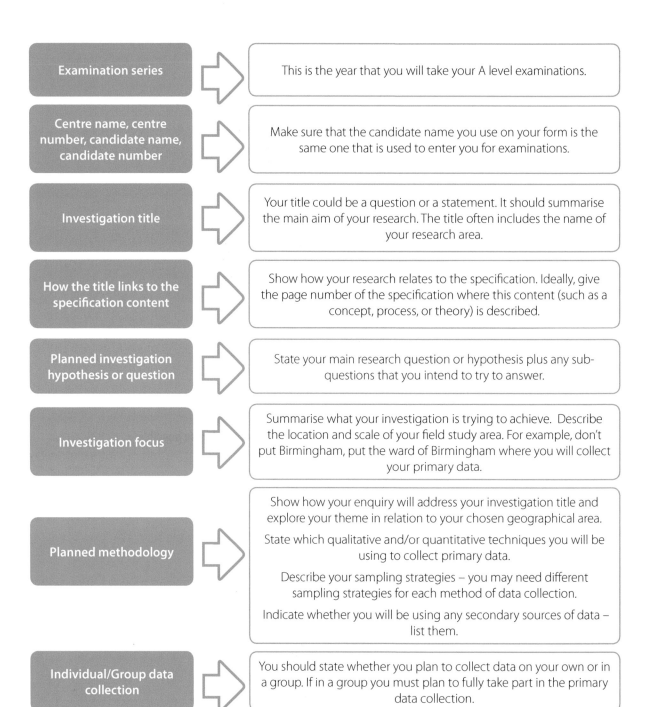

Examination series	This is the year that you will take your A level examinations.
Centre name, centre number, candidate name, candidate number	Make sure that the candidate name you use on your form is the same one that is used to enter you for examinations.
Investigation title	Your title could be a question or a statement. It should summarise the main aim of your research. The title often includes the name of your research area.
How the title links to the specification content	Show how your research relates to the specification. Ideally, give the page number of the specification where this content (such as a concept, process, or theory) is described.
Planned investigation hypothesis or question	State your main research question or hypothesis plus any sub-questions that you intend to try to answer.
Investigation focus	Summarise what your investigation is trying to achieve. Describe the location and scale of your field study area. For example, don't put Birmingham, put the ward of Birmingham where you will collect your primary data.
Planned methodology	Show how your enquiry will address your investigation title and explore your theme in relation to your chosen geographical area. State which qualitative and/or quantitative techniques you will be using to collect primary data. Describe your sampling strategies – you may need different sampling strategies for each method of data collection. Indicate whether you will be using any secondary sources of data – list them.
Individual/Group data collection	You should state whether you plan to collect data on your own or in a group. If in a group you must plan to fully take part in the primary data collection.

Figure 7.1 How to complete your Independent Investigation Proposal Form.

Action Point 2

Read your teacher's comments and consider what (if any) changes you might need to make to your plan.

When you get your Proposal Form back, read the comments very carefully.

The purpose of these general comments is to allow you to take the initiative for any amendments that need to be made to the plan. Your teacher is not allowed to give you specific advice that tells you exactly how to change or improve your plan, so:

1   read the comments very carefully;
2   make a list of the issues that have been raised. Some common issues are shown in the left hand column of Figure 7.2;
3   use this book to find solutions;
4   keep a record of how you intend to address each issue. An example is shown in Figure 7.2.

Figure 7.2 How to deal with the comments on your proposal.

List of issues raised on the proposal form	How I might deal with this issue
1 The teacher has suggested that my plan is rather ambitious.	My research is about urban sustainability. I must decide if it is the scope or scale of the investigation that is at fault. 1 The concept of sustainability is very broad so I can reduce the scope by focusing on one or two clearly defined elements of sustainability. 2 I should reduce the scale of my research so I focus on one or two wards rather than the whole city.
2 It has been suggested that I am relying very heavily on just one method of data collection.	I had hoped to rely mainly on questionnaires. I could use Step 3 (pages 28-94) to choose another qualitative technique (like re-photography) and a quantitative technique (like cleanliness index) to improve the range of data types. This will give me a wider range of opportunities when I present and analyse the data.
3 My teacher has commented that I haven't indicated how I will sample the data.	I obviously need to choose a suitable sampling strategy. I will read Step 4 (pages 95-106) and select suitable strategies for each of my three data collection methods.
4 My teacher has raised ethical concerns about my proposal.	I need to consider what questions I really need and how I should phrase them.

QUESTION My proposal has been returned and I think I need to start again because the comments suggest that my research does not match the specification. Can I ask my teacher to show me some successful proposals or a list of suitable titles?

ANSWER No, your teacher is not allowed to give you an 'off-the-shelf' title for an investigation. If you need to go back to the beginning then you should do three things urgently.

1   Read Step 1. It explores different styles of investigation. Choose a style of investigation that interests you.
2   Download the specification and check that any new research questions are focused on some aspect of the specification.
3   Resubmit a new proposal form.

Review Points

Tick off each review point before moving on to Step 8.

I have completed the Proposal Form with all the relevant information. ☐

I have read the comments provided by my teacher. ☐

If necessary, I have written an action plan so that I can amend my proposal. ☐

Collect primary data

Action points

1 Design data collection forms to record your primary data.
2 Conduct a pilot survey and review its success. Amend the design of your sampling/data collection and data collection forms if necessary.
3 Follow your data collection methods and sampling strategy methodically.
4 Reflect on your methods, making a record of strengths, limitations, and anything that is unexpected.

Action Point 1

Design data collection forms to record the primary data.

Figure 8.1 Geo-locate sample locations using What3words. delay.voter.doll is the geo-location for the centre of Centenary Square, Birmingham.

You need a reliable way to record primary data as you collect it. This means designing data collection forms before you begin your fieldwork. These could be electronic forms accessed on a laptop, tablet, or smartphone, or paper forms that you fill out with a pen. The form needs to contain **fields** – empty spaces where you can record each item of data that you collect.

Whatever type of data is being collected there are some general rules you should follow.

▶ Data collection forms need to be easy to use.
▶ Data should always be **geo-located**. Always include a space on the form to record the location where the data was collected.
▶ Always record somewhere on the form when data was collected.

Geo-location

All the primary data you collect (including any photos) should be geo-located. This means recording accurate location details on your data collection forms. You could do this using the postcode district or with an OS grid reference.

You can use an app on your smart phone to accurately geo-locate your fieldwork site while you are working. Some apps record the location, altitude, and the time the photo was taken (as in Figure 8.2). Alternatively, you can check the OS grid reference of your site when you return from the fieldtrip. If you don't have an actual OS map of your fieldwork site you can use a website to find the reference such as the National Library of Scotland website (see Figure 8.3).

What3words is a free app that uses combinations of three words to identify geo-locations. The system assigns three words to a global grid of squares that each have a dimension of 3 metres by 3 metres. This means that the app can provide a very detailed geo-location. You could use it to identify the location of each sample point. Other researchers could find your exact sample location later by using the app.

Latitude: 52.478672
Longitude: -1.909143
Elevation: 116.49m
Accuracy: 3.2m
Time: 04-06-2019 12:27
Note: Centenary square 2

Powered by NoteCam

Figure 8.2 Geo-locate your photos by using a smart phone app.

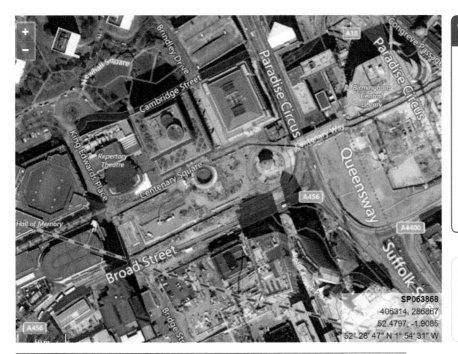

SP063868
406314, 286867
52.4797, -1.9085
52° 28' 47" N 1° 54' 31" W

Weblink

https://maps.nls.uk/geo/explore/side-by-side Use the National Library of Scotland website to view historic maps next to modern satellite images. The six inch map option is a useful scale. The geo-location is given in the bottom right of the screen.

SP is an Ordnance Survey reference for a 100km area (or tile) that covers part of the West Midlands. 063866 is a six figure reference within that tile. It pinpoints Centenary Square in Birmingham.

Figure 8.3 Geo-locate your data collection points. The National Library of Scotland website provides six figure references and precise latitude/longitude references for the location of the cursor. This image shows the location of Figure 8.2.

Different ways of recording data

Figure 8.4 describes three different types of form that you may need to design.

Figure 8.4 Different types of data collections forms.

Continuous data forms → Where you need spaces to record actual measurements as you collect the data. You may need to use a table within the form so that you can record data of the same type (for example, wind speed) collected in different places or at different times.

Tally sheets for categories of data → Where you are interested in counting the total number of individuals in each category, for example, a traffic or pedestrian survey.

Individual data forms → Where data from each individual in the sample is collected on a separate form. Most questionnaire surveys are carried out in this way.

Continuous data

Data that can be measured on the interval or ratio scale.

Frequency

Frequency of sampling is about distance between readings (in time or space).

Timing

Timing of sampling is important because readings may vary over time (during the day or week).

Continuous data collection forms

If you are planning to use specialist equipment that records **continuous data** such as a thermometer, anemometer, light meter, clinometer, or noise meter you will need to design a form that has fields where you can accurately record each reading. The form should include the units of measurement, especially if the equipment you are using has more than one. For example, wind speed can be measured in knots, metres per second, or kilometres per hour.

Think about the **frequency** and **timing** of the readings you intend to take and make sure that your form has enough fields. For example, if you are investigating an ecosystem such as a woodland or sand dune you may intend to take readings of wind speed, available light, and soil temperature every 25 metres along a transect. Design your form with enough fields for each sample point so that you can fill it in systematically as you move along the transect.

Temporal variations are another factor that needs to be considered. You may need to take several readings in which case you need more fields on the form. Infiltration rate experiments, for example, need readings taken every few minutes. You might want to investigate how noise levels vary throughout the day. Again, you need to consider the frequency and timing of these readings and design a form with enough fields.

Continuous data, such as wind speed and noise levels, can vary considerably as you are measuring them. It's a good idea, therefore, to record several readings on your form so that you can calculate an average later.

Date:		Location:					
		Wind speed (metres per second)			Soil temperature (°C)	Available light (lux)
Sample site	Distance from the start of the transect (metres)	Reading One	Reading Two	Reading Three		
1	0					
2	25					
3	50					
4	75					
5	100					
6	125					

Figure 8.5 Example of a continuous data form.

Tally sheets to collect in categories

Where data can be broken down into categories (for example, types of plant, land use, or traffic) you can add boxes to your form so you can record the number of items in each category. Using a tally mark is a quick and reliable way to record information that you are counting. You can also group numerical data into categories and use tally marks to record the number of individuals who belong to each group. For example, if you are doing a sediment analysis, you can group the pebble sizes into categories. Similarly, you could estimate the age of a participant and group people's ages into categories. Any numerical groups must be **contiguous**. An example of a correct tally sheet is shown in Figure 8.6 and an incorrect one in Figure 8.7.

> **Contiguous**
>
> Contiguous numbers are in sequence. The groups of numbers 'touch' one another without any gaps or overlap so it is impossible for any number to (a) not be part of a group or (b) fall into more than one group.

> **Test your understanding**
>
> Study Figure 8.7 State how this form could be improved.

Age of shoppers

Location ....

Date ....   Time ....

Age group	Number of shoppers	Total
0-19	IIII	4
20-39	JHT JHT JHT IIII	19
40-59	JHT JHT	10
60+	JHT I	6

Figure 8.6 A correct tally sheet.

Beach survey data collection sheet

Date ....   Site 1

Pebble sizes (mm)	Number of pebbles
10 or less	JHT JHT JHT I
10-20	JHT IIII
25-40	JHT I
40-50	IIII
More than 50	

Figure 8.7 An incorrect tally sheet.

Individual data forms

When you are collecting data you need to be able to record raw (unprocessed) data so that it is of greatest use to you later in your investigation – when you are analysing the data. One key consideration is whether you will need to drill down, through all of the data that has been collected, to investigate the original source – the individual person that you interviewed, or the individual reading from the quadrat, clinometer, or anemometer. If so, you will need to use a separate form for every individual in your sample. This is typically how the data from a questionnaire is recorded. You design your questions and then print multiple copies – one for each person in your sample. If you use a tally chart to record evidence from different respondents to a questionnaire it will be impossible to analyse how individual people responded to different questions when you come to the analysis stage. This would be a major problem as it would severely limit the depth of your analysis. See page 145 for more information about how to deal with individual data forms prior to their analysis.

Action Point 2

Conduct a pilot survey and review its success. Amend the design of your sampling/data collection and data collection forms if necessary.

A pilot survey is an opportunity to check that your proposed methods of sampling and collecting data are going to work as you expect. Think of it as a dry-run of your fieldwork. The aim is to collect a **small** sample of data so that you can check that everything is working as you expect. A pilot survey is an opportunity to check that:

▶ you are aware of the potential risks at your fieldwork site;
▶ access to the site is as you expected;
▶ you know how to use any specialist equipment;
▶ the data collection forms are working effectively.

With good planning (and some luck!) you will hopefully find that you have designed suitable and efficient ways of collecting the data you need to answer your research questions. However, if you find that something isn't working as you expected, a pilot survey should provide the evidence that you need to amend the design of your sampling strategy or data collection methods.

> A good investigation is characterised by critical thinking. A pilot survey is a great idea. It shows that you have tested your methods.

Pilot questionnaires

Pilot surveys are a particularly good way of testing the usefulness of questions in a draft questionnaire. If you are going to use a questionnaire (see page 71) you will want to use some closed and some open questions. Open questions allow the person you are interviewing to say whatever they want in response. The following are examples of open questions that you might use in a fieldwork enquiry about place and identity.

1 Which features do you like best about this town?
2 What makes this town different from others you know well?
3 What gives this place its unique identity?

Using open questions like these have advantages but it is time-consuming to record all the possible responses that people might give. So, it's a good idea to use a pilot survey with a few people to see what kinds of answers you are likely to get when you carry out the full survey. After the pilot survey, you can look at the answers that people gave and put them into categories. So, in a pilot survey, the open question *'Which features do you like best about this town?'* was asked. Imagine that:

▶ 5 people said friendly people;
▶ 4 people talked about history or historic buildings;
▶ 3 people said that good schools were an important feature of the town;
▶ 3 people said they liked the multicultural atmosphere;
▶ 1 person talked about locally owned (independent) shops.

As a result of this pilot survey you can now design a closed question for your full questionnaire that looks like Figure 8.8.

1. Which features do you like best about this town? Tick up to 3 boxes.
The people ☐
The town's history ☐
Buildings/architecture ☐
Local schools ☐
Cultural activities ☐
Multicultural atmosphere ☐
Independent shops ☐
Others ☐
If others, please describe the feature(s) …

Figure 8.8 Using a pilot survey to create option boxes for the data collection sheet.

Action Point 3

Follow your data collection methods and sampling strategy methodically.

You are now ready to begin fieldwork and collect the primary data needed for your investigation. There are a few golden rules for collecting data in the field.

▶ **Always work safely.** Be aware of your environment and others working around you. If you are working alone, make sure other people know where you are and what time you intend to finish.
▶ **Record data at the time it is collected** – not later. It's easy to forget important details.
▶ **Write your results neatly** if you are working on paper. This seems obvious but you need to be confident that you can read the results later.
▶ **Save your work regularly** if you are collecting data electronically.
▶ **Make sure you understand exactly what is required** if you are collecting data as part of a team.
▶ **Take multiple measurements** if data is varying (like wind speeds or noise levels).
▶ If data isn't going to be used and analysed, **don't bother collecting it.**

Working with others

You are allowed to work collaboratively when collecting primary data. If you are on an organised field trip (or residential course) you may be expected to work as part of a team. Indeed, it may be safer and more practical to do so because:

▶ a team can collect data from multiple locations at the same time. For example, to record the number of pedestrians at different locations across a city centre at a single point in time it is essential to collect data as part of a team;

> it is easier to carry out some data collection methods, like surveying a beach profile, in pairs or teams.

Even if your investigation is not part of an organised field trip you can still ask another student or group of students to help you collect the data. Remember that any data collected by the team should be collected using your data collection sheets and in answer to your investigation question.

Personalise your data collection

If you have collected primary data as part of a team you should think about how you can also demonstrate some independence. For example:
> do not feel compelled to use all the data that is collected by a team;
> disregard data that has no direct relevance to your own research questions or hypotheses;
> select the data that is relevant to answer your own research questions;
> ideally, collect some data independently of the group. This data must be **valid**, of course.

Moderators expect to see candidates selecting relevant data from a large dataset.

Valid

For data to be valid it must be relevant to the aims of your investigation.

Action Point 4

Reflect on your methods, making a record of strengths, limitations, and anything that was unexpected.

Critical reflection on your methods is an important part of the investigation. You will need to write an evaluation and a substantial number of marks is available for this. However, you may be writing your evaluation days or weeks after the data has been collected so it is important to make a record of strengths, limitations, and anything that is unexpected as you go along.

Primary data can suffer from two main types of limitation:
> issues with **accuracy**;
> issues with **reliability**.

Accuracy

Accuracy - how close a measurement is to the actual (or true) value.

Reliability

Reliability - how certain you can be that your measurements are true.

Accuracy and reliability of data

For data to be accurate it needs the equipment to be used correctly and the result to be recorded carefully in the correct units. For example, if you are using specialist equipment, such as scales to weigh samples of soil or vegetation, make sure the scales have been zeroed correctly. If you are using a ruler to measure the length of a pebble you are relying on your eye to judge where the measurement starts and ends. Using callipers means you can measure the true value exactly without any guesswork. Measuring in millimetres is more accurate than measuring to the nearest centimetre. Take care to record data accurately on your collection form.

Figure 8.9 Use the correct equipment to improve accuracy of data.

For data to be reliable it needs to be collected in such a way that, if the fieldwork is repeated, a similar set of data would be collected. Reliability is achieved by strictly following the same sampling procedures each time the data is collected.

▶ If you are repeating a technique, such as an infiltration rate experiment, on a number of different occasions, it is important to follow exactly the same method each time.

▶ If you are working as part of a team to collect data, it is important that every member of the team uses exactly the same method.

For example, imagine a situation where a large team of students split up across an urban area to conduct a traffic count at numerous locations and all at the same time. Unreliable data would be collected if:

▶ the teams had not synchronised their watches so data was not collected at the same time;

▶ or some teams used stopwatches to keep to exactly 3 minutes but others did not.

Evaluation

Consider the limitations of your primary data, including the accuracy and the reliability of your data collection methods.

Moderators are looking for data collection methods that are appropriate. They expect the data to be plentiful and meaningful. However, more is not always better. There is no point collecting a lot of data that is not relevant to the research questions.

QUESTION Do I have to do a pilot survey?

ANSWER It is not essential to conduct a pilot survey but it is a really good idea. It may add a little time to the investigation but it's better to spend time now checking that methods work as you expect than wasting time collecting data that isn't going to help your investigation. It can also save time in the long run by enabling you to ask closed questions which are quicker to process and analyse.

QUESTION Will I be allowed to work with a friend to collect data?

ANSWER Yes, you can work with a friend or as part of a team to collect primary data. Some data is impossible to collect on your own, for example, you need at least two people to collect data for a slope or beach profile. In fact, working as part of a team can have real advantages. For example, a team can collect data simultaneously from several different sites. This will allow you to identify spatial patterns. However, you must collect any secondary data on your own.

Review Points

Tick off each review point before moving on to Step 9.

I have designed data collection forms. ☐

I have conducted a pilot survey. ☐

I have amended my data collection form in response to the results of my pilot survey. ☐

I have collected data and considered the issues of accuracy and reliability. ☐

I have made a record of strengths and limitations of my methodologies and noted anything that was unexpected. ☐

STEP 9

Begin the write-up

Action points

1   Write an introduction that outlines your aims, reviews the relevant geographical literature, and describes the context, scale and location of the fieldwork.

2   Write a methodology that describes and justifies your data collection methods and sampling strategy.

Action Point 1

Write an introduction that outlines your aims, reviews the relevant geographical literature and describes the context, scale, and location of the fieldwork.

The introduction to your report needs to be concise. Ideally it will be between 500 and 750 words. It needs to do three things.

1   Outline your aims.
2   Provide an overview of your literature review.
3   Locate the site of your fieldwork (see Figure 9.1).

Figure 9.1 Key elements to cover in your report's introduction.

Outline your aims

Describe the overall aim of your investigation and state your research questions.

Review the literature

Explain how your review of the literature inspired you to begin your investigation. Use the literature to provide a theoretical context for the investigation.

Locate the fieldwork

Describe the scale and location of your fieldwork. Include a map at an appropriate scale.

The introduction must:

▶   set out the **context** for your investigation;

▶   explain your **aim**. What was it you hoped to achieve? You must also **justify** your investigation - in other words, explain why you selected this aim and how the investigation links to the specification.

▶   summarise the **theoretical background**. What theoretical aspect of geography have you been researching? This may be a concept, model, theory, process, or contemporary issue.

> It is essential to give the aims of your research a theoretical context by referring to a review of relevant geographical literature.

Use what you discovered in your **literature review** to explore the context. There is no need to go into a lot of detail but you do need to make connections between theory in the textbooks and the purpose of your research. This may take the form of a prediction – using the literature to predict a possible outcome of the research. Alternatively, it may take the form of a comparison – comparing your own fieldwork location to findings in other people's research to determine whether your location is typical or atypical of the theory. This is what is meant by 'comparative context' in some mark schemes – it does not mean comparing two fieldwork locations.

Figure 9.2 Create geographical context in your introduction.

A mediocre report	A great report
• Fails to discuss geographical theory. • Fails to make any reference to geographical literature or refers to only one source. • Describes the aims but fails to explain why the investigation was chosen. • Provides only small scale maps to locate the investigation.	• Shows understanding of the geographical **theory** that underpins the research. • Refers to a **range** of at least three different sources in the geographical literature. • Explains **why** you think your research is relevant. • Provides a map to locate the investigation which is of an appropriate **scale**.

Geo-locating your investigation

It is important to give an accurate description of the location and scale of your fieldwork site in the introduction of your report. The best way to do this is by giving Ordnance Survey grid co-ordinates and also by providing a map of the location. The map should be at a large scale – one that shows significant details of your fieldwork site. It could be a large scale OS map or GOAD map, or a labelled sketch map that you have drawn, or a map downloaded from a website. Figure 9.4 shows an example of a suitable location map.

> The style of map shown in Figure 9.3 is used by some students but the scale of this map is unsuitable.

Figure 9.3 Do not use this type of map to locate your site.

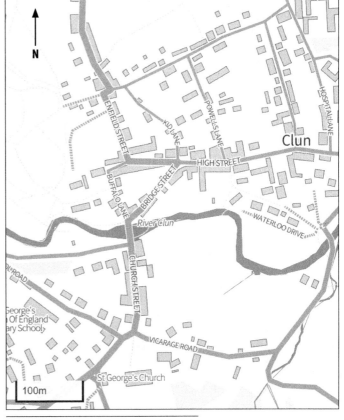

Figure 9.4 Use a map at an appropriate scale to locate your fieldwork site. This map shows Clun, Shropshire.

Writing in the third person

The correct way to write your report is in the third person. This means you should avoid using the personal pronoun ('I did this…'). Figure 9.5 shows examples of sentences written in the third person (on the left) and with a personal pronoun (on the right). If you can't get the hang of this, don't worry too much. You shouldn't lose marks if you do lapse into the style used in the right column of this table.

Figure 9.5 How to write your report.

You should use this style	You should avoid this style
• The aim of the investigation was to research the perception of different groups of people to the risk of flooding. • Qualitative data was collected using a questionnaire.	• My aim was to research the perception of different groups of people to the risk of flooding. • I used a questionnaire to collect qualitative data.

Action Point 2

Write a methodology that describes and justifies your data collection methods and sampling strategy.

> A good report will include a clear, concise description of methods of data collection. A great report will justify why data was collected in a particular way.

After the introduction, the next section of your report should describe the methods you used to collect data for your investigation. This is an important section in terms of marks available (see Appendix 1 for details of the mark scheme used by your exam board). You should aim to write between 750 and 1000 words. The moderator will expect to see specific details about:

▶ your choice of sampling strategies;
▶ the methods used to collect primary data;
▶ reference to the ethical dimension and risk assessment of your investigation.

Take a step-by-step approach to describing your methods. Be clear and concise. Your description should tell the reader:

▶ where data was collected;
▶ when it was collected;
▶ how it was collected.

Furthermore, you should justify your methods. This means you should:

▶ explain why particular data was collected;
▶ explain why data was collected in a particular way. This may include a reference to your risk assessment – if you adjusted the data collection method to make it safe.

Provide details of your sampling strategy

> Include significant details of your sampling strategy. In particular, a great report will discuss elements such as sample size and the timing and frequency of sampling points.

As you write this section think about your audience – the people who are going to read it. They will be a geography teacher and a geography moderator. Regard them as an 'informed' audience. They know what a clinometer is and what systematic sampling means so you don't need to spell out the techniques as though the person you are writing for is unfamiliar with these things. However, they won't know the details that are individual to your research. So, if you used a systematic sampling strategy, they will know what this means but they won't know how many sample points you used, or how far apart they were, so these are the kinds of detail you should provide. Make sure you refer to:

▶ the **frequency of your sample** – not only the number of sample points but also how far apart they were in terms of both distance and time;

▶ the **timing of your sample** – whether you made observations at different times of the day or week to take into account of any temporal variations;

▶ the **location of your sample points** and why you chose these locations. A good way to do this is with an annotated map showing the location of each sample point (see Figure 3.35 in Step 3).

Figure 9.6 Elements of the methodology.

A mediocre report	A great report
• Assumes that the reader knows very little so over-describes basic survey methods. • Omits important details such as the size of sample or when/where the sample was taken. • Justifies why the data that has been collected helps answer the research questions. • Fails to mention the ethical dimension of your research.	• Provides a step-by-step description of the method that could be replicated by the moderator. • Provides details of sample size, timings, and frequencies. • Justifies why data helps the research and explains why data was collected in a particular way. • Considers the ethical dimension and explains how you ensured that your research was respectful to people and the environment.

QUESTION Should I integrate the evaluation of my method into this section or wait until the end of the report?

ANSWER You could evaluate your methods in this section. However, if you are studying OCR, WJEC, or Eduqas Geography you should probably wait until later. This is because the marker and moderator will be looking for a separate evaluation section that comes towards the end of the report. If you are studying AQA or Edexcel Geography it's possible to integrate the evaluation of your methods into this section if you find that helpful.

Review Points

Tick off each review point before moving on to Step 10.

I have written a short introduction to my investigation that:

▶ describes the aim of my research ☐

▶ explains the theoretical context and refers to relevant literature ☐

▶ describes the scale and location of the fieldwork. ☐

I have written a methodology that:

▶ provides details of my sampling strategy and considers the accuracy and reliability of this strategy. ☐

▶ describes and justifies the methods I used to collect data ☐

▶ considered the ethical dimension of my research. ☐

Collate the data

Action points

1 Collate your raw data and use it to create summary tables.

2 Sort results by category.

Having written about your sampling strategies and data collection methods your next steps (Steps 10, 11, and 12) all involve making sense of your data. Steps 10-12 can be time-consuming so allow sufficient time in your schedule. You must work independently when collating, sorting, processing, presenting, and analysing data.

Action Point 1

Collate your raw data and use it to create summary tables.

Collate

To collate data means to gather together and combine data – usually by creating tables that summarise the evidence.

Your raw data may have been collected in the field on numerous separate data sheets – especially if the data was collected by a team of people. You may also need to collate together the secondary data you have found. Your first action point in trying to make sense of your data is to **collate** it into forms that will be easier to handle. The usual way to do this is to create summary tables that can be included in your report.

The purpose of collation is to bring together all similar data into the same place so that similarities and differences, or trends and patterns, in the data can be spotted.

▶ You may need to gather together **data by location** – so that one table summarises all of the data collected at a particular sample point.

▶ Alternatively, you may need to **create tables that sort the data by variable** – so that one table summarises all of the data collected for a particular variable (such as light, noise, or graffiti) at all sample points. This kind of table would help you draw a map.

▶ Tables can also be used to gather together **data that shows a potential correlation**. Putting all of the data into a table which has rows for sample points and columns for variables that may show a correlation (such as property prices, amount of traffic, and noise levels).

Figure 10.1 Use summary tables like this one to bring your data together.

	A	B	C	D	E	F
	distance along transect (m)	wind speed (m/s)	% cover sea sandwort	% cover marram grass	% cover restharrow	% cover that is open
1						
2	0	12	25	0	0	75
3	50	10	0	45	0	55
4	100	8	0	60	15	25
5	150	7	0	65	20	15

Use of spreadsheets

You could create your tables in a spreadsheet (such as Excel) and then use the computer programme to draw your charts and graphs (see pages 146–174).

Alternatively, you could create your tables in a spreadsheet and then copy and paste them into your written report when you are writing up. The advantage of using a spreadsheet (rather than a table in a word processing programme) is the ability to sort and rank order the data in a spreadsheet. This may prove useful when you are presenting and analysing the data.

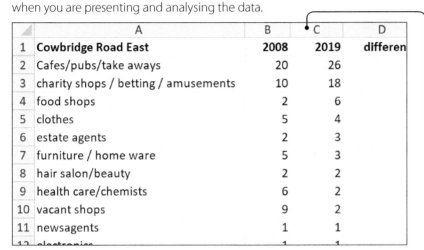

Figure 10.2 Use a spreadsheet to rank order the data in your summary tables.

1. Data has been transferred from tally sheets into a spreadsheet. Notice that the data has already been sorted on column C.

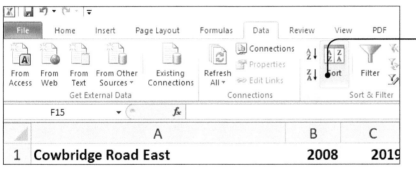

2. Use the mouse/keypad to select all the cells that contain your data. Then, click on the Sort button on the toolbar.

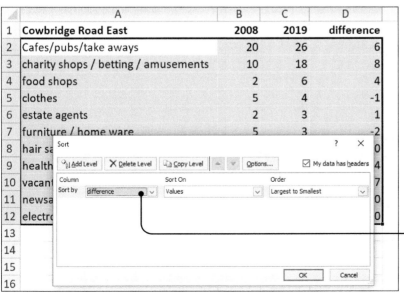

3. Select to sort on 'difference' which is the heading for column D.

4. The finished spreadsheet has sorted the data so that the shops that show the greatest increase are now in row 2.

	A	B	C	D
1	**Cowbridge Road East**	**2008**	**2019**	**difference**
2	charity shops / betting / amusements	10	18	8
3	Cafes/pubs/take aways	20	26	6
4	food shops	2	6	4
5	estate agents	2	3	1
6	hair salon/beauty	2	2	0
7	newsagents	1	1	0
8	electronics	1	1	0
9	clothes	5	4	-1
10	furniture / home ware	5	3	-2
11	health care/chemists	6	2	-4
12	vacant shops	9	2	-7

Stem and leaf plots

Stem and leaf plot

A stem and leaf plot is a simple way to categorise raw data whereby each data value is split into a stem (the first digit or digits) and a 'leaf' (usually the last digit).

A **stem and leaf plot** is a simple way to sort raw data into categories. You may need to do this before you can draw a histogram (see page 159). A stem and leaf plot simply records the frequency of data values that fall into each category of base 10. So, for example, imagine that you have collected data on pebble size from a beach or glacial environment (in millimetres or centimetres). By copying your raw data into a stem and leaf plot you can quickly see the frequency that data falls into each category. For example, in Figure 10.3, every pebble that is between 30mm and 39mm long is recorded in the stem for 3. This stem has a frequency of 30, in other words, 30 pebbles fall into the category 30-39mm.

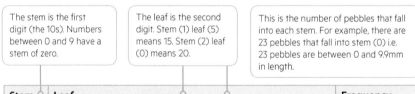

The stem is the first digit (the 10s). Numbers between 0 and 9 have a stem of zero.

The leaf is the second digit. Stem (1) leaf (5) means 15. Stem (2) leaf (0) means 20.

This is the number of pebbles that fall into each stem. For example, there are 23 pebbles that fall into stem (0) i.e. 23 pebbles are between 0 and 9.9mm in length.

Figure 10.3 Raw data displayed as a stem and leaf plot.

Stem	Leaf	Frequency
0	3 3 4 4 5 5 5 6 6 6 7 7 7 7 7 8 8 8 8 9 9 9 9	23
1	2 3 4 5 6 7 8	7
2	0 2 2 3 3 4 4 4 5 6 6 6 7 9 9	15
3	1 1 2 2 3 3 3 3 4 4 4 4 4 4 5 5 5 5 6 6 6 7 7 7 7 8 9 9 9	30
4	0 2 2 3 3 4 4 4 4 5 5 6 6 7 9 9 9	17
5	0 5 7 9	4

Action Point 2

Sort results by category.

The data you have collected may need sorting, for example, imagine you have collected from two locations on a beach you might want to sort the data by pebble size, shape, or geology.

The data from questionnaires will need sorting before you are able to present any of your findings. This is because the raw data from questionnaires is usually recorded on separate data collection sheets – one separate sheet for each person in your sample.

Imagine a questionnaire with six closed questions, two open questions, and a sample size of 60. In Figure 10.4 the sample has been sorted on one field – whether each participant was a local resident or a visitor. The graphic has been colour-coded to show whether participants responded yes (green) or no (blue) to questions one and two. In fact, the data can be sorted using any of the closed questions. For example, imagine that question 1 requires a yes/no response. You can sort the data in subsequent questions depending on how people responded to question 1.

You could use an electronic database to sort the data from questionnaires.

Alternatively, use a spreadsheet with columns for questions and rows for respondents and use the sort function in a similar way to Figure 10.2.

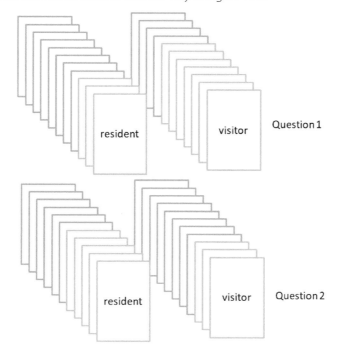

Figure 10.4 Using individual data forms will allow you to sort the data on any field.

QUESTION Do I need to include all of my completed data collection sheets in the report so that the moderator can see my raw data?

ANSWER No, you should only include summary data tables in your report. You could include some or all of your raw data in an Appendix at the end of your report. The marker/moderator may then be able to use the Appendix if they need to clarify something – perhaps because your report is confusing. The Appendix will not be marked.

Review Points

Tick off each review point before moving on to Step 11.

I have collated my raw data into summary tables. ☐

Where appropriate, I have sorted the data into categories. ☐

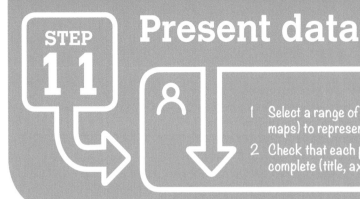

STEP 11

Present data

Action points

1 Select a range of suitable techniques (charts, graphs, maps) to represent the data you have collected.

2 Check that each presentational technique is accurate and complete (title, axis labels, scale lines, north arrows, keys).

11.1 Presenting data

Present data

To present data means to represent your data in a visual form such as a graph or map.

You have come to the part of your investigation where you need to **present** the data you have collected using suitable techniques such as pictograms, charts, graphs, or maps. Once you have presented your data you will be able to analyse it – look for patterns, trends, or connections in the data (Step 12 Analysis). The processes of presenting and analysing data are connected so it is a good idea to read both Step 11 and Step 12 before you begin drawing any graphs or maps. You **must work independently** when selecting and drawing the charts, graphs, and maps in your report.

Action Point 1

Select a range of suitable techniques (charts, graphs, maps) to represent all of the data.

Appropriate/Suitable

Appropriate or suitable data presentation methods are those that are most relevant and pertinent to the type of data and what it is showing.

You need to think about the type of data that you have collected. Then choose an **appropriate** or **suitable** technique to present it accurately and in a way that enables you to identify patterns and to interpret what the data is telling you. The purpose of presenting the data and analysing it is to help you answer your investigation aim, enquiry questions, or prove your hypothesis.

Select suitable data

If your data collection strategy has been designed well then your data will have perfect validity. In other words, every scrap of data that has been collected will be relevant to your aims. Consequently, **all** of the data should be presented and analysed in some way. Indeed, if you choose to ignore some data you could be accused of poor research. This is because by failing to present and analyse valid data you may miss some important trend or pattern and come to the wrong conclusion.

An example of frequently collected irrelevant data is data on gender. If you have collected data on gender, double check now whether it has any relevance to your research questions.

However, let's be honest – you have probably collected some data that, with hindsight, you now realise is irrelevant to your research questions. This may be data that you collected as part of a group – the data is valid for someone else's investigation but not to yours. At this stage, you should ignore this data. Only present data that is relevant to **your** investigation.

Select suitable charts and graphs

There are lots of different types of graphs you can draw. However, choosing which graph to draw is not just about personal taste. The style of graph you draw depends on the type of data that is being presented. Certain rules apply to the presentation of categorical data, data that can be ranked (on the ordinal scale), and continuous data (measured on the interval or ratio scales). Figure 11.2 gives some advice on graph selection.

> Select a suitable way of representing each dataset. Think carefully about the type of data and the most appropriate way of graphing or mapping it.

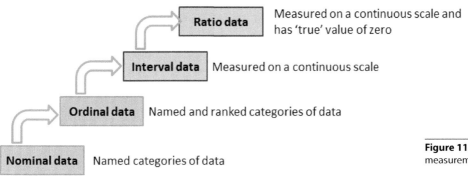

Ratio data — Measured on a continuous scale and has 'true' value of zero

Interval data — Measured on a continuous scale

Ordinal data — Named and ranked categories of data

Nominal data — Named categories of data

Figure 11.1 Types of data and measurement scales.

Type of data	Context	Suitable graphs to select
Categorical (Nominal scale)	Data that can be counted and put into categories, e.g. types of vehicle in a traffic survey, or footfall counted at different locations around a town centre.	Bar charts (vertical or horizontal). See section 11.2 in this Step. Compound bars. See Figure 11.13. Pie charts. See Figure 11.17.
Ordinal	Data that can be put into categories that can be ranked, e.g. bipolar scores, cleanliness index, EQI surveys.	Bar charts. Radar charts. See page 163. Pie charts.
Ratio or interval	Data that can be measured on a continuous scale such as time, wind speed, water depth, plant height, or distance along a transect.	Histograms. See page 159. Line graphs. See Figure 11.14.
Bivariate data where both data sets are interval or ratio	Data where one variable (always shown on the y-axis) is dependent on a second variable such as wind speed and altitude.	Scatter graphs. See page 164.
	Where one variable is orientation and the other is measured on the interval/ratio scale such as wind speed, or pebble length.	Rose diagrams. See page 161.

Figure 11.2 Examples of graphs that suit different types of data.

Avoid misleading graphs

A good graph allows you to see the data clearly. If the graph is badly drawn it could be misleading – making it difficult to see patterns or make comparisons. You should review each graph to make sure that you haven't fallen into one of the common mistakes that can be made at this stage of the investigation.

Remember to:
1 **make sure you have selected a suitable graph**. Follow the rules described in Figure 11.2;
2 **ensure the origin for the y-axis is correct** – usually it should start at zero. Study Figure 11.4. At first glance this graph gives the impression that more than four times as many pedestrians were seen in High Street than at Mardol. However,

If you use Excel to draw a graph make sure you check it carefully. Excel can draw a variety of graphs but they aren't all appropriate for the type of data you want to represent.

the y-axis starts at 40 not zero, so differences in height between the bars have been exaggerated and the difference between the two sites is twice the number not four times the number. There are some exceptions to this rule (see Figure 11.16 on page 156);

3 **be careful with pie charts**. They can be over-used in some investigations – the moderator will be looking for a suitable range of techniques. Sometimes a pie chart is unsuitable because there are too many data categories. If you have lots of small slices the pie becomes difficult to read and ineffective. In Figure 11.18 there are too many slices in each pie. In this case a bar chart showing frequency of shop type whould have been more effective. Figure 11.3 shows some common pitfalls which lead to the creation of a misleading graph.

Common error	Examples	How to avoid
Using an unsuitable graph.	Selecting the wrong graph can misrepresent your data and mislead the reader. The worst case scenario is using a line graph to present data that is in discrete categories because a line graph should only be used to present ratio (continuous) data.	Make sure you have selected a suitable graph. Follow the rules described in Figure 11.2.
Providing a false origin for the y-axis.	Study Figure 11.4. The difference in height between the bars is exaggerated because the y-axis begins at 40 rather than zero.	Ensure that the y-axis starts at zero.
Using a pie chart when there are many data categories.	Study Figure 11.18. These pie charts are difficult to read and ineffective because there are too many small slices.	Use a pie chart when you have a limited number of categories to present.

Figure 11.3 Common errors when presenting data – and how to avoid them.

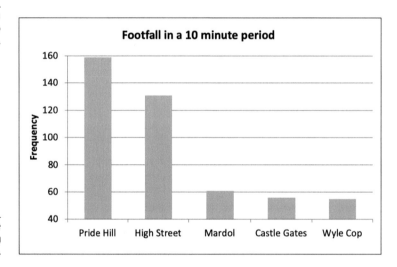

Figure 11.4 Failing to start the axis at zero creates a misleading impression of the data.

Select suitable maps

Cartographic techniques are used to present data in map form. They say a picture is worth a thousand words. If so, a map can tell the story of your data, in particular, it can say a lot about:

▶ the geographical distribution of your data – whether data is dispersed, spread evenly, clustered, or concentrated;

▶ whether some areas are under-represented or over-represented by a certain feature;

▶ direction, orientation, or movement of data.

Just as with graphs, you need to select maps that are suitable for the data you have collected. Figure 11.5 describes the main cartographic techniques that are available to you.

Cartographic technique	Sampling	Type of data	Example
Located bars or located pie charts.	Point	Nominal, ordinal, ratio, or interval data that has a small range of values.	Bars to represent bipolar or EQI scores that are located on a map where the data was collected. See page 173.
Proportional symbols.	Point	Nominal, ratio, or interval data that has a very large range of values.	Shapes, such as circles or squares, the area of which represents the value of the data. See page 171.
Proportional arrows or flow lines.	Point	Nominal or ratio data that represents movement and which has an orientation.	Arrows, the width of which represents the value of the data, to show traffic flow or pedestrian movement. See page 173.
Desire lines.	Point	Nominal data that represents movement and which has both an origin and destination.	A map in which each line represents the movement of an individual who has moved to a rural location as a result of counter-urbanisation. See page 167.
Isolines.	Point	Nominal, ratio, or interval data that has been point sampled and which represents an environmental gradient.	Isolines join places on a map which have the same value. A contour map is an example of an isoline map. See page 169.
Choropleth.	Area	Nominal or ordinal data that represents evidence collected from an area rather than from a point.	A choropleth uses colour or density shading to represent larger or smaller values on a map. See page 168.
Dot maps	Point	Nominal data that falls into a single category.	To give a visual representation of the spatial distribution of your data, such as the distribution of vacant shops in a town centre. See page 166.

The importance of the sampling strategy

To use primary data to draw a map you will have needed to collect data from points across your field study area – a systematic method of **point sampling** would be most appropriate. With this type of sampling strategy you can use your data to draw located bars, proportional symbols, flow lines, or isolines.

Alternatively, you can overlay a map of your field study area with an arbitrary grid pattern. This enables you to use a systematic method of **area sampling** (rather than than point sampling) to collect data for each of the areas on your grid. In Figure 11.6 data was collected about perceptions of flood risk in each area coloured yellow on the map. This allowed the construction of a choropleth map (Figure 11.31 on page 168).

Figure 11.5 The main cartographic techniques.

Point sampling

Point sampling is where data is collected from discrete individual places.

Area sampling

Area sampling is where data is collected from defined specific areas, for example, by using a quadrat.

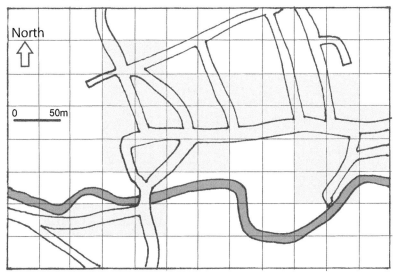

Figure 11.6 A student's map of the field study area has been overlain with an arbitrary grid.

Creating maps from qualitative data

If you have used a questionnaire to collect your primary data, you will be able to draw a map as long as one or more of your questions was about places. Figure 11.7 shows an example. In this investigation, the student asked about 50 children, aged 8, to name places in the UK that they had visited. The resulting data was plotted on a map and isolines used to join places with the same number of responses.

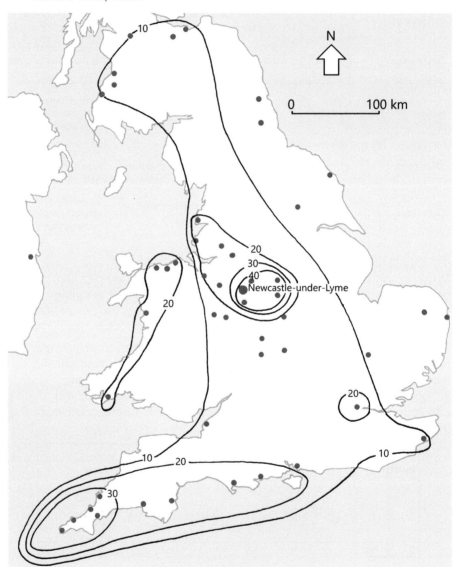

Figure 11.7 An example of an isoline map. It shows places known by a class of 8 year olds who live in Newcastle-under-Lyme.

Creating maps from secondary data

If you can't draw a map using primary data then you should consider whether you can use secondary data instead. It may be possible to use the census or other big data to draw a choropleth map. The census data in Figure 11.19 provides a suitable example – in this case you would need to find an outline map of the wards and then devise a suitable colour shading technique to present the data: the darker the shading, the greater the value. See page 168 for more information about choropleth maps.

Use a range of methods

When your investigation is marked, the teacher and moderator will be looking for:

▶ graphs and maps that are suitable for the data and that have been drawn accurately;
▶ evidence that shows you have a range of graphical and cartographic skills.

Some Independent Investigation mark schemes reward the use of more 'sophisticated' (OCR) or a 'range' (AQA) of presentation methods. Consequently, it is better to use a variety of different charts, graphs, and maps rather than repeating the same type of graph over and over. If you are aiming for a high mark then you will want to create a wow factor. You might achieve this by:

▶ using some techniques that are technically more difficult (in terms of the amount of data and the style of graph or map). Isoline maps and maps using proportional symbols, for example, are technically much more difficult to draw than a dot map;
▶ layering some techniques on top of one another. For example:
  • by locating and annotating photos onto a map;
  • locating bar charts or pie charts on top of a choropleth map;
  • locating charts or kite diagrams above a cross section or beach profile.

It could be argued that methods of data presentation fall on a continuum from simple to more sophisticated methods. Figure 11.8 shows one interpretation of this idea – it is based on experience of drawing these techniques rather than any exam board guidance. Don't avoid the 'simple' methods. If they are suitable then they should be used. However, it would be a good idea to use a variety of methods from across this continuum.

Evaluation

Think about the importance of planning ahead when you design your sampling strategy or the questions for your questionnaire. Lack of planning can limit your ability to use a cartographic technique.

Maps are a very effective way to show patterns over an area and you should consider using one in your report to present some of your data.

Figure 11.8 Methods of data presentation fall on a continuum of sophistication.

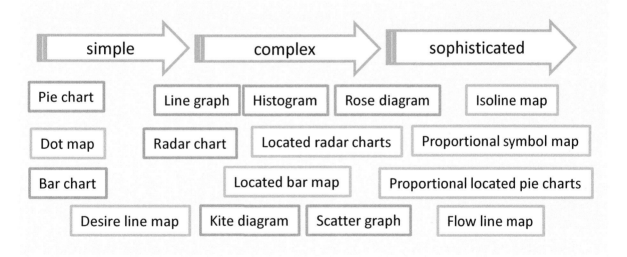

Check that each presentational technique is accurate and complete (title, axis labels, scale lines, north arrows, keys).

As you complete each graph or map you must check that it is accurate and complete. It is important to get the details right so that people who view your graph can fully understand what it is telling them about the data. A good graph or map will have each of the elements shown in Figure 11.9.

| Title | | Give all of your tables, graphs, maps, and photos a title. You can add a unique and consecutive figure number – like the captions in this book. |

| Axis labels | | Make sure you have stated what data is represented on both the x-axis and y-axis. |

| Units of measurement | | If you have used ratio or interval data make sure that the units of measurement (e.g. metres or mm per hour) are included on the axis. |

| Key / legend | | If you have used colours or symbols on your graph or map make sure you have included a key (or legend) that explains what these mean. |

| Scale line | | Every map must have a statement of scale or a scale line showing a representative length, e.g. 100m or 1km. Alternatively, write 'not to scale' if your map is not drawn to scale. |

| North arrow | | Every map must have an arrow that points north. |

Figure 11.9 Checklist for completing each presentational technique.

Check that you have represented the data accurately. For example, check that each axis is labelled and that you have included the unit of measurement.

The people who mark and moderate your report will be making judgements about the following:

▶ is the data presented using a suitable and effective technique?
▶ have you used a range of appropriate methods to present the data?
▶ is each graph or map complete? Use the checklist in Figure 11.9.
▶ is each graph or map accurate?

Pages 153-174 describe useful graphic and cartographic methods for presenting data. Use this information to choose methods of data presentation that are appropriate for your investigation and the data you have collected.

> If you use Excel to draw a graph make sure you check it carefully. Excel can draw a variety of graphs but they aren't all appropriate for the type of data you want to represent.

Simple graphs and charts

Bar charts, line graphs, and pie charts are relatively simple methods of presenting data and you are almost certain to use one of these. Try to extend the range of presentation methods by choosing some others that are more complex or sophisticated.

Bar charts

Bar charts clearly show the category with the largest and smallest values so they are useful for analysing similarities and differences between categories or places.

Bar charts can be used in two main circumstances. When you have collected data from:

1 **different locations:**
   ▶ show the locations on the x-axis;
   ▶ use the y-axis to present:
     • **nominal data** such as the number of pedestrians;
     • **ordinal data** such as the score from an EQI;
     • **interval/ratio (continuous) data** such as decibel readings;
2 **different categories**, such as categories of land use or shapes of pebble, and you want to plot the frequency of each category i.e. the number that you counted
   ▶ show the categories on the x-axis;
   ▶ use the y-axis to present the number you have counted.

Some categories have a logical sequence and should be shown in the correct order. An example is shown in Figure 11.10. However, if your categories have no particular sequence then it's a good idea to put your data in rank order by value from largest to smallest – making comparison easier, as shown in Figure 11.11.

Bar charts

Suitable for comparing categorical data.

Figure 11.10 Features of a bar chart.

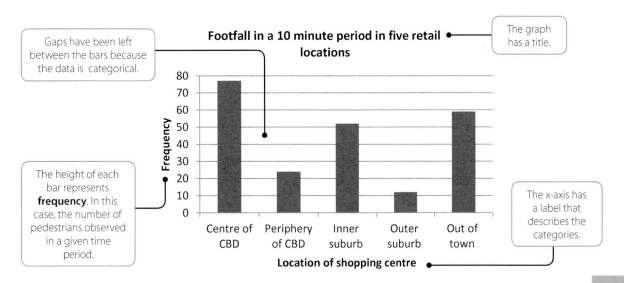

Gaps have been left between the bars because the data is categorical.

The graph has a title.

The height of each bar represents **frequency**. In this case, the number of pedestrians observed in a given time period.

The x-axis has a label that describes the categories.

Footfall in a 10 minute period in five retail locations

Frequency

Location of shopping centre

Centre of CBD · Periphery of CBD · Inner suburb · Outer suburb · Out of town

Bar charts usually have vertical bars (or columns) but it is possible to draw horizontal bars instead. Horizontal bars are useful if your category names are very long because it is easier to label horizontal bars (see Figure 11.11).

Figure 11.11 Put data in rank order to make patterns easier to analyse.

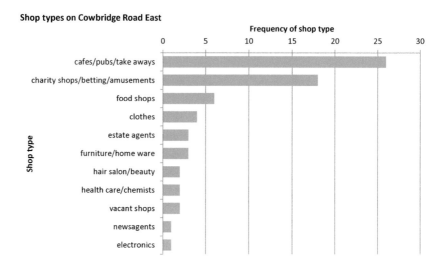

Decrease and increase can be shown by using positive and negative numbers on either the x-axis (like Figure 11.12) or the y-axis (if you want a column graph). Bar charts with negative values can be used to analyse change over time.

Figure 11.12 This bar chart includes negative values so that we can show how the number of each type of shop has decreased as well as increased over time.

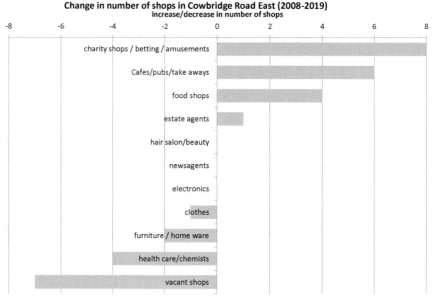

A **compound bar chart** is used to categorise data on the y-axis as well as on the x-axis. An example is shown in Figure 11.13 where:

▶ the x-axis has been used to represent data from five different locations; and
▶ the bars show frequency of shop type based on a simple three-way classification.

This type of chart works best if the number of categories within the bar is small.

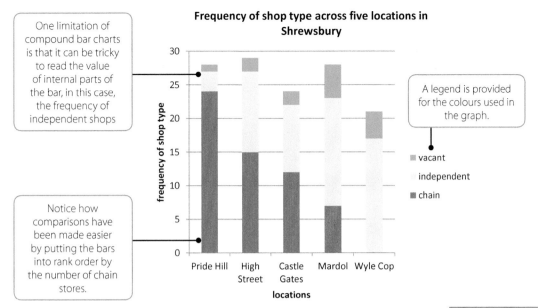

Frequency of shop type across five locations in Shrewsbury

One limitation of compound bar charts is that it can be tricky to read the value of internal parts of the bar, in this case, the frequency of independent shops

A legend is provided for the colours used in the graph.

■ vacant

independent

■ chain

Notice how comparisons have been made easier by putting the bars into rank order by the number of chain stores.

Figure 11.13 Use compound bar charts to present a breakdown of data within each category.

Test your understanding

Can you justify the choice of data presentation technique used in Figures 11.11 to 11.13? Why have bar charts been used? What are the strengths?

Line graphs

Line graphs are used to present interval or ratio data. In most cases, the x-axis is used to represent time (as in Figure 11.14) or distance (as in Figure 11.15). The y-axis can then be used to plot the value of any other variable that can be measured on a continuous scale such as height, temperature, sound level, velocity (for example, infiltration rate or wind speed). Figure 11.16 shows the height of plants growing on a transect that cuts at right angles across a footpath.

Line graphs

Suitable for showing trends in continuous data.

Figure 11.14 The features of a line graph. This presents data collected during an infiltration rate experiment (see page 60).

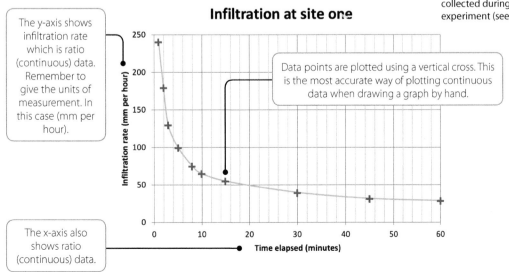

Infiltration at site one

The y-axis shows infiltration rate which is ratio (continuous) data. Remember to give the units of measurement. In this case (mm per hour).

Data points are plotted using a vertical cross. This is the most accurate way of plotting continuous data when drawing a graph by hand.

The x-axis also shows ratio (continuous) data.

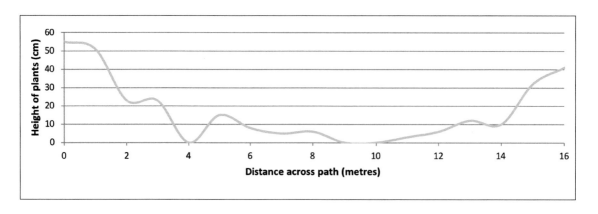

Figure 11.15 Cross section across the footpath showing plant height.

Line graphs are a useful way to present changes along an **environmental gradient** where data such as plant height, wind speed, soil depth, temperature, or light intensity has been collected systematically along a transect. For example, you could use a line graph to show how wind speed varies across a sand dune ecosystem in which case the x-axis would be used for distance (metres) and the y-axis for wind speed (metres per second).

Figure 11.16 also shows an environmental gradient. In this case the researcher has measured wind speeds at different altitudes above sea level on a transect up a slope. Consequently, in this example, the y-axis represents movement along the transect because height is the important factor rather than horizontal distance. The origin of the y-axis is at 220m because the slope started at 220m not sea level.

Environmental gradient

An environmental gradient is a gradual change in a variable across space (or time).

Figure 11.16 Line graph of wind speeds. Notice that the graph shows height of the hill on the y-axis.

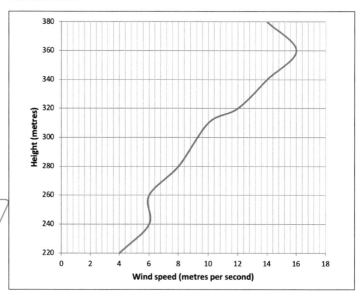

Choose a variety of different ways to represent your range of data. There is no point in drawing the same style of graph over and over again.

Pie charts

Pie charts

Suitable for comparing percentage data.

Pie charts are a simple way to present proportional or percentage data. The complete circle represents 100% of the population and the sector, or slice of the pie, represents a percentage of the total. Pie charts are an effective way to make simple comparisons of proportion. You will notice that opinion polls always refer to percentage or proportion of the population. For example, in Figure 11.17 it's easy to see that only 25% agreed with question 1 whereas 75% agreed with question 2.

Keep the number of sectors in your pie chart small (5 or less). The most effective pie charts are often those that represent binary decisions – yes/no or agree/disagree. This is because it's easy for the person reading the graph to visualise the major slices of the pie and equate them to proportions. If you have lots of small slices the pie becomes difficult to read and ineffective.

Figure 11.17 Pie charts are suitable for presenting results from questionnaires. They are effective if the number of slices is small.

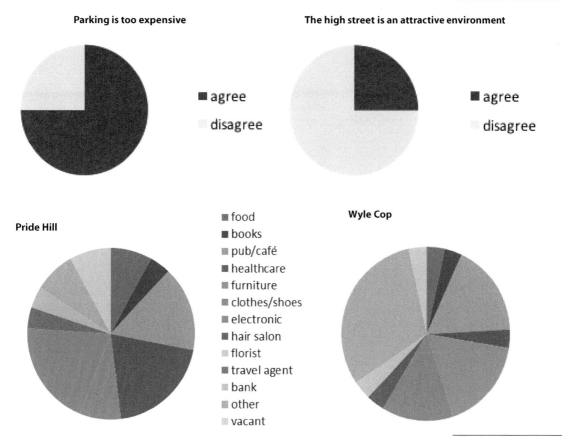

Figure 11.18 Pie charts are much less effective when the number of slices is large.

When to use pie charts

Pie charts are useful in two main circumstances.

1 **You have collected primary data from a questionnaire and you want to represent how people responded to each closed question.**

   You could use a bar chart to record frequency. But what does it mean if 20 people responded yes to question 1? 20 responses might only represent 5% of the whole. A pie chart is suitable because it allows you to compare the proportion of people who responded in each way.

2 **You have collected secondary data from the census or some other source of big data.**

   You want to compare the data for two different places (wards, towns, or regions) but these places have very different populations which make the comparisons of the raw data very tricky. Look at Figure 11.19. It shows data from the 2011 census for wards of Newcastle-under-Lyme in Staffordshire. It's an example of raw data – data that hasn't been processed.

> **Evaluation**
>
> Pie charts are not effective if they have more than 4 or 5 sectors.

Notice that each ward has a different total number of residents. Loggerheads has most retired people. It also has more residents than other wards so it's difficult to know whether it has more or less of its fair share of retired people. To make comparisons between wards easier we need to convert this raw data into percentages.

Location	Ward	Residents	Retired
Inner urban	Town	5,063	467
	Knutton & Silverdale	4,313	439
	Cross Heath	5,887	622
Suburban	Westlands	5,659	792
Rural-urban fringe	Keele	4,129	93
	Loggerheads	6,948	1,068
Newcastle		123,871	14,830

To calculate the percentage of the population of Loggerheads ward that is retired you need to follow these steps.

One Divide the number of people in Loggerheads who are retired by the total number of residents in that ward. So, divide 1,068 by 6,948.

Two Multiply the answer (from Step One) by 100. So, multiply 0.1537 by 100. The answer is 15.37. This is the percentage of all residents in Loggerheads who are retired.

Three You can round the number up or down to the nearest whole number. If the number ends .49 or less, round it down. If it ends .50 or more, round it up. So 15.37 would round down to 15%.

Figure 11.20 Representing some of the data from Figure 11.19 as a bar chart and pie chart.

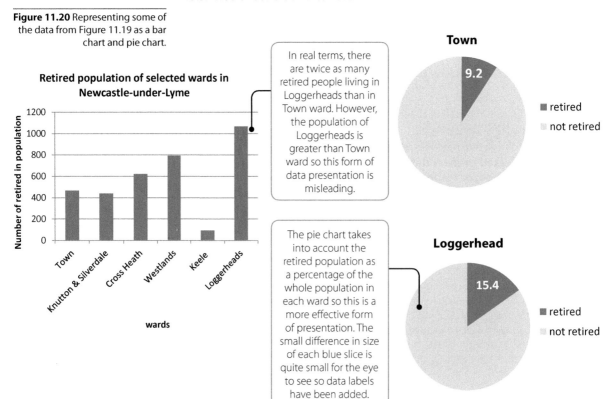

Retired population of selected wards in Newcastle-under-Lyme

In real terms, there are twice as many retired people living in Loggerheads than in Town ward. However, the population of Loggerheads is greater than Town ward so this form of data presentation is misleading.

Town

9.2

■ retired
■ not retired

The pie chart takes into account the retired population as a percentage of the whole population in each ward so this is a more effective form of presentation. The small difference in size of each blue slice is quite small for the eye to see so data labels have been added.

Loggerhead

15.4

■ retired
■ not retired

More complex charts and graphs

Histograms

A **histogram** is a type of graph that uses bars. It may look similar to a bar chart but there are some important differences between histograms and bar charts that are shown in Figure 11.21. The key difference is that the x-axis of a histogram is used to present continuous categories of data (such as time, slope angle, height, or distance) whereas the x-axis of a bar chart is used to present categories of discrete, **nominal data** (such as different locations where data was collected, or categories of vehicle, vegetation, shop, or land use). In a histogram the value of each bar is represented by its area rather than its height. If all the intervals on the x-axis are equal, the histogram is easy to plot and read on the y-axis.

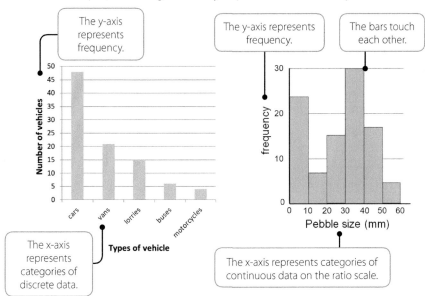

Figure 11.21 The difference between bar charts and histograms.

Why use a histogram

Histograms can be used wherever it is possible to divide continuous data into equal-size categories. For example, you could use a histogram to show:

▶ **population structure**, where the x-axis is used to show age categories from 0-99. An age-sex pyramid, like the one on page 123, is a pair of histograms turned through 90 degrees;

▶ **the frequency of pebbles** which fall into categories based on pebble length (as in Figure 11.21);

▶ **the frequency of rainfall events** where the x-axis is used to show categories of duration of rainfall (in minutes).

Histograms are useful because their shape represents the distribution of data within a large data set. They can be used to visualise the distribution of data between the categories. This allows the analysis of distribution patterns such as modal class, range, **skewness**, and outliers. See page 180.

In geography fieldwork, the commonest use of a histogram is to plot pebble distributions. The measurement of pebble length (in millimetres) provides you with ratio data on a continuous scale. By organising the range of pebble sizes into equal-size categories you can count the frequency of pebbles in each category. The resulting histogram, like the one in Figure 11.21, shows the distribution of pebble sizes which, in turn, tells us something about how well the pebbles have been sorted by wave action.

If you are drawing pairs of graphs, make sure you format the axes so that the y-axis in each graph uses exactly the same intervals and maximum value. This will make visual comparisons easier.

In Figure 11.22 a pair of histograms has been used to present another large data set. This time the x-axis presents categories of the Cailleux Index (see page 77). Low values on this Index represent very angular pebbles, high values represent very rounded pebbles. The value of drawing a pair of histograms is that we can compare the distribution of pebble shapes which, in turn, allows us to interpret something about the depositional environment in which they were formed.

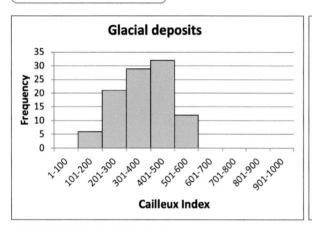

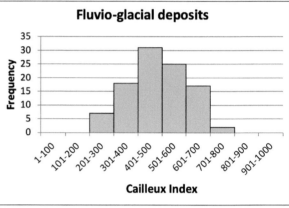

Figure 11.22 Pair of histograms to represent sediment roundness in two deposits found in a previously glaciated environment.

Test your understanding

Compare the distribution of pebbles in the pair of histograms in Figure 11.22. What are the main similarities and differences? How does the construction of the histograms make comparisons easier?

How to draw a histogram

In a histogram it is the area of the bar that represents its value. So, in theory, you can use unequal sized categories. For example, in a histogram showing population structure you could have categories 0-19, 20-35, 36-65, 66-90. However, this makes both construction and analysis of the histogram tricky. The bars will be of unequal widths and the people viewing the histogram may underestimate the true value of the wider bars. Consequently, it is preferable to ensure that the intervals on the horizontal axis are equal in size. This means each bar must be the same width. To draw a histogram follow these directions.

One Divide your continuous scale into equal-sized intervals to create the categories. Too few categories, or too many, and any patterns will be hard to identify. It will depend on the range of data but between 5 and 12 categories is sensible. Plot these categories on the x-axis.

Two Count the frequency of your data that falls into each category. In a larger data set you could sort the data in a spreadsheet first, before organising it into categories using a tally chart.

Three Create a y-axis that is long enough to include your largest frequency.

Four Draw the bars of your histogram. The bars must touch each other. Use the same colour to colour each bar. Different colours would suggest that each bar represents something different and these aren't different things – they are all pebbles!

Rose diagrams

A rose diagram is a type of histogram that is used to present data that has direction and frequency. Like a histogram, this type of chart divides the orientation data into categories of equal size. Instead of plotting the frequency as bars on a y-axis the frequency is plotted as bars on polar graph paper (a type of circular graph paper that has divisions every 10 degrees).

Why use a rose diagram?

A rose diagram gives a visual presentation of data that has an orientation in the landscape. For example, you could use a rose diagram to present the orientation of pebbles in a depositional environment such as:

▶ a glacial moraine or scree slope;
▶ the direction of striations or corries in a glaciated landscape;
▶ wind direction.

In each case the length of the bars represents frequency, for example:

▶ the number of pebbles whose axes lie in the same orientation as the slope;
▶ the number of corries that face north;
▶ the number of hours that the wind blew from the south-west.

How to draw a rose diagram

One Divide your data into equal-sized categories. To present pebble orientation data (like Figure 11.23) each category should represent 10 degrees. To do this you could use a spreadsheet to rank your data and then organise it into categories using a tally chart.

Two Label the frequency on the primary (north-south) axis.

Three Plot the data as a series of tapering bars.

Pages 56–57 explain the data collection method that was used to collect the data that is represented in Figure 11.23. Notice how each bar has been plotted with a symmetrical, mirror image bar on the opposite side of the chart. This is because the blocks that were measured lay on an axis which pointed in two opposite directions. For example, 8 stones lay on an axis that was recorded as being between 70 and 80 degrees. However, the axis of these stones also pointed between 250 and 260 degrees.

Pages 56–57 explain the data collection method that was used to collect the data that is represented in Figure 11.23.

Rose diagrams

Suitable for presenting orientation of continuous data.

Weblink

https://www.waterproofpaper.com This is one of several websites where you can download free graph paper, including the polar graph paper with divisions every 10 degrees that you need to draw a rose diagram.

Figure 11.23 A rose diagram showing orientation of stones at the Stiperstones, Shropshire.

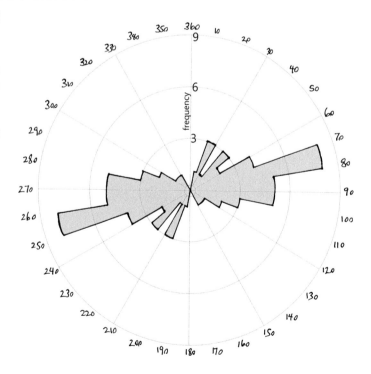

Test your understanding

Wind is always measured in the orientation that the wind is blowing from, whereas the axis of a pebble always points in two opposite directions. Think about how a wind rose diagram would differ from Figure 11.23.

Kite diagrams

Kite diagrams

Suitable for presenting changes in percentage cover across an ecosystem.

A kite diagram takes its name from its similarity in shape to a flying kite and its symmetrical shape. Kite diagrams are used to present changes in percentage data collected during a transect survey such as a vegetation survey (see page 85). Kite diagrams can have multiple x-axes – one for each species of plant in the survey.

Why use a kite diagram?

Kite diagrams are useful because they allow you to visualise changes in percentage plant cover as you move through an ecosystem. For example, you could use a kite diagram in an investigation of zonation in a sand dune ecosystem to visualise how plant species change from the embryo dunes through the yellow and grey dunes. You might compare the changes shown by your kite diagram to **abiotic** changes along the environmental gradient such as how wind speed, soil moisture, and soil temperature change along the transect.

Abiotic

The abiotic factors are the non-living factors of the environment that influence vegetation such as light, moisture, and temperature.

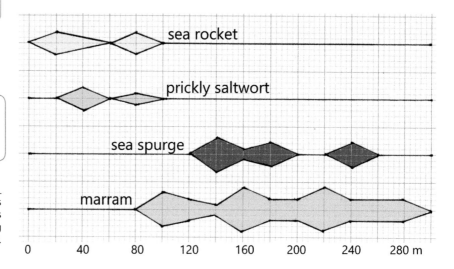

In the y-axis each small blue square represents 10% vegetation cover.

Figure 11.24 A kite diagram has been used to represent the changes in percentage cover of plants along a sand dune transect.

How to draw a kite diagram

One Choose the plant species that you are going to present. You can present the data from one species, or multiple species, on the same horizontal scale that will represent the length of your transect.

Two Plot the primary x-axis on graph paper to represent the length of the transect. For each species of plant plot a separate x-axis that is parallel to the primary x-axis.

Three For each species of plant, label the y-axis from 50% (above the x-axis) to 50% (below the x-axis).

Four For each species, plot two points equidistant from the horizontal central line, equivalent to half of the percentage cover that was recorded for the species at that point on the transect. When the graph is complete, the width of the kite diagram will represent the full value of the percentage cover (see Figure 11.24).

Five When all the points have been plotted for the first species, join all the points above the x-axis with a rule. Do the same for the points below the x-axis. Colour the space between the horizontal lines.

Six Repeat this process for each species of plant. You should use different colours for each species.

Radar charts

Radar charts are a way of representing the values observed for multiple variables. These variables must have something in common and have the same scale, for example, you could use a radar chart to present bipolar scores. An example is shown in Figure 11.25. It represents data collected using a bipolar survey where two locations within Cardiff city centre were judged using nine different bipolar statements, each focusing on a different aspect of the urban environment.

Why use a radar chart?

Radar charts are often used to represent data collected using attitudinal surveys or EQIs. They are useful for making comparisons. In Figure 11.25 each polygon represents a different location so the polygonal shape provides a visual comparison of the qualities of the two places.

Radar charts can also be used to compare the perceptions of different groups of people, for example, to compare perceptions of locals and visitors, or people of different ages.

Radar charts are useful to compare features because the eye is drawn to the different areas and shapes of each polygon.

1 In Figure 11.25 we can see that the area covered by the polygon for Location A is considerably larger than the polygon for Location B, meaning that the overall impression is that the urban environment is much more favourable at A than at B.

2 The shapes reveal interesting similarities and differences. In some respects the two sites are similar: the variable street lighting receives the same positive score at each site whereas green spaces has a negative score at each site. Other variables display a wide difference, especially in building design and cleanliness, where Location A scores much more highly than Location B.

> **Radar chart**
>
> Suitable for presenting ordinal data such as EQI and making comparisons between locations.

> Radar charts should only be used if each axis has the same scale, for example, a bipolar or EQI score. Do not be tempted to add secondary data from the census that is measured on a different scale. You cannot use a mixture of different kinds of data on a radar chart.

Figure 11.25 A radar graph to represent bipolar scores.

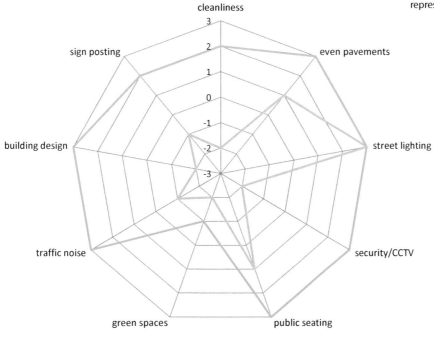

Location A   Location B

Scatter graphs

A scatter graph (also known as a scatter plot) is a type of graph that is used to show the link (or correlation) between two sets of data. To draw a scatter graph you will need **bivariate data**. That is two sets of data (or variables) that you think may be connected in some way.

Why use a scatter graph?

A scatter graph is a useful way of representing a link between two sets of data. If bivariate data is closely connected, the graph will show a dense pattern of plots scattered diagonally across the graph. In each of the examples shown in Figure 11.26 you could use a scatter graph to represent the potential link between the two variables.

Figure 11.26 Examples of bivariate data.

Fieldwork context	Variable One	Variable Two
1 A sandy beach.	Wind speed (metres per second).	The height that sand is carried (by the wind) above the beach (in centimetres).
2 A transect up a hillside between 150m and 400m above sea level.	Height above sea level (metres).	Wind speed (metres per second).
3 A pebble beach.	The average size of sediment (millimetres).	Distance along the beach – measuring in the same direction as the movement of longshore drift (metres).
4 An eroded footpath in a honeypot site.	Distance from the car park (metres).	Width of the area affected by erosion (metres).
5 Study of 10 different soil samples.	Infiltration rate (cubic cms per minute).	Percentage of the soil composition made of clay particles.
6 The area around a busy main road.	Noise levels (decibels).	Distance from the road (metres).
7 A housing area close to an attractive urban park.	Distance from the park (metres).	House prices (£1,000s).
8 A study of a river channel over several days.	The discharge in the river channel (in cubic metres per second).	The amount of rainfall each day (in millimetres).
9 A larger urban area.	Population density (number of people living per km^2).	Distance from the city centre (km).
10 A larger urban area.	Population density (number of people living per km^2).	The percentage of households who do not own a car.

An important idea that you need to understand when plotting a scatter graph is the concept of the dependent and independent variable. Think about the first pair of variables in Figure 11.26. On a windy day, sand bounces up the beach in a process called saltation. In a gentle wind most sand particles rise only 10mm from the beach. In stronger winds the height increases to a maximum of about 50cm. The height achieved by the sand grains depends on the strength of the wind. So, wind speed is the **independent variable** and height is the **dependent variable**. In an investigation of house prices close to an attractive urban park, distance from the park is the independent variable and house price is the dependent variable.

Test your understanding

Think about the variables shown in Figure 11.26. In each pair, identify the dependent and the independent variable.

How to plot a scatter graph

One Think about how the two variables may be connected. For example, in Figure 11.27, a student has collected data from the Census about the educational background and occupations of people living in 14 different neighbourhoods in Cardiff. The student thinks it is likely that more people will have professional occupations in wards where more people have a degree. If so, the percentage of people in professional occupations will be the dependent variable because the value of this number will depend on the percentage of people who have degrees – not the other way around.

Two Draw a pair of axes. The dependent variable must be plotted on the y-axis. The independent variable – in this case the percentage of people with a degree – should go on the x-axis. Try to make the two axes about the same length as each other so that the finished graph is square. This will make it easier to see any patterns on the graph.

Three Label each axis.

Four Plot the points for each ward onto the graph. Vertical crosses are the best way to plot each point. These will line up with the vertical and horizontal grid lines on your graph paper – so your plots should be accurate and easy to read.

Five Calculate the mean value (M) for each variable. Plot this point onto your graph – perhaps using a different style or colour so that it stands out from the other points on the graph.

Six Draw a **line of best fit** on your graph.

To draw a line of best fit accurately follow these rules.
▶ The line must pass through the mean value (M).
▶ The line should also follow the trend of the other points but it doesn't need to go through any of them or join them up.
▶ There should be the same number of points on each side of the line of best fit.
▶ The line of best fit does not have to go through the origin of the graph.

The analysis of scatter graphs, and the correlations that they show, is discussed on pages 178-179.

> ### Line of best fit
>
> A line of best fit represents the trend shown in bivariate data.

Ward	% of residents with a degree	% of residents in professional occupations
Adamsdown	28	14.5
Butetown	33	20.1
Caerau	10	5.4
Canton	50	32.8
Cathays	22	13.4
Ely	9	6.1
Grangetown	22	13
Llanishen	31	19.5
Pontprennau	38	23.8
Rhiwbina	35	27.9
Riverside	32	20.1
Rumney	13	9.2
Splott	26	17
Whitchurch	37	26.8
Mean	27.57	17.83

Figure 11.27 Census data for education and occupation in selected wards of Cardiff.

Figure 11.28 Scatter graph representing the relationship between the bivariate data in Figure 11.27.

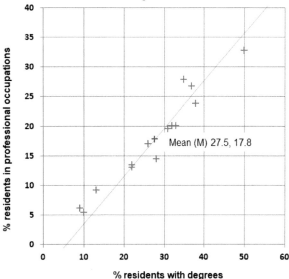

Cartographic techniques

Geographers are interested in spatial patterns. These are patterns that exist in two dimensions so they can be represented on a map. Can you represent some of the evidence from your fieldwork on a map? You can use either primary or secondary data to draw your map.

Dot maps

A dot map is the simplest kind of map you can draw. They show the location of data that falls into a single category. To draw a dot map you need:
▶ a base map of your study area;
▶ to know the exact location of each item of data.

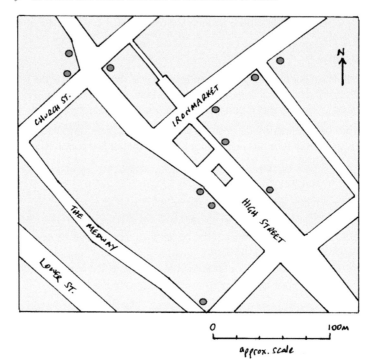

Figure 11.29 A dot map showing the location of vacant shops, Newcastle-under-Lyme (2018).

Why use a dot map?

A dot map is useful because it gives a visual representation of the spatial distribution of your data. For example, in an investigation of urban places you could use a dot map to show the distribution of CCTV cameras, cash points, primary schools, vacant shops, or speed bumps. In an investigation of a glaciated upland you could use a dot map to show the distribution of corries or scree slopes. Distribution patterns shown on a map can be described using qualifying words such as regular, nucleated, scattered, clustered, random, or linear.

If you draw the distribution of two related items on the same map (such as banks and cash points, or CCTV cameras and burglar alarms) you can compare the distribution patterns.

You can analyse the distribution of features on a map using Nearest Neighbour Analysis (see page 197) or by calculating the interquartile area (see page 199).

Desire line maps

A desire line map is another very simple type of map. It uses thin straight lines to show how places are linked together by data.

Why use desire line maps?

The most common use of a desire line map is to present the movement of people, for example:

▶ commuters travelling to and from work;

▶ visitors to a honeypot site;

▶ the origin of people who have recently moved into a community, for example, in a study of the impacts of counter-urbanisation on a village or the gentrification of an inner urban area.

How to draw a desire line map

To draw desire lines you need to know exactly where each line begins so you need to ask the commuter or visitor the name of their home town rather than the name of a county.

One Download or sketch a map to use as a base map.

Two Plot a straight line for each item of data. In Figure 11.30, the line should begin where the visitor lives and end at the location of the honeypot site.

Three Give your map a scale line and a north arrow. This is essential so you can describe the pattern made by the desire lines.

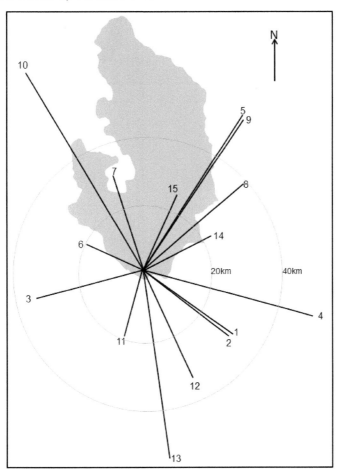

Figure 11.30 A desire line map showing visitors to Dovedale. The area coloured green shows the Peak District National Park.

Choropleth maps

A choropleth is a type of map where darker colours (or darker shading) are used to represent higher data values. They are versatile because you can use a range of different types of data to draw this type of map – as long as the data values can be divided into class sizes. Choosing the right class sizes, however, is the key to a good choropleth.

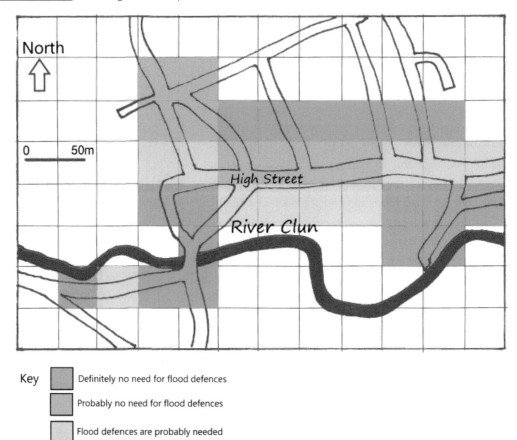

Key

☐ Definitely no need for flood defences

☐ Probably no need for flood defences

☐ Flood defences are probably needed

☐ Flood defences are definitely needed

Figure 11.31 A choropleth map of Clun, Shropshire, showing perceptions of flood management.

Why use choropleth maps?

A choropleth is useful because it is a visual representation of the magnitude of the data. The darker colours or shades clearly show where data values are higher. This makes them easy to understand and to identify patterns and anomalies.

If you have used a sampling strategy where you have sampled data systematically from areas across your field study area you can draw a map like Figure 11.31. This map shows residents' perceptions of the need for flood defences. You could use a similar technique to choropleth EQI scores.

A choropleth represents data from geographical areas rather than specific points so you don't need to know pin-point locations for your data. This makes them ideal for using with secondary data sources (such as the census) which attributes data to postcodes, wards, or counties rather than to exact locations.

How to draw a choropleth map

The patterns on a choropleth map will only be clear if you have chosen to divide your data into a sensible number of data classes. Too few classes of data and smaller variations in the data will not be shown. On the other hand, too many classes and the map will be covered in different colours and it will be impossible to see any spatial patterns. As a rule of thumb, four classes is probably the least and seven the most classes you should use.

One Make a simple base map or download one. It must show the areas (for example, wards) that match your data.

Two Decide how many classes you are going to use. The safest way to do this is to look at your range of data and divide this into four, five, or six equal-sized classes.

Three Create a key. Use dark colours for the highest values and lighter colours for lower values.

Four Colour each area on the map. Do this by checking the data value for each area and comparing it to the key.

Isoline maps

An isoline is a line on a map that joins places that have an equal value. A contour map is the most commonly used isoline map where each line on the map represents places that have an equal height. The distance between the isolines tells us something about gradients in the data. If the isolines are close together then the data is changing quickly. On a contour map this would indicate a steep gradient.

An isoline map is commonly used to present continuous data such as air pressure (isobars) or temperature (isotherms) or rainfall (isohyets). However, they can be used in human geography too, for example, to show the density of pedestrians in a city centre.

isoline maps

Suitable for presenting the density of data.

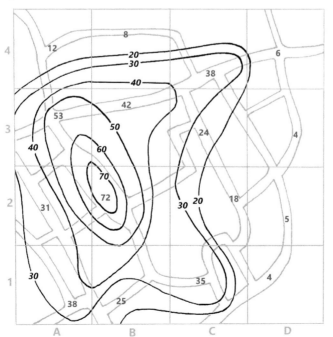

Figure 11.32 An isoline map of pedestrian density in Cardiff.

How to draw an isoline map

To draw an isoline map you will need lots of data points across a map. In Figure 11.32 each dot represents a point where footfall was counted for 10 minutes. To draw an isoline you simply need to join places that have the same data values. It sounds simple but, in order to do this, you need to be able to interpolate - which means to find values that lie between other values.

Study Figure 11.33. There are 2 places where a value of 20 was recorded. You could join these up with an isoline but it would be easier if there were more points. To create more points you need to interpolate – do this by estimating where 20 lies on a continuum between adjacent data values. Each of the red dotted lines has been drawn between values where 20 should be somewhere on the line. Using this method gives another 9 places that have a value of 20.

Figure 11.34 shows how to interpolate the data and draw an isoline for 20. Everywhere inside this line has more than 20 pedestrians. Everywhere outside this isoline has fewer than 20 pedestrians.

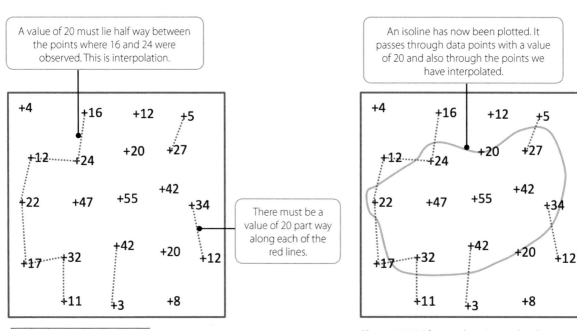

Figure 11.33 How to interpolate values on an isoline map.

Figure 11.34 After you have interpolated additional values you can draw an isoline.

Maps with located charts and symbols

If you have collected data from different locations across your study area then you have the option of drawing charts or graphs on a base map to indicate the location of the data. Each of the following forms of graphical presentation can be located on a map:

▶ bar charts or compound bars;
▶ pie charts;
▶ proportional arrows – where the width of the arrow is in proportion to the data (see page 173);
▶ proportional symbols - where the area of the symbol is in proportion to the data (see below).

Why use maps with located charts and symbols?

Use a map with located symbols, such as the located pie charts in Figure 11.35 to give a visual presentation of any spatial patterns in your data.

Figure 11.35 A map of Shrewsbury with located pie charts to show percentage of independent shops in selected streets.

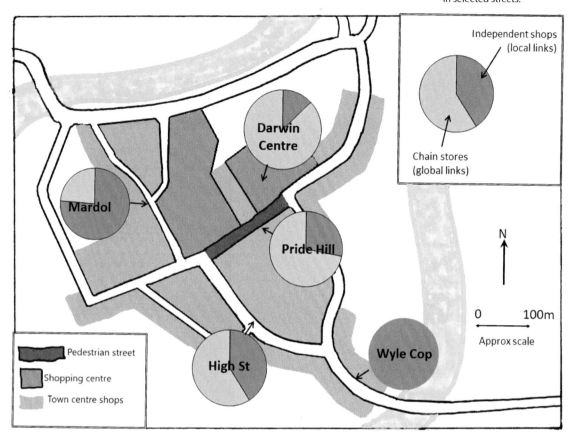

Proportional symbols

A proportional symbol map uses symbols (usually squares or circles) of different sizes to represent the data. The larger squares/circles represent larger data values – it is the **area** of the symbol that is in proportion to the value. Proportional symbols are useful if you have a large range in your data. This is because it is their area rather than their height that represents the data value – meaning that even large data values can be represented with quite a compact shape. On the other hand, it is difficult to estimate the size of a proportional symbol by eye – people viewing your map will tend to underestimate their size.

Proportional symbols

Suitable for presenting spatial distribution of data that has a large range.

How to draw proportional symbols

To draw a proportional square or circle you need to follow these instructions.

One Calculate the square root of each piece of data. Put the number in to a calculator and press this √ button. Add your answers to a table like Figure 11.36.

Two Decide on a scale for the symbols. The square root for Raven Meadows is 29.3. A simple scale would be 1:1 so, for Raven Meadows, you would draw a square with a side that is 29mm long, or a circle with a radius of 29mm. If this scale doesn't work well you could consider halving (to make all symbols smaller) or doubling (to make all the symbols larger) all of the square root numbers in your table.

Evaluation

Have you selected a suitable and effective cartographic technique? Can you justify its choice? Can you identify its strengths and weaknesses?

Three Download or sketch a simple map that can be used as a base map.

Four Draw each symbol. The centre of each symbol should be located carefully in the right place. It is ok to overlap symbols.

Five Draw two symbols of different sizes at the edge of your map to make a scale. Use whole numbers that are close to the top and bottom of your range of data.

Six Give your map a scale line and north arrow.

Figure 11.36 Number of parking spaces available in Shrewsbury (2018).

Car park	Number of spaces	Square root ($\sqrt{}$)
Bridge Street	48	6.9
Raven Meadows	856	29.3
Saint Julian's Friars	272	
Wyle Cop	240	
Frankwell	720	
Shrewsbury Station	189	

Figure 11.37 Proportional squares showing number of parking spaces available in Shrewsbury (2018).

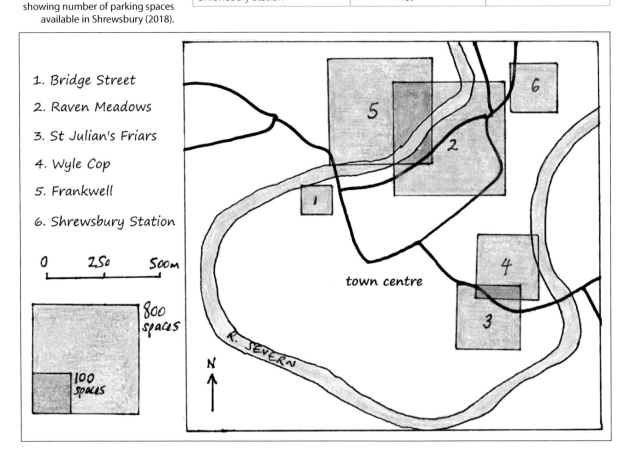

1. Bridge Street
2. Raven Meadows
3. St Julian's Friars
4. Wyle Cop
5. Frankwell
6. Shrewsbury Station

0   250   500m

800 spaces

100 spaces

town centre

R. SEVERN

N

Why use located bars on a map?

On this type of map it is the **height** of the bars that represents the data values. This type of map is easy to draw and gives a useful visual impression of any spatial patterns in the data. They are particularly useful if the range of data is quite small. This means located bars are particularly useful to represent ordinal data such as bipolar or EQI scores, like Figure 11.38.

Located bars can also be used to present nominal data such as the number of shop types at a given location. However, if you are presenting nominal data which has a very large range you will have some very long bars. Look at the data for parking spaces in Figure 11.36. The range of data is from 48 to 856 so it would be difficult to fit the longest bars onto a map. In this case it would be much better to draw a proportional symbol.

Figure 11.38 Located bars on a map representing bipolar scores.

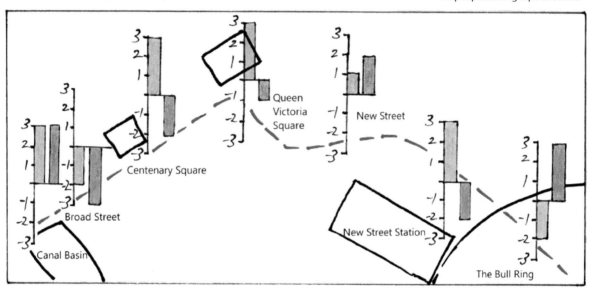

Why use a flow line (or proportional arrow) map?

A flow line map uses proportional arrows to show flows, for example, flows of traffic or the movement of pedestrians. The **width** of each arrow is in proportion to the value of the flow. Proportional arrows can be used to show:

▶ flows from an area (such as a county) or a place (such as a town);
▶ data that has an amount and direction but where you don't know where the movement began (for example, traffic on a road).

One Draw a simple base map.

Two Create a scale for the width of your arrows. This needs to be small enough so that your largest arrows will fit on the map.

Three Draw each arrow onto the base map so that they point in the direction of flow. The width of the arrows should be in proportion to the data.

Four Add a scale line, north arrow, and key to your map.

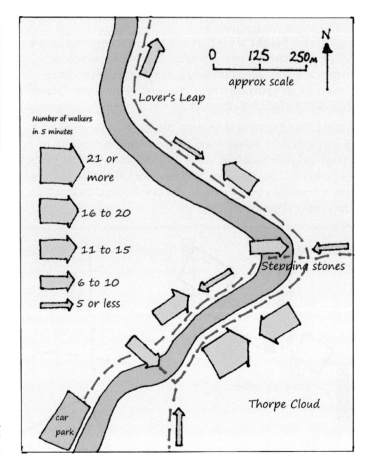

Figure 11.39 A flow line map showing pedestrian flows.

QUESTION Do I have to use GIS to present data?

ANSWER GIS can be a useful tool to present geo-located data across a map but you don't have to use GIS. It is advisable to present some of your data on a map as this will help you to analyse spatial patterns. You can create very effective maps by hand. It is perfectly acceptable to use a ready-made map and then add proportional symbols, located bars, isolines, or annotated photos to this base-map. Indeed, this method of over-laying data onto a base-map is considered to be one of the more sophisticated ways of presenting data.

Analysis

Action points

1 Research and select appropriate methods of analysis to reveal the meaning of quantitative and qualitative data.

2 Apply methods of analysis so you can describe patterns and trends and find meaning in your data.

3 Where relevant, use statistical tests to examine apparent relationships in your data. Always test the significance of any statistical tests you have used.

4 Write up your analysis in your report. Interpret your findings and integrate the written analysis with the presentation of your data.

Analysis is a methodical process. Think of yourself as a detective. You need to examine each piece of evidence carefully. By looking for connections, patterns, or trends in the data, analysis allows you to make sense of the evidence and tell the story revealed by the data. This means that great analysis moves beyond describing the data - it goes on to make inferences about what your sample of data means in relation to the wider geographical issue, concept, or process that you are investigating. This chapter has four parts:

▶ 12.1 describes what you will need to do in order to analyse your data;
▶ 12.2 describes methods of qualitative analysis;
▶ 12.3 describes methods of quantitative analysis;
▶ 12.4 describes three useful statistical tests.

Read parts 12.2 to 12.4 before selecting methods of analysis that are suitable for your own investigation.

Analysis

Analysis is a process which examines data in detail so that the wider story of the data can be understood.

12.1 Analysing your data

Analysis is a methodical process and an important stage of the investigation. You need to examine each piece of evidence carefully. First, you need to choose the methods of analysis which are appropriate for your data.

Action Point 1

Research and select appropriate methods of analysis to reveal the meaning of quantitative and qualitative data.

Analysis is a really important stage of the investigation, without it you cannot make sense of the data and you won't be able to come to any firm conclusions. As both the analysis and conclusions are worth a lot of marks, you need to get the analysis right. Be prepared to spend several hours analysing your results.

Methods of analysis

Effective analysis uses methods that are specifically designed to suit the type of data that you are investigating.

There are many different methods of analysis. Some are very straightforward – you will have used them many times before. Others are quite technical – you will probably have to research them (using Sections 12.2, 12.3, and 12.4) to make sure you apply them correctly. You will probably find yourself using several different methods. You can analyse:

▶ photos and other images by annotating the evidence revealed by the image;
▶ text and transcripts of interviews by finding meaning in significant words and phrases;
▶ graphs and maps by describing (or annotating) significant patterns and trends;
▶ raw numerical data by calculating the mean, median, mode, or by describing the range, or interquartile range;
▶ whether it is likely that patterns in your sample of data represent patterns in the wider population. To do this you will need to apply an appropriate statistical test.

Select the most appropriate methods

Sometimes analysis is described as deconstruction – an act of taking the data apart to reveal its true meaning. If so, a sledgehammer approach isn't going to help you but selecting the right key might just help you unlock the story of your data. You need to select appropriate methods to help you do the analysis.

There are a range of methods available to you. These are summarised in Figure 12.1. Pages 177-221 describe different methods that are useful when analysing geographical data. Your first job is to research these methods and select the ones that are most appropriate to help you answer the aims of your investigation.

Figure 12.1 Methods of analysis.

Data type	What you are analysing	Method	Pages
Qualitative	Patterns and trends in speech or written text.	Text (or discourse) analysis.	184-187
		Coding.	187-188
	Ascribing meaning to significant features of an image.	Annotation.	189
		Analysis of re-photography.	189-190
		Coding of images.	191-192
		Image elicitation.	192
Quantitative	Numerical patterns and trends.	Measures of central tendency (mean, median, mode).	193-194
		Measures of dispersion (range, interquartile range).	195-196
	Spatial patterns.	Nearest neighbour analysis.	197-199
		Interquartile area.	199-201
		Location quotient.	201-203
	Sediment shape.	Zingg analysis.	203-204
		Cailleux index.	205
	Statistical tests.	Chi square test.	206-211
		Mann Whitney test.	211-214
		Spearman's Rank Correlation Coefficient.	214-218

Action Point 2

Apply methods of analysis so you can describe patterns and trends and find meaning in your data.

Analysis of quantitative data

Quantitative data is structured. It can be easily counted, arranged in rank order, or compared to find similarities and differences. Consequently, trends, patterns, and anomalies can be identified relatively easily which enables you to begin to tell the story of the data. Analysis will help you to describe:

- **trends** – where data measured on a continuous scale follows a sequence;
- **central tendency** – a measure of the 'average' value of your data;
- **patterns** – how data is distributed. This includes measures of dispersion – in other words, describing the range of values in your data;
- **correlations** – how two sets of data are connected;
- **anomalies** – data that doesn't fit the general pattern or trend.

Trends

Numbers measured on a continuous scale may follow a sequence or trend. Does the data (and therefore the line of the graph) follow any kind of sequence? If so, is it going up or down? The nature of any trend can be analysed by drawing a line graph and then adding annotations to identify the main features, for example:

- decreasing - the values are going down;
- increasing - the values are going up;
- exponential - an increasing trend in which the data on the y-axis is doubling in value for every unit on the x-axis so the trend gets steeper and steeper;
- fluctuating - the values in the data vary up and down in a repeated pattern.

Use an adjective to describe the steepness of the line and, therefore, the rate of increase or decrease such as:

- abruptly or suddenly;
- gently or slightly;
- gradually or steadily;
- sharply or rapidly.

Figure 12.2 Annotation has been used to identify trends on this hydrograph for the River Esk in Cumbria.

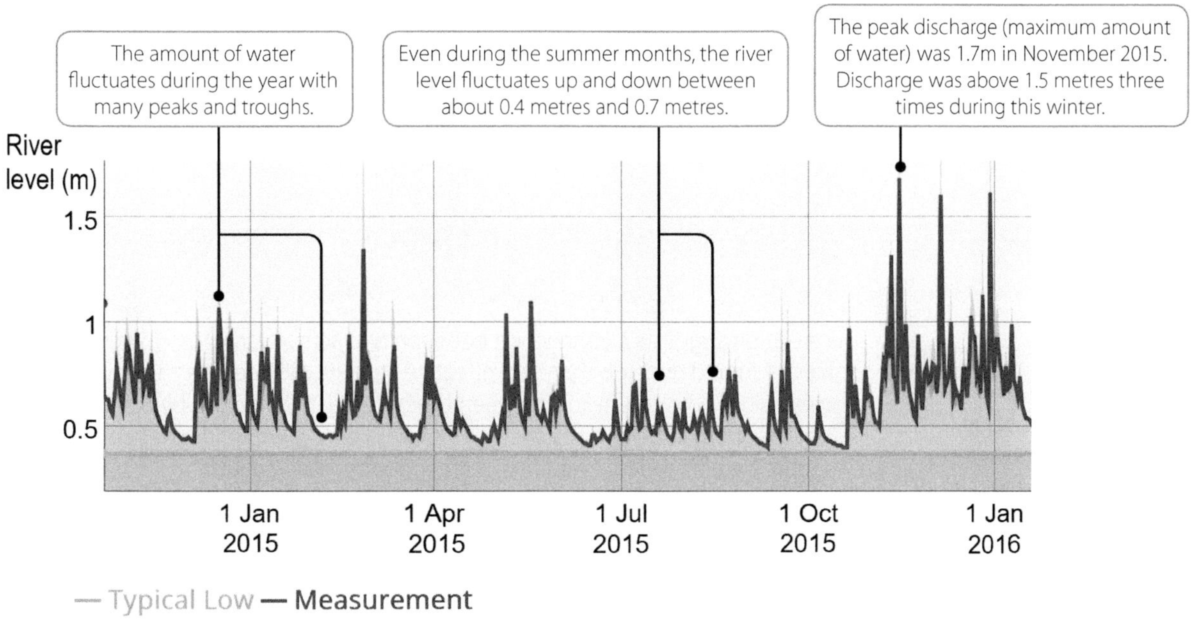

The amount of water fluctuates during the year with many peaks and troughs.
Even during the summer months, the river level fluctuates up and down between about 0.4 metres and 0.7 metres.
The peak discharge (maximum amount of water) was 1.7m in November 2015. Discharge was above 1.5 metres three times during this winter.
River level (m)
1.5
1
0.5
1 Jan 2015
1 Apr 2015
1 Jul 2015
1 Oct 2015
1 Jan 2016
— Typical Low — Measurement

Central tendency

Central tendency is a summary of a dataset that describes its central value. We commonly think of it as the 'average' figure. You can use mean, median, and mode to describe central tendency. Each has its own purpose:

▶ **mean** is used with **continuous data** measured on the **ratio and interval scales**;
▶ **median** is used with **ordinal data** – categorical data that is ranked. In some circumstances it can be used with other categorical data;
▶ **mode** is used with **categorical data**.

The calculation of central tendency is described on pages 193-194.

Correlations

Correlation is demonstrated by the interdependence of two variables. Your analysis may reveal that two datasets are connected. You can use a scatter graph (see page 164) to analyse correlations. Figure 12.3 shows three possible scenarios.

▶ Chart A suggests that as the dependent variable increases so the independent variable also increases. Analysis of this graph would suggest that there is a direct relationship or **positive correlation** between the two variables.
▶ Chart B suggests that as the dependent variable decreases so the independent variable increases. Analysis of this graph would suggest that there is an inverse relationship or **negative correlation** between the two variables.
▶ Chart C suggests that there is no correlation between the two variables as the points are scattered across the graph without making any pattern.

A scatter graph does not necessarily prove a correlation, especially if you have a limited amount of data. You can extend your analysis by using Spearman's Rank Correlation Coefficient (see page 214) which is a statistical test. This tests the probability that an apparent correlation, found in sample data, is representative of an actual correlation in the whole population.

Figure 12.3 The analysis of scatter graphs is used to suggest correlation.

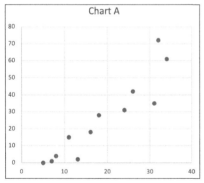

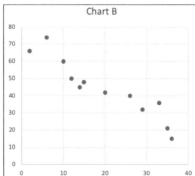

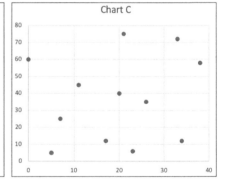

Correlation and causality

Correlation suggests a connection between two sets of variables. However, analysis should not stop there. An effective analysis will interpret the correlation by explaining the causal link between the two variables. Do this by using your understanding of geography theory to explain why values of the dependent variable are affected by variations in the independent variable.

Effective analysis will explain the **causality** that underlies your correlation. For example, in a study of secondary data from 20 European cities of similar latitude, a student found a negative correlation between distance from the Atlantic and average January temperatures – the further east the city, the colder the January

Causality

Causality means that changes to the values of the dependent variable can be explained by changes in the independent variable.

temperature. In this example, there is a causal link that explains the relationship – the temperature decreases with distance from the ocean because continental land masses heat up and cool down much more quickly than oceans.

Common cause correlations

Beware of jumping to conclusions about causality. It is relatively common to find that a scatter graph suggests a correlation between two variables. However, the variations you observe in the independent variable may not be caused directly by the independent variable. It may be that a third factor (one that you may not have measured) is actually the cause of the correlation.

For example, in studying the Census data for Cardiff, a student noticed that the percentage of households in inner urban wards who did not own a car was higher than in suburban wards. The student plotted a scatter graph with distance from the CBD on the x-axis. The graph showed a negative correlation. However, in this example, it is not possible to demonstrate a causal link between the two sets of data. It is more likely that a third factor is at play. It could be that:

▶ households in the inner city are poorer and cannot afford a car, so income is the third factor;

▶ fewer homes in the inner city have driveways so there are fewer places to park a car;

▶ people living in the inner city have access to frequent buses and trains so don't need a car.

Patterns

Identifying patterns in your data is another way to analyse it. Is data distributed in a particular way? For example, is data distributed at regular intervals or is there some degree of clustering? Alternatively, there may be no obvious pattern because data is distributed randomly.

A histogram is an effective way to visualise a distribution pattern in continuous categorical data. For example, histograms can be used to analyse the dispersion of data such as pebble size, pebble shape, or age of the population. See Figure 12.4. The data patterns can be described in the following ways.

▶ **Skewness** A description of an asymmetric distribution of data. Skewness is used to describe the distribution of data across a histogram. See Figure 12.4b.

▶ **Outliers** Data that is separate from the main group of data values in a dataset. An outlier may be very much bigger or smaller than the next closest data value See 12.4c..

Skewness

A description of an asymmetric distribution of data.

Outliers

Data that is separate from the main group of data values in a dataset.

Bimodal

A bimodal distribution is one that has two modes, i.e. two categories of the histogram are significantly larger than any others.

Figure 12.4 Histograms can be used to analyse the dispersion of data between continuous categories such as pebble size, pebble shape, or age of the population.

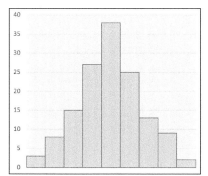

Figure 12.4a Normal distribution.

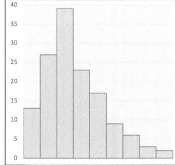

Figure 12.4b A skewed distribution.

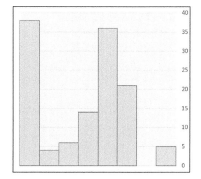

Figure 12.4c A bimodal distribution which also has an outlier.

Spatial patterns

Spatial patterns can be presented using a dot map, choropleth, or isoline map. The patterns presented on a dot map might be described as random, clustered, linear, or regular, see Figure 12.6. Patterns on a choropleth represent the density of the data so can be used to analyse areas that are over- or under-represented. An isoline map can be analysed to reveal gradients, peaks, and troughs. Whatever the type of map, annotation is an effective way to show the analysis, as shown in Figure 12.5.

Figure 12.5 Use annotations to analyse patterns on maps.

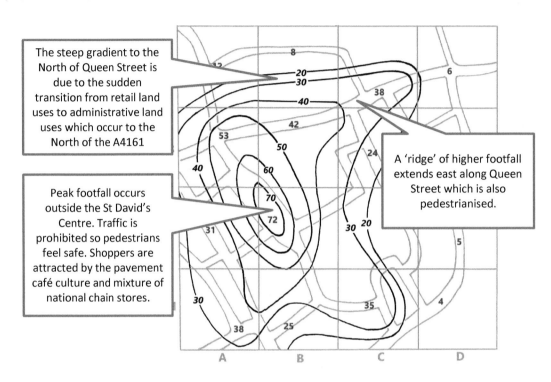

The steep gradient to the North of Queen Street is due to the sudden transition from retail land uses to administrative land uses which occur to the North of the A4161

A 'ridge' of higher footfall extends east along Queen Street which is also pedestrianised.

Peak footfall occurs outside the St David's Centre. Traffic is prohibited so pedestrians feel safe. Shoppers are attracted by the pavement café culture and mixture of national chain stores.

Clustered Values (or points on a map) are concentrated into small groups.

Linear Features (on a map or photograph) are spread out along lines.

Random Values (or features on a map or photograph) are at irregular spaces and show no clear pattern.

Regular Values (or features on a map or photograph) are repeated at even spaces.

Figure 12.6 Useful descriptive words to make sense of patterns in data.

Dispersion

Dispersion (or variability) is a description of how data is dispersed (or spread) across the range of data values. You might be interested in the **range** which is the difference between the highest and lowest values. Where the range is very large it is useful to exclude the lowest and highest values and concentrate on the data in the middle of the range – in which case you would calculate the **interquartile range.** Interquartile range is effective at describing the dispersion in the central 50% of the values and prevents the data from being overly influenced by the largest and smallest values. See page 195.

Anomalies

Anomalies are individual data values that don't fit the overall pattern or trend. These values may need explanation. They may be due to experimental error. On the other hand, real-life geography can be messy – some data is affected by variables that you haven't yet considered.

Analysis of qualitative data

Qualitative data is less structured than quantitative data. For example, people may respond in unexpected ways to your questions. Interviewees sometimes repeat themselves, ramble, or go back to reinforce a point. So the analysis of qualitative data has to try to create some order. By analysing unstructured qualitative data you will break the evidence down into smaller chunks so that it becomes easier to recognise repeated patterns or common elements.

If your investigation includes qualitative data such as images, questionnaires, participant observation, or text (either from interviews or written accounts) there are a handful of methods of analysis that can be used.

▶ The results of **closed questions** from a questionnaire can be sorted and the results quantified – so you effectively use **quantitative analysis techniques**.

▶ **Text analysis** is a technique that can be used to analyse longer passages of text, such as interviews, blogs, or responses to open questions. Various forms of text analysis are examined on pages 184-188.

▶ Notes taken during participant observation can also be analysed using text analysis.

▶ Images such as mental maps, photos, and artworks can be analysed using various forms of **annotation** (see page 189). It is also possible to use a form of coding to analyse the elements of an image (see page 191).

Text analysis

Text analysis (also known as discourse analysis) covers a wide variety of techniques that attempt to understand the meaning given by individuals to what they say or write.

Qualitative data is subjective

Qualitative data is usually more subjective than quantitative data. This is an important feature of qualitative data that makes it valuable to you as a researcher.

The transcript of an interview is more than just words. It represents the voice of the interviewee. An interviewee has opinions that are based on their experience, their perception of the world around them, and their values. They will choose words and phrases carefully to emphasise certain values that they hold. They will also choose to ignore other words and phrases to exclude some ideas and emphasise the values that they hold most strongly.

The same is true of images. People take and manipulate images to create a representation of the world around them. This representation is likely to emphasise some features and exclude others.

The fact that qualitative data is subjective is what makes it useful to us in any research that is primarily concerned with perception. The aim of a perception study is to understand how and why different groups of people view the world.

Statistical tests

Statistical tests allow the researcher to move from describing patterns seen in the sample data to making **inferences** about the wider meaning of the data. As a researcher you have collected a sample of data. If your sample is representative of the whole population then it should be possible to use your data to make inferences about data patterns in the wider world. For example, imagine you have conducted a questionnaire into people's perceptions of rebranding. You notice that people with similar socio-economic and demographic characteristics in your sample share a similar view of rebranding whereas another group in your sample has a very different view. We can use a statistical test to make inferential statements about the perceptions of the whole population based on the data collected in the sample.

Inference

An inference is a conclusion about the wider population that is reached by analysing evidence in the sample.

The use of statistical tests relies on an understanding of two concepts.

Statistical significance. When we ask if something is statistically significant we mean does this data signify (or really mean) anything?

▶ It could be that your sample is very small, or you happen to have collected some data that is full of anomalies and which is not representative of the whole population. If so, your data is unlikely to signify anything.

▶ On the other hand, a carefully collected sample may reveal evidence that is symptomatic of the wider population. The way to find out is to conduct a statistical test. The test should tell us whether or not the evidence that can be seen in the data is signifying a pattern, difference, or relationship that occurs in the whole population.

Probability. Statistical tests rely heavily on the concept of probability. We cannot be certain that evidence in our sample is proof of wider patterns, differences, or relationships in the wider population. However, a statistical test provides the researcher with objective information about the likelihood (or probability) that inferences made from sample data are valid.

What is probability?

It is important to realise that statistical tests provide you with probability rather than certainty.

Probability is actually a simple concept. Imagine flipping a coin. You have a one in two chance of it coming down a head. Similarly, you have a one in six chance of rolling a six on a dice. We express probability as a:

▶ ratio, for example, one in six;
▶ fraction, for example $\frac{1}{6}$;
▶ percentage, for example, 16.66%;
▶ decimal fraction, for example, 0.16.

Statistical tests usually use decimal fractions to express a probability.

In an A level Geography Investigation, we would be persuaded by a probability of 0.95. In other words, sample data is considered to have significance if the result of a statistical test has a probability of nineteen in twenty.

Hypothesis testing

Whichever statistical test you use the approach is the same.

One State the null hypothesis (H_0): that the evidence seen in the sample data is not representative of the population from which the sample was taken.

Two State the alternative hypothesis (H_1): that the evidence seen in the sample data is representative of the whole population.

This may seem a bit convoluted but it's the way statistical tests should be conducted. Think of yourself as a detective again. The data is pointing towards a suspect but your suspect remains innocent until proven guilty.

Three Conduct the appropriate statistical test.

Four Check the significance of your result. By comparing the result of your test to a table of **critical values** you can determine whether or not the null hypothesis can be rejected and, therefore, whether your data signifies that a pattern, difference, or relationship is likely to occur in the whole population.

Statistical tests look scary but they are actually quite easy to apply. You feed in your data and the test crunches the numbers. What a statistical test is really doing is working out a probability – the probability that the patterns seen in

---

Critical values

Critical values are the values above (or below) which the null hypothesis may be rejected.

the sample data does not represent patterns in the population – which, you will remember, is the null hypothesis.

A worked example

The following worked example illustrates some of the concepts we have considered so far. As you read the example, think about:

▶ the inference that could be made from samples A, B, and C;
▶ whether the sample size is large enough;
▶ how increasing the sample size might affect the significance of the result.

Imagine you have been collecting data about the distribution of heather in a moorland ecosystem. You decide to draw a scatter graph to visualise the data. Figure 12.7 shows four possible scatter graphs. The first chart shows data from the whole population, it represents data values from every possible point where data could be safely collected. This chart shows that there is no clear relationship between steepness of the slope and the percentage cover of heather. The two variables do not seem to be connected. Charts A, B, and C represent data from 3 different possible samples of the whole population.

▶ Chart A indicates a positive correlation between the two variables. The conclusion seems to be that more heather is found on steeper slopes.
▶ Chart B indicates a negative correlation between the two variables. The conclusion seems to be that less heather is found on steeper slopes.
▶ Chart C indicates that there is no relationship between the two variables.

Sample size obviously influences the probability that the sample is **representative** of the whole **population**. The probability that a small sample (6 or less in this example) will represent the whole population is low. A larger sample (12 or more) is much more likely to represent the whole population.

Population

The name given to all of the data from which you select a sample is the population.

Representative sample

Representative sample reflects the features/characteristics of the whole population.

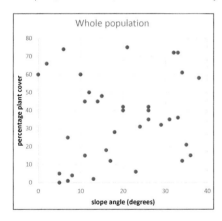

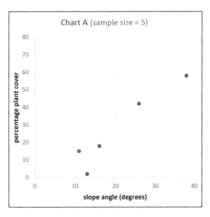

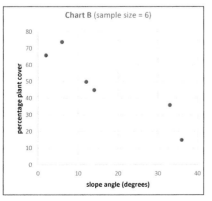

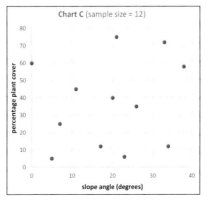

Figure 12.7 The first chart shows data from the whole population. Charts A, B, and C each show data from a sample of points. Only C is a representative sample.

Each of these three different conclusions is possible but only Chart C represents the whole population. You can use a statistical test to estimate the probability that the data collected in your sample are a true representation of the population.

One State the null hypothesis (H_0). There is no correlation between the two variables.

Two Set up an alternative hypothesis (H_1). In this case, there is a relationship between slope angle and percentage heather cover.

Three Conduct the statistical test. In this example, Spearman's Rank Correlation Coefficient would be the suitable choice.

Four Compare the result of the statistical test to a table of critical values. This table tells you whether or not the null hypothesis can be rejected. As mentioned before, there is no certainty in statistical tests. By comparing the result of your test to the table of critical values you can determine whether or not the null hypothesis can be rejected. Geography research requires a probability of 0.95 (in other words a 19 in 20 chance). In practice, you are testing the null hypothesis, so you actually compare your result against a significance level of 0.05 (a 1 in 20 chance).

> Always consider the significance of any statistical test you have carried out by checking the appropriate table of critical values.

Types of statistical test

You must choose a statistical test that is suitable for your data type – whether it be categorical, ranked (ordinal), or continuous. There are three main tests and, if you choose to use one of them, they are described in part 12.4. When you read these descriptions you should note that each test has certain conditions (for example, relating to sample size) that must be met for the test to be valid.

> Select a suitable statistical technique to analyse your data. Think carefully about the type of data. Make sure you can justify your choice.

12.2 Methods of qualitative analysis

Part 12.2 describes methods of qualitative analysis. They fall into these main groups:
- ▶ text analysis, including coding;
- ▶ analysing visual evidence;
  - • using annotation to analyse images;
  - • analysis of re-photography;
  - • coding images taken by others.

If you have qualitative data, use these pages to read about methods of analysis that you could adopt in your own investigation.

Text analysis

Text analysis (also known as discourse analysis) covers a wide variety of techniques that attempt to understand the meaning given by individuals to what they say or write.

Text (or discourse) analysis

Text analysis can be used to analyse any pieces of extended writing such as:
- ▶ responses to open questions in questionnaires;
- ▶ transcripts of interviews;
- ▶ transcripts of discussions of a focus group;
- ▶ blogs, articles, or advertising copy from a secondary source such as the internet.

The first step is to decide on the purpose of your analysis. This should relate to the aims of your research and/or the objectives of your research questions. For example, if your aims were to investigate how different groups of people feel about an issue you could use text analysis by looking for the emotional language they used in their responses. In this case, adjectives that convey how the respondents feel may be worth identifying and counting. Alternatively, if your aims were to examine the advantages and disadvantages of a particular change (such as gentrification of an urban environment) you might choose to use **coding** to identify recurring advantages and disadvantages that are identified by different groups of people.

When analysing textual evidence there are a number of questions you might ask.

- Who wrote the text and what was their aim? Does the text make a statement that reveals the personality of the author? Do they have a clear left-leaning, right-leaning, or environmental standpoint?
- Who is the intended audience for this text?
- What are your first impressions? What are the significant parts or details in the text?
- Are their different ways of reading the text? Could it have different meanings to different people?
- What doesn't the text say? Has something been deliberately ignored or omitted? Why might this be significant?

Simple ways to analyse text

Text is an important source of evidence. It can provide both facts and opinions. The way that the text is written may tell you something about what somebody thinks of a geographical issue – their perception.

How do you analyse any patterns or trends when your evidence is in words? There are a number of simple things you can do.

One Use one colour of highlighter to identify facts and another colour to identify opinions. In Figure 12.8, one fact has been highlighted in yellow in interview A. One opinion is highlighted in green.

Two Consider the tone of the text – what kinds of words are used? Are the words mainly positive or is a negative tone used in some of the text? You can count the words or phrases that have a positive tone and then compare those words/phrases that have a negative tone in a bar graph. In Figure 12.8, one positive phrase has been highlighted in pink in interview B. One negative phrase is highlighted in blue.

Three Copy and paste your text into an online tool that counts the frequency of words that are used. The text of the interviews in Figure 12.8 has been analysed in this way and the top 20 words used in each interview are shown in Figure 12.9. You can analyse these lists.

- Are the words mainly nouns that identify physical features of the environment, or human features?
- Are there many adjectives? The number of times that adjectives such as 'beautiful', 'pretty' and 'friendly' have been used can be graphed using a bar chart. This will tell you something of the positive (or negative) perception of a place.

> **Coding**
>
> Coding is a way of analysing each phrase in a document, identifying common features, and categorising these features using a number of 'codes' which summarise the key points made by the respondent.

Figure 12.8 Photo of Borth (a small seaside town in west Wales) and transcripts of two interviews (below).

Interview A Borth is a small seaside town in West Wales. It is a wild and natural place that is close to nature. The estuary is constantly changing: the light shines on the water and reflects off pools of water on the beach. Birds soar in the sky above. This place is magical. It's as though the landscape is alive. The light is beautiful. I think it's because the weather changes so much and we have light that reflects off the estuary and the waves. The beach is glorious. When the tide is out a long way the wet sand glistens and shines in the light. The sand is soft and clean. I think the beach is really beautiful. I love walking along the pebbles looking for things that have been washed up in the tide. The beach is a lovely place but it can be wild in the winter when the storm waves crash against the pebbles. Then you know that nature can have wild forces.

Interview B Borth is a friendly place. Local people are very friendly and want to help. I like the main street with its cheap cafes and shops selling holiday souvenirs. You can get most things in the local shops but not everything so we have to drive quite a long way to do some shopping - like clothes. The main street has pretty little cottages on either side. Some of the old cottages are made out of pebbles off the beach. The town has a lot of interesting history. There are special legends about the place too - legends about the sea and the drowned forest. I think the history of the place is very interesting. Borth is pretty in the summer and the beach is beautiful but it can be rather bleak here in the winter and sometimes I feel quite isolated.

Figure 12.9 Text analysis of the two interviews to identify the most frequently used words.

Interview A

Primary word	light	beach	place	wild	pebbles	sand	beautiful	water	nature	estuary
Frequency	4	4	3	3	2	2	2	2	2	2
Primary words	shines	reflects	think	waves	tide	glorious	much	weather	landscape	magical
Frequency	2	2	2	2	2	1	1	1	1	1

Interview B

Primary word	place	legends	history	beach	cottages	pretty	shops	main	borth	friendly
Frequency	3	2	2	2	2	2	2	2	2	2
Primary words	local	very	street	quite	interesting	isolated	sometimes	old	beautiful	cafes
Frequency	2	2	2	2	2	1	1	1	1	1

Presenting the evidence of text analysis

If you turn text into something else it can help you to analyse it and make sense of it. The following are simple ways to represent text in another form.

One Create a word cloud (or wordle). A word cloud (or wordle) gives a very visual way of analysing perceptions. The size and position of each word in the 'cloud' is in proportion to its importance in the original text. In Figure 12.10 a pair of word clouds has been used to represent the commonest words used by two groups of residents in a remote rural location to describe rural life – one word cloud represents words used by teenagers, the other by retired residents.

Weblink

http://www.textfixer.com/tools/online-word-counter.php

Figure 12.10 Present the results of simple text analysis in a word cloud.

Two Create spider diagrams. Use a spider diagram to identify the connections that bring meaning to the text. For example, in Figure 12.11 red clouds are used to identify human features and green clouds for physical features. It then uses connections to explain why these features are important. The most important conclusions of this analysis have been highlighted in orange.

Figure 12.11 Analyse connections in a text document by making links in a spider diagram.

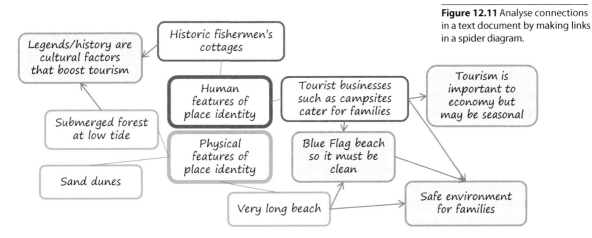

Analysing text through coding

Coding is a slightly more complex form of text analysis. Coding involves analysing each phrase in a document, identifying common features, and categorising these features using a number of 'codes' which summarise the key points made by the respondent. You can code primary data such as an interview or a discussion of a focus group. Alternatively you can code secondary data such as a blog.

Coding is used to sort text into useful categories. The researcher is able to choose the categories and these will depend on the aims of the investigation. Examples of categories could include:

▶ perceived **factors** that influence vulnerability to flooding;
▶ **causes** of inequality or deprivation;
▶ **social** and **economic effects** of gentrification;
▶ perceived **strengths** and **limitations** of a rural community;
▶ **short term** and **long term** implications of regeneration.

Coding requires written text. So, if you want to analyse an interview or discussion you will need to transcribe what was said. You could use apps to do this. Many offer a free trial period. To carry out coding you should follow these actions.

Coding

Coding is a way of analysing each phrase in a document, identifying common features, and categorising these features using a number of 'codes' which summarise the key points made by the respondent.

One Clean the data. Interviewees often repeat themselves, hesitate, ramble, or go back to reinforce a point. There is no point coding this kind of text so carefully delete any text that is repeated and any irrelevant remarks.

Two Think about the aims of your research. Use this to create a number of possible categories that you can use as codes. For example, to assess people's perception of the impacts of regeneration you could use the following codes.

1. Economic impacts +/-.
2. Environmental impacts +/-.
3. Accessibility.
4. Reputation.
5. Sustainability.
6. Local identity.
7. Job creation.
8. Short term impacts.
9. Long term impacts.

Three Read the transcript carefully. Use a highlighter pen to mark phrases that can be categorised using your codes. Keep a note in the margin of the transcript to show how each phrase has been categorised. Codes can be used more than once. An example is shown in Figure 12.12.

Four As you read more transcripts you may need to **expand your list of codes.** Just add add more codes and repeat the process a number of times.

Five Use your completed coding exercise to **compare the way that different people respond.** Look for similarities and differences. In the example shown in Figure 12.12 you can quantify (count) the positives and negatives or analyse the range of different impacts that are identified by each respondent.

Figure 12.12 Using coding to analyse the perceived advantages (highlighted in green) and disadvantages (highlighted in blue) of regeneration.

Codes used in Response 1
1 Short term
2 Economic impact (negative)
3 Accessibility (negative)
4 Accessibility (negative)
5 Economic impact (negative)
6 Environmental impact (negative)
7 Economic impact (negative)
8 Economic impact (negative)
9 Accessibility (negative)
10 Accessibility (negative)
11 Economic impact (negative)
12 Reputation (negative)

Codes used in Response 2
1 Economic impact (negative)
2 Short term
3 Long term
4 Environmental impact (positive)
5 Reputation (positive)
6 Identity
7 Reputation (positive)
8 Identity
9 Sustainability
10 Short term
11 Accessibility (negative)
12 Long term
13 Accessibility (positive)
14 Accessibility (positive)
15 Economic impact (positive)

Response 1
For the last few months[1] the regeneration project has been a catastrophe for business[2]. The construction of the tramway means the road is closed to traffic[3]. There is nowhere to park[4] so we are getting less passing trade[5]. Pedestrians complain about the constant banging and clattering of construction[6]. Overall we have seen a drop in footfall of maybe 20%[7] and out takings are down[8] too. The constant road works[9] are another problem because delivery vehicles get stuck in traffic[10] which is adding to their costs[11]. I think this entire nuisance is putting off visitors coming to the city[12] for a day-out.

Response 2
I will admit that the construction work is noisy[1], but it won't go on for ever[2]. In the long-run[3] all of the construction work is transforming the city[4]. We are going to be a world class city[5]. It's something we should all[6] be proud of[7]. They are saving the important historical features[8] of the city by giving them a new purpose[9]. Okay, at the moment[10] I can see that the road works are causing a nuisance for drivers[11] but if you can work around it I think in 3 years-time[12] all of these problems will be forgotten. We will have a better tram system[13] so getting around the city will be easy[14]. And it's going to be cheap[15].

Test your understanding
Identify the main similarities and differences between the responses given by the two interviewees in Figure 12.12. What might explain these differences?

Analysing visual qualitative evidence

Images such as photos, posters, leaflets, and artwork are all potentially useful sources of qualitative evidence. You can analyse:

▶ photos you have taken yourself;
▶ photos taken by participants in a survey;
▶ images available in secondary sources such as tourism leaflets or websites.

Using annotation to analyse images

Annotation means to add text to source material – either your own or those you have found in secondary sources. It is commonly added to photographs but it can also be added to:

▶ field sketches, transects, and cross sections;
▶ maps;
▶ graphs;
▶ screen shots of satellite images or GIS images.

Analysis of a photo means that you need to break the image down into its elements by identifying the different features of the landscape that have been included (or excluded) from the image. In Figure 12.13, annotation has been used to help explain the wider processes operating within this coastal environment.

> If you are going to take and annotate a photo for your investigation you should provide a reference for its location. An OS grid reference is often best.

Weblink

http://www.gridreferencefinder.com/ Use this simple website to find six figure grid references for your fieldwork locations and photos.

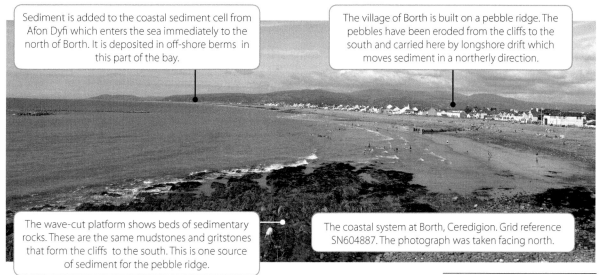

Sediment is added to the coastal sediment cell from Afon Dyfi which enters the sea immediately to the north of Borth. It is deposited in off-shore berms in this part of the bay.

The village of Borth is built on a pebble ridge. The pebbles have been eroded from the cliffs to the south and carried here by longshore drift which moves sediment in a northerly direction.

The wave-cut platform shows beds of sedimentary rocks. These are the same mudstones and gritstones that form the cliffs to the south. This is one source of sediment for the pebble ridge.

The coastal system at Borth, Ceredigion. Grid reference SN604887. The photograph was taken facing north.

Figure 12.13 Effective labelling and annotation of a photo.

Analysis of re-photography

Re-photography allows you to identify change in the environment since the original image was made. Your analysis should involve careful annotation of the differences that you observe between the old and the new images. What has changed and what remains the same?

Effective analysis should also involve interpretation and inference, for example:

▶ What processes may have caused this change?
▶ How might these changes affect people or the environment?
▶ Can we infer that the same changes would occur in other, similar, circumstances and environments?

Figure 12.14 Analysis of re-photography using a photo taken in the 1960s of Newcastle-under-Lyme.

In this way an effective analysis will demonstrate an understanding of theoretical geography. In Figures 12.14 and 12.15 the annotation refers directly to the literature review and a footnote gives a reference for the source. Also notice how, in Figure 12.15, the annotation refers to the 'voice' of the artist.

> Historical façades of Georgian buildings have been conserved while the building behind the façade has been completely replaced. Façadism, however, has a history of controversy[2] in town planning.

> Trees improve the aesthetics of the urban environment by adding natural forms. It is argued that they reduce traffic noise and help to improve air quality[1].

> The historic monument has been conserved. The experience for the pedestrian has also been improved by planting trees and banning traffic.

1. Woodland Trust (2012), Urban Air Quality. Accessed online 06/05/2019.
2. Richards, J. (1994), Facadism, Routledge.

Figure 12.15 Analysis of re-photography using a painting of Salmon Lane in Limehouse, London , painted in 1987, compared with a photograph of the street in 2019.

> The Victorian pub of the painting has been replaced by living accommodation. A quarter of the UK's pubs closed in the period 1982-2017[1]. The loss of traditional places for people to meet may lead to a decline in identity and social cohesion.

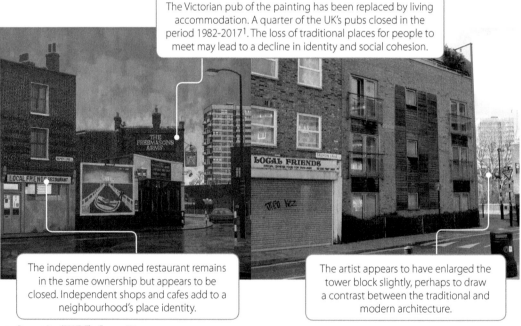

> The independently owned restaurant remains in the same ownership but appears to be closed. Independent shops and cafes add to a neighbourhood's place identity.

> The artist appears to have enlarged the tower block slightly, perhaps to draw a contrast between the traditional and modern architecture.

1. *Why London's pubs are disappearing.* (2017), The Economist.
https://www.economist.com/britain/2017/08/24/why-londons-pubs-are-disappearing
Accessed online 06/05/2019.

Coding images taken by others

You may want to analyse images created by others, for example:

▶ photos taken by participants in a survey that you organised (see Image elicitation);

▶ images such as artwork from secondary sources;

▶ images that are included on websites or leaflets that promote tourism to a particular place, for example, 12.17.

In order to understand these images you need to think about the issues shown in Figure 12.16.

Figure 12.16 Understanding who, how, why, and for whom an image was created.

Who created this image? ⇨ Can you find the name of the artist or photographer? Are they famous? Was the image paid for by a business, charitable organisation, or political party?

Did they have an agenda? ⇨ Did the creator of the image have a reason for publishing it? Were they trying to represent a particular point of view? Were they trying to make the viewer see something new or in a different way?

What did they decide to include and why? ⇨ Is the subject matter provocative or thought-provoking? Is the image trying to represent the place in a particularly positive (or negative) light? Does the image create a clear sense of identity?

What did they exclude and why? ⇨ Is something missing from the image? Has the image been cropped in such a way that you cannot see a feature of the landscape?

Why code images?

The purpose of coding is to identify recurring features that occur in the images. From this analysis you should be able to make inferences about the meaning that is conveyed in the images. For example, if you were to code the paintings of the artist Doreen Fletcher, who created the image shown in Figure 12.15, you would see that small independent shops, cafes, and pubs are a recurring theme in her paintings of the East End of London. From this, we might infer that people who collect these paintings are interested in the social history of the East End.

How to code images

Images may be analysed using a process of coding which uses similar principles to the coding of text (see pages 187).

To analyse a group of images you need to:

One Study the images and identify the features that occur in them.

Two Create codes based on the features you can see in the images. These are your codes. Codes can be very simple, such as 'positive' or 'negative' features of the environment. They can be more complex, such as 'sustainable', 'attractive', 'historic', 'monotonous', 'contemporary', 'bustling', 'congested', 'empty', 'grey' or 'colourful' to describe the features of an urban environment.

Three Tally the number of times each code is used in the group of images. The results can be sorted by frequency and this data could then be graphed using a bar chart.

Four To make the analysis slightly more sophisticated, the codes could be grouped by type (for example, historical features, physical features, social features).

Figure 12.17 Images of historic buildings in Bishop's Castle feature prominently on many of these tourist information leaflets.

An example of a coded image is shown in Figure 12.19. To illustrate how coding can reveal patterns, study Figure 12.18. This table shows the total number of codes identified in images used in tourism leaflets for Bishop's Castle, a small rural town in Shropshire.

Figure 12.18 Tallies of images seen in tourism leaflets.

Code	Total number of times seen in the images
Historic building	23
Historic artefact	20
Interesting architectural details	19
Historic image/painting	14
Colourful street scene	12
Crowds of people	12
Blue skies	11
Participants	10
Festivals/events	9
People smiling	8
Open countryside	8
Town hall	7
Road closure	7
Breweries / pubs	6
Walking/tours	6
Vintage vehicles/classic cars/trains	5

Figure 12.19 How to code an image using simple descriptive terms or phrases.

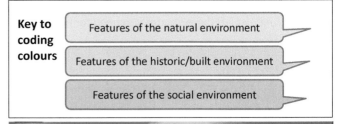

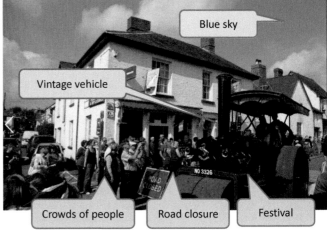

Photo elicitation

An interesting way to collect a group of images is to ask a small focus group to take photos of their local environment – perhaps focusing on the features that they like and dislike. This process is known as photo elicitation. Collate and display the images. Ask the focus group to meet with you and discuss the images with them – making a transcript of the discussion. This process will allow you to code both the images and the text of the discussion. This analysis should enable you to analyse what the images represent and why they were chosen. You may be able to draw inferences about how the wider community perceive their local environment.

> **Test your understanding**
>
> Consider the findings that are shown in Figure 12.18. How would you interpret this analysis? What are the key messages that are promoted by the images in these leaflets?

This section 12.3 describes methods of quantitative analysis, descriptions of central tendency and dispersion, and more specialised methods that can be used to analyse spatial patterns or describe shapes of pebbles. If you have quantitative data, use these pages to read about methods of analysis to use in your own investigation. Statistical tests are described in section 12.4.

Central tendency and dispersion

The first few of these methods are universally helpful – you will almost certainly need to use them at some point.

Measures of central tendency

Use a measure of **central tendency** to describe the central point in your dataset. There are three different ways to describe central tendency. These are mean, median, and mode.

Type of data	Recommended measure of central tendency
Nominal	Mode
Ordinal	Median
Interval/Ratio (not skewed)	Mean

Figure 12.20 Recommended measures of central tendency.

Evaluation

Mean can fail to represent the central point fairly if the dataset includes outliers (extreme values) or a very wide range of values.

Mean

Use mean for continuous data (data measured on the ratio and interval scales) such as distance, temperature, velocity, or price (such as house price).

To calculate the arithmetic mean value of a dataset:

One Sum all the data to find the total. The total is often shown by the Greek symbol Σ.

Two Divide the total value by the number of items of data.
For example, to calculate the mean value for Site A in Figure 12.21:
mean = 4.2 + 3.9 + 3.7 + 3.8 + 4.1 = 19.7/5 = 3.94

Figure 12.21 A student has collected data on wind speeds at three locations on a hillside. The data is shown in the table below (values in metres per second).

	Individual readings					Mean
Site A – lower slope	4.2	3.9	3.7	3.8	4.1	3.94
Site B – middle slope	3.9	4.2	4.4	4.2	4.0	4.14
Site C – upper slope	4.8	5.1	4.7	4.8	5.2	4.92

Calculating the mean is especially useful if data has been recorded several times and varies a little each time. For example, you might take five wind speed readings at each location (as in Figure 12.21) and find the mean. The wind may be gusty so each reading is different. By calculating the mean you can average out these variations. By calculating the mean for the three sites in Figure 12.21 it is possible to analyse how wind speeds vary with height on this transect.

Median

Use median as a measure of central tendency for continuous data or data measured on an ordinal scale (such as a Likert Scale).

The **median** is the middle value when all your data is arranged in rank order. To find the median value:

One Put the data in rank order.

Two The median is the middle value in an **odd** number of items of data. In Figure 12.22, the median value is 8.

Three If you have an **even** number of items in your dataset, the median is the mean value of the two values that are in the middle of the rank order. In Figure 12.23, the median value is $\frac{40+44}{2} = 42$

Median is a useful measure to use if you have extreme values or outliers in your dataset. These extremes will affect the mean but the median is unaffected so will still give you a fair measure of the central point in your data. For example, a student has collected data on the length of commute for a group of workers in an office in Cardiff. The data for eleven workers is shown in Figure 12.22. The mean value for this dataset is 23.78 miles. The median value is 8 miles. You can see that the mean has been distorted by the one worker who does a super-commute of 103 miles. In this case the median is a better representation of central tendency than mean.

Figure 12.22 Length of commute (miles).

1	2	4	6	7	8	12	18	22	31	103

22	25	27	32	35	40	44	48	52	55	58	60

Figure 12.23 Pebble length (mm)

Mode

Mode is a useful measure of central tendency in categorical data. The mode is the most frequently occurring value in your dataset. For example, in Figure 12.24, the mode is 17 years.

16	16	16	17	17	17	17	17	18	19	19	19

Figure 12.24 Age of people surveyed (years).

You would describe the category that has the largest frequency as the **modal class**. For example, in Figure 12.26 the modal class of pebbles is the category 20 – 39.99mm and in Figure 12.25 the modal class for the bipolar survey is -1.

Pebble size (mm)	Number of pebbles
0 – 19.99	21
20 – 39.99	35
40 – 59.99	18
60 – 79.99	15
80 – 99.99	10

Figure 12.26 Pebble size (mm)

	2	1	0	-1	-2	
Pavements are in good condition	2	3	5	18	12	Pavements are in poor condition

Figure 12.25 Bipolar survey results.

Measures of dispersion

Dispersion is a description of how your values are spread (or dispersed) through a dataset.

Range

The simplest measure of dispersion is **range**. This is the difference between the highest and lowest value in your dataset. This is often a useful comparative figure – the range of one dataset may be very different from the range of another, even if the mean or median value of the two datasets is similar. For example, in Figure 12.29, quadrats have been used to sample pebbles at two different locations on a beach. The median value (shown in the green cell in the table) is 14mm at each location. However, the ranges are very different.

▶ Quadrat 1 the range is 75 - 8 = 67mm
▶ Quadrat 2 the range is 25 - 7 = 18mm.

The large difference in range suggests that wave action has moved pebbles up and down the beach and has sorted them by size – leaving pebbles with a very narrow range of sizes further up the beach.

> Remember to interpret any analysis. In the example shown in Figure 12.29 the difference in range can be interpreted by sediment sorting.

Figure 12.29 Pebble sizes at two locations on Vik beach, Iceland.

Length of pebbles (mm)	
Quadrat 1	Quadrat 2
75	25
60	22
45	20
39	20
20	18
18	17
16	15
14	14
11	12
10	11
9	10
9	9
8	9
8	8
8	7

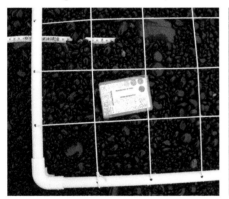

Figure 12.27 Quadrat 1. Pebbles close to the water's edge.

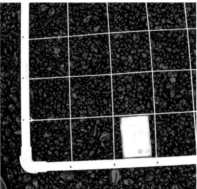

Figure 12.28 Quadrat 2. Pebbles 5 metres from the water's edge.

Interquartile range

The **interquartile range** is another way of measuring the dispersion of values in a dataset. The interquartile range is the difference between values that are one quarter and three quarters through the dataset so it excludes the largest and smallest values. It is used when the overall spread of values is rather large. To find the interquartile range:

One Put the values into rank order and identify the median value. In Figure 12.29 it is in the green cell.

Two Identify the lower and upper interquartiles. The lower quartile is the mid-value between the lowest value in the dataset and the median. It is in the orange cell in Figure 12.29. The upper quartile is the mid-value between the median and the highest value and the dataset. It is in the yellow cell in Figure 12.29.

Three Calculate the interquartile range by subtracting the value of the lower quartile from the value of the upper quartile.
▶ Quadrat 1 the interquartile range is 39 - 9 = 30mm.
▶ Quadrat 2 the interquartile range is 20 - 9 = 11mm.

Dispersion graphs

The range of values in a dataset can be presented visually using a **dispersion graph**, like Figure 12.30, or a box and whisker graph, like Figure 12.31.

To make a dispersion graph:

One Set out your categories of data on the horizontal axis. In Figure 12.30, these are different locations within Borth.

Two Mark the vertical axis with a range of values for your data. In Figure 12.30, this is house prices. The highest value is £380,000 so the axis is marked at £50,000 intervals up to £400,000.

Three Plot each value in your dataset as a small vertical cross. In this case, each cross represents the value of one house that is for sale in Borth.

Dispersion graphs can be used to analyse differences in range or interquartile range (IQR). In Figure 12.30 the median house price at each location has been plotted in red and the IQR annotated with a curly bracket. This allows the difference between the two locations (in terms of median, range, and IQR) to be clearly seen.

To construct a box and whisker graph you need to have calculated the interquartile range. The 'box' on a box and whisker graph represents the interquartile range. The 'whiskers' represent the maximum and minimum values. A box and whisker graph is quicker to draw than a dispersion graph so is appropriate where the dataset is very large.

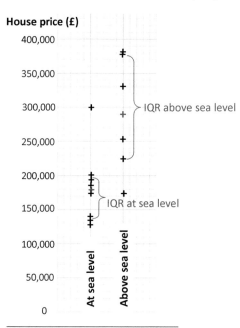

Figure 12.30 Dispersion graph showing range of house prices in Borth (2017).

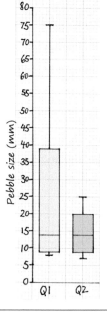

Figure 12.31 A box and whisker graph to represent the data shown in Figure 12.29.

Specialised methods of analysis

So far, we have examined the most common forms of quantitative analysis. In this section we will examine some more specialised forms of analysis. These methods are only suitable if you want to analyse spatial distributions or the shapes of pebbles. Only select methods of analysis that are suitable for your data.

Nearest neighbour analysis

Nearest neighbour analysis is a simple statistic that is used to analyse a distribution pattern on a map such as the distribution of vacant shops on Figure 12.32. You can, of course, describe a distribution pattern using adjectives like regular, random, or clustered. Nearest neighbour analysis allows you to quantify a distribution pattern by giving you a number – the Nearest Neighbour Index (referred to as **R**).

The Nearest Neighbour Index generates a number between 0 and 2.15 where:
- ▶ 0 = the points are perfectly clustered (they are on top of each other);
- ▶ 1 = the points are distributed in a completely random pattern;
- ▶ 2.15 = the points are distributed in a completely regular pattern.

The Nearest Neighbour Index (**R**) is calculated using the following equation:

$$R = 2 . \bar{D} \sqrt{\frac{n}{A}}$$

Where $\bar{D}$ = mean distance between each point and its nearest neighbour;

n = total number of points in the survey (= dots on the map);

A = area of the map.

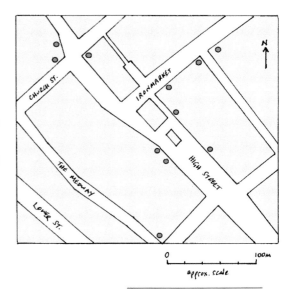

Figure 12.32 Dot map showing the distribution of vacant shops in Newcastle-under-Lyme (2019).

When to use Nearest Neighbour Analysis

Use Nearest Neighbour Analysis to analyse spatial patterns. If you have drawn a dot map (see page 166) you have presented a spatial pattern. Nearest neighbour analysis gives this pattern a number. So, for example, you could use Nearest Neighbour analysis to describe the pattern made by:
- ▶ drumlins in an environment that has been glaciated;
- ▶ CCTV cameras in an urban environment;
- ▶ vacant shops in a town or city centre.

Why use Nearest Neighbour Analysis

Calculating the Nearest Neighbour Index is particularly useful if you want to compare the pattern made by two geographical features. For example, you could use it to compare:
- ▶ the distribution patterns made by two different services. For example, you could use it to compare the distribution of GP surgeries and care homes for the elderly;
- ▶ compare how a distribution pattern changes over time. For example, by using a combination of primary data research and images on Google Street View you could compare how the distribution of vacant shops has changed over a 5-year period.

How to use Nearest Neighbour Analysis

To calculate the value of the Nearest Neighbour Index (**R**) you will need a dot map which shows the distribution of the feature you are testing. The process is simple and involves measuring the distance between each individual point and its nearest neighbour. These distances are indicated by the red lines on Figure 12.33.

One Draw a dot map. In this map, each dot represents one vacant shop.

Two Identify each dot on the map with a unique letter or number.

Three Measure the distance between each dot and its nearest neighbour. You can measure in millimetres or you can use the scale line of the map. It doesn't affect the result as long as you use the **same** units of measurement when you calculate the area of the map.

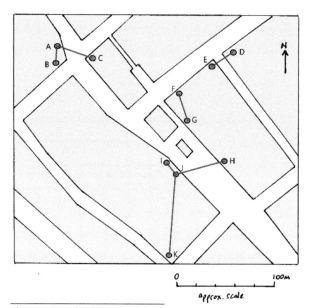

Figure 12.33 The distance between each vacant shop and its nearest neighbour.

Shop	Nearest neighbour	Distance (cm)
A	B	0.8
B	A	0.8
C	A	1.8
D	E	0.8
E	D	0.8
F	G	1.4
G	F	1.4
H	J	2.5
I	J	0.8
J	I	0.8
K	J	4.0
	ΣD	15.9

Figure 12.34 A table is used to record the distance between each point and its nearest neighbour.

Four Record the measurements in a table, like Figure 12.34. Notice that some dots on the map make reciprocal pairs. For example, the closest shop to A is B and the closest shop to B is A.

Five Calculate the mean of all the observed distances ($\bar{D}$) by adding all the distances together (ΣD) and dividing by the number of dots (n) on the map. In this example:

$$\bar{D} = \frac{15.9}{11} = 1.45$$

Six Calculate the area of the map (A) by multiplying the width by the height. Make sure the same units of measurement are used as when measuring the distances between the dots. In this example distances have been measured in centimetres:

$$A = 14 \times 12 = 168$$

Seven Calculate the Nearest Neighbour Index (R) using the equation. A worked example for Figure 12.36 is shown below.

$$R = 2.\bar{D}\sqrt{\frac{n}{A}}$$

$$= 2 \times 1.45 \sqrt{\frac{11}{168}}$$

$$= 0.74$$

Eight In this case, an Index of 0.74 indicates that the pattern is random.

Limitations of Nearest Neighbour Analysis

Nearest Neighbour Analysis has some significant limitations. If you are aware of these limitations you should be able to reduce their risk by visually checking the dot map.

Example	Limitation	Solution
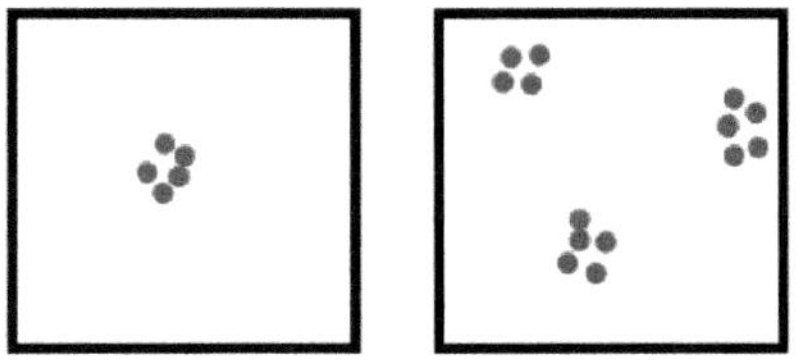	Nearest Neighbour Analysis cannot recognise a multi-clustered distribution. These two patterns would generate a very similar value for R.	Check the map visually for multiple clusters.
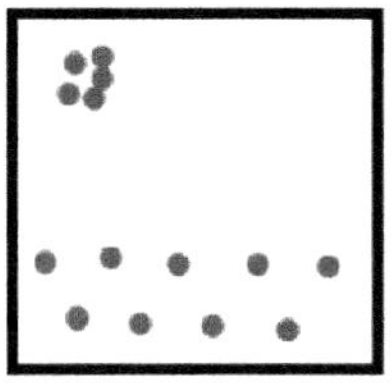	A value of 1 will be generated by a random pattern. However, a similar value will be generated if the map contains a mixture of clustered and regular distribution patterns.	Check the map visually for multiple patterns.
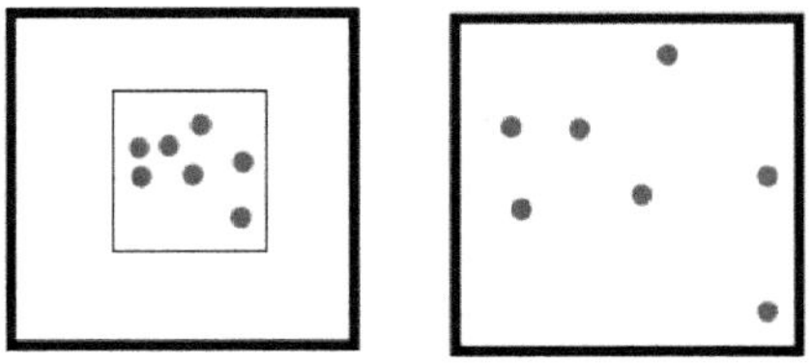	The overall size of the map will influence the value of R. These two patterns are identical but the one on the left will give a value that is closer to zero.	Define the area of the map using relevant criteria (such as an actual boundary) and crop off any unnecessary areas of the map.

Figure 12.35 Limitations of Nearest Neighbour Analysis.

Interquartile Area and Index of Dispersal

Interquartile area is a simple measure of spatial dispersal. It uses the same principles as interquartile range (see pages 195-196).

When to use Interquartile Area

Use Interquartile Area if you want to analyse a dot map such as Figure 12.32. You will need **at least** 8 points on the map. Use this simple method to calculate the area of map covered by points between the lower and upper quartile in the range. A low value will indicate clustering while a high value will indicate dispersal.

Why use Interquartile Area

Interquartile Area is used to measure the clustering or dispersal of features across a map such as villages, schools, post offices, CCTV cameras, drumlins, or specific plant species in an ecosystem. Like Nearest Neighbour Analysis, this method is particularly useful if you want to **compare** the pattern made by two geographical features. It does not suffer from the same limitations as Nearest Neighbour Analysis.

How to calculate Interquartile Area

To calculate Interquartile Area you must mark the features on a dot map.

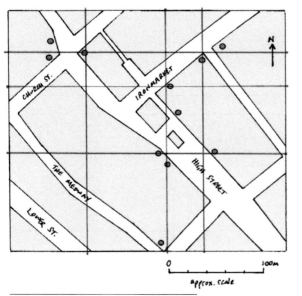

Figure 12.36 To calculate Interquartile Area

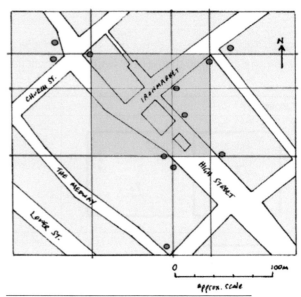

Figure 12.37 The interquartile area is tinted in pale blue.

One Count the total number of points (n). In Figure 12.36 there are 11 vacant shops. Calculate the median. In this case, the median shop is sixth in sequence. If the map has an even number of points, the median is midway between the two central points.

Two Count the number of points from the left of the map. Put a line through the median. This is shown with a vertical green line on Figure 12.36.

Three Count the number of points from the top of the map and add a horizontal line through the median. Note that the horizontal and vertical lines do not have to go through the same shop (they don't in Figure 12.36).

Four Add two vertical lines to indicate the upper and lower quartiles. As Figure 12.36 has a total of 11 points these go through the third and ninth points. Repeat this process by adding horizontal lines that go through the third and ninth points.

Five The area in the centre of the map (which has been tinted in pale blue in Figure 12.37) is the Interquartile Area. A small area indicates clustering whereas a large area indicates dispersal.

Index of Dispersal

You can take the analysis of interquartile area one step by further by using it to create an Index of Dispersal (Id).

The formula is
$$Id = \frac{Q}{A}$$

Where   Q = the interquartile area;
        A = the total area of the map.

The Index of Dispersal is a number which describes clustering and dispersion across a map.

If Id = 0, there is maximum clustering of dots around the median point on the map.

If Id = 0.25, there is a uniform distribution of points.

If Id = 1, there is maximum dispersion of dots around the median point on the map.

To calculate Index of Dispersal (Id):

One Calculate the interquartile area, as described in the method on page 199.

Two Calculate the total area of the map. Use the same units of measurement for each calculation.

Three Apply the values for each area to the formula. In our worked example for Figure 12.37:

$$Id = \frac{30}{168} = 0.178$$

This result indicates a clustered pattern.

Location Quotient

Location quotient is a statistical method used to analyse the spatial dispersion or concentration of data. It is particularly useful for measuring how concentrated a particular economic activity, occupation, demographic, or socio-economic group is in a geographical area. Alternatively, it could be used in a vegetation survey to analyse the spatial concentration of certain plant species.

Why use Location Quotient

Location quotient is a ratio that uses percentage data to compare small regions (for example, wards or postcodes) to larger regions (for example, towns or counties). Use location quotient to identify small regions that have a concentration – or more than their fair share – of that type of data. This concentration may give the region a distinctive or unique character. For example, location quotient could be used to identify regions that have a concentration of:

▶ students;
▶ retired people;
▶ people employed in manufacturing (or any other occupation);
▶ a particular ethnic group.

When to use Location Quotient

Location quotient is most often used to analyse spatial concentrations in secondary data, for example, data collected from the census. For example, in Figure 12.38, a student has collected data from the census. The table shows the percentage of people in each ward who are students in the Borough of Newcastle-under-Lyme. This borough contains a campus university in the ward of Keele. This ward has a student population of 64.71% (see cell B16 in the spreadsheet in Figure 12.38). Clearly there is a concentration of students in this ward. You can use location quotient to analyse whether students are over- or under-represented in any other wards.

How to calculate Location Quotient

The location quotient is the ratio between the percentage of a specific group (within a smaller region) and the percentage of the whole of that specific population within the wider region. To calculate the location quotient (LQ) use the following equation:

$$LQ = \frac{\% \text{ students in each ward}}{\% \text{ students in the borough}}$$

The quickest way to do this is in a spreadsheet as shown in Figure 12.38.

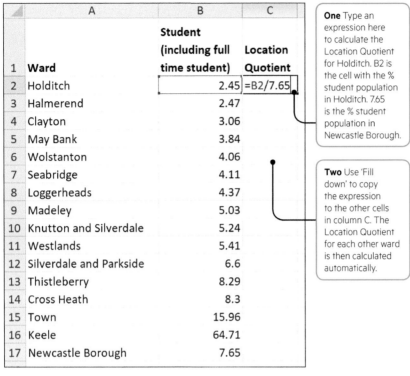

	A	B	C
	Ward	Student (including full time student)	Location Quotient
1	Ward	Student (including full time student)	Location Quotient
2	Holditch	2.45	=B2/7.65
3	Halmerend	2.47	
4	Clayton	3.06	
5	May Bank	3.84	
6	Wolstanton	4.06	
7	Seabridge	4.11	
8	Loggerheads	4.37	
9	Madeley	5.03	
10	Knutton and Silverdale	5.24	
11	Westlands	5.41	
12	Silverdale and Parkside	6.6	
13	Thistleberry	8.29	
14	Cross Heath	8.3	
15	Town	15.96	
16	Keele	64.71	
17	Newcastle Borough	7.65	

One Type an expression here to calculate the Location Quotient for Holditch. B2 is the cell with the % student population in Holditch. 7.65 is the % student population in Newcastle Borough.

Two Use 'Fill down' to copy the expression to the other cells in column C. The Location Quotient for each other ward is then calculated automatically.

Figure 12.38 Use a spreadsheet to calculate the Location Quotient for each ward.

Ward	% student population (including full time student)	Location Quotient
Holditch	2.45	0.32
Halmerend	2.47	0.32
Clayton	3.06	0.40
May Bank	3.84	0.50
Wolstanton	4.06	0.53
Seabridge	4.11	0.54
Loggerheads	4.37	0.57
Madeley	5.03	0.66
Knutton and Silverdale	5.24	0.68
Westlands	5.41	0.71
Silverdale and Parkside	6.6	0.86
Thistleberry	8.29	1.08
Cross Heath	8.3	1.08
Town	15.96	2.09
Keele	64.71	8.46
Newcastle Borough	7.65	

Figure 12.39 A table of demographic data showing % population and Location Quotient for the student population of Newcastle-under-Lyme.

Analyse Location Quotient using a choropleth

The spatial patterns made by Location Quotient values are best analysed visually on a choropleth map. To construct useful classes for a choropleth map using Location Quotient follow these steps.

One Complete the Location Quotient calculation for each area of your map. Figure 12.39 gives the Location Quotients for each ward.

Two Put the data into rank order – this makes the selection of the correct classes for the choropleth easier and more likely to be accurate.

Three Create three classes for the choropleth.
▶ Location Quotient from 0 - 0.79.
▶ Location Quotient from 0.8 - 1.09.
▶ Location Quotient of 1.1 or above.

Four Colour the map using the three classes described above.

In Figure 12.40, the wards that have the darkest shading have a greater concentration of student population than you would expect if the student population had an even distribution across the borough. You could say that students are over-represented in these wards. Students are under-represented in those wards with the lightest shading while those wards in the central class have about the share of students that you might expect.

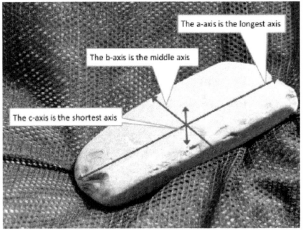

Figure 12.40 A choropleth map of Newcastle-under-Lyme using Location Quotient classes.

Location Quotient 1.1 or above

Location Quotient 0.8 - 1.09

Location Quotient 0 - 0.79

Zingg analysis

The construction of Zingg diagrams allows you to analyse three dimensional shapes, for example, the shape of pebbles found on a beach or in a fluvio-glacial deposit. To conduct Zingg analysis you need to measure each of the three axes in a sample of pebbles as shown in Figure 12.41.

Why use Zing Analysis

Use Zingg analysis to categorise the shape of pebbles from a coastal, fluvio-glacial, or glacial deposit. Pebble shape is influenced by two main factors:

▶ Geology;
▶ sorting whilst the sediment is being transported.

If you have pebbles that are largely from the same rock type then transport will be the principle factor that has sorted them by shape. Use Zingg analysis to compare:

▶ the shapes of pebbles from different parts of the beach profile;
▶ to determine the impact of longshore drift on pebble shape;
▶ to determine the influence of geology on pebble shape.

How to use Zingg Analysis

To conduct a Zingg analysis you need to calculate the ratios of the b/a and c/b axes. The relationship between these two ratios is used to describe the three dimensional shape of each pebble in one of four categories as shown in Figure 12.42. Figure 12.43 shows five pebbles. Pebbles 2 and 5 have a similar shape (they are both blades). Each of the other pebbles is typical of a sphere, disc, or rod.

The a-axis is the longest axis

The b-axis is the middle axis

The c-axis is the shortest axis

Figure 12.41 A three dimensional shape is described by measuring each axis.

Shape	b/a	c/b
Spheres	>0.67	>0.67
Discs	>0.67	0.67
Rods	0.67	>0.67
Blades	0.67	0.67

Figure 12.42 The ratios define pebble shape.

Figure 12.43 Pebbles used in the Zing analysis that follows.

The quickest way to calculate these ratios is by using a spreadsheet.

One Enter the length of each axis for your sample of pebbles into a spreadsheet.

Two Calculate the b/a ratio for pebble 1 using the formula:

= cell value of b / cell value of a.

Repeat the process to calculate the c/b ratio as shown in Figure 12.44.

Three Use the copy down function to calculate the b/a and c/b ratios for all other pebbles. The completed table is shown in Figure 12.45.

Four Use the b/a and c/b ratios to plot a scatter graph. Plot c/b on the x-axis and b/a on the y-axis.

Five Analyse the finished graph. Figure 12.46 shows the completed Zingg diagram for the 5 pebbles. You can see that pebbles 2 and 5 both fall into the same part of the diagram that describes blades.

Figure 12.44 How to calculate Zingg values using a spreadsheet.

	A	B	C	D	E	F
1	pebble	a axis (cm)	b axis (cm)	c axis (cm)	b/a	c/b
2	1	3.2	2.5	2.3	0.78125	=D2/C2
3	2	4.5	2.7	1.5		
4	3	4.8	1.5	1.5		
5	4	6.3	5.6	1.8		
6	5	4.5	2.5	0.8		
7						

Calculate the c/b ratio by using this formula. Then, fill down to calculate the ratio for all other pebbles.

Figure 12.45 The ratios for this sample of pebbles.

Pebble	a axis (cm)	b axis (cm)	c axis (cm)	b/a	c/b
1	3.2	2.5	2.3	0.78	0.92
2	4.5	2.7	1.5	0.60	0.56
3	4.8	1.5	1.5	0.31	1.00
4	6.3	5.6	1.8	0.89	0.32
5	4.5	2.5	0.8	0.56	0.32

Figure 12.46 Plot your results on a Zingg diagram.

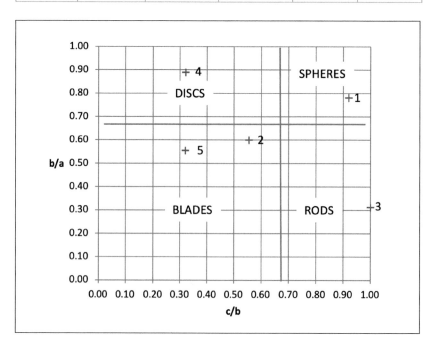

Cailleux Index

Another method for describing pebble shape is the Cailleux Index of roundness. The Cailleux Index describes the roundness of a two-dimensional shape. The values of the index range from 0 to 1000, where 1000 is a perfect circle.

Cailleux Index $= \frac{2r}{A} \times 1000$

Where $2r$ = twice the radius of the sharpest corner

A = the length of the a-axis

Why use Cailleux Index

The Cailleux Index is useful for telling us about the depositional environment. Environments in which sediment is carried further distances tend to have less angular corners and less variability of values on Cailleux Index.

How to use Cailleux Index

The data you have collected should be analysed by considering the ratio between the radius of the sharpest corner and the length of the a-axis (see page 74). To calculate Cailleux Index follow this calculation.

Cailleux Index $= \frac{2r}{A} \times 1000$

For pebble 1 (Figure 12.43) Cailleux Index $= \frac{2}{3.2} \times 1000 = 625$

Figure 12.47 shows the value of each of the pebbles in the sample shown in Figure 12.43.

Pebble	a axis (cm)	Radius (cm)	Index of roundness
1	3.2	1	625
2	4.5	1.5	667
3	4.8	1	417
4	6.3	3	952
5	4.5	1	444

Figure 12.47 How to calculate Cailleux Index.

Interpreting the analysis of Cailleux Index

Having calculated Cailleux Index you should analyse the data using measures of central tendency (median) and dispersion (range and interquartile range). This is a useful analysis to compare pebbles from two different locations, for example, two different locations on a beach profile. In comparing two samples, the sample that has the smaller range and smaller interquartile range will have been subject to greater attrition which would indicate that it has been transported further.

12.4 Statistical tests (tests of probability)

This section 12.4 describes three commonly used statistical tests:
▶ Chi Square test;
▶ Mann-Whitney U test;
▶ Spearman's Rank Correlation Coefficient.

Suppose you have identified an apparent relationship in your data or apparent differences between the frequency of data in various categories. You should use a statistical test to examine probability - the probability of whether or not the apparent relationship or differences in the sample data is a true representation of relationships or differences in the whole population.

**Where relevant, use statistical tests to examine apparent relationships in your data.
Always test the significance of any statistical tests you have used.**

As you read this section remember three important things.

▶ **You must choose a statistical test that is suitable for your data type** – whether it be categorical, ranked (ordinal), or continuous.

Select a **suitable** statistical technique to analyse your data. Think carefully about the type of data. Make sure you can justify your choice.

▶ Each test requires certain criteria to be met, for example, about sample size.

▶ **Always consider the significance of any statistical test you have carried out.** In other words, calculating the value of Chi Square, Mann-Whitney, or Spearman's Rank is not the end of the test. You must also check the value you have calculated against the relevant table of critical values which are printed in Appendix 2. By comparing the value you have calculated to the critical values in the table you can decide whether or not you can reject the null hypothesis. Understanding the significance of your result allows you to make conclusions about the wider population

▶ **You do not have to conduct a statistical test.**

Chi Square test

The Chi Square test is used to make comparisons between data in different categories.

The formula for the Chi Square test is:

$$X^2 = \sum \frac{(O - E)^2}{E}$$

where Σ = the sum of;
O = observed frequency;
E = expected frequency.

When and when not to use Chi Square test

The Chi Square test is a statistical test that can **only** be used with categorical data where you have counted the **frequency** of individuals in each category.

Expected frequency

The expected frequency is the number you would expect to have in each category if the data was distributed randomly between the categories.

To conduct a Chi Square test your data **must** satisfy the following criteria:
▶ the data must be expressed as frequencies;
▶ the data must be grouped into two or more categories;
▶ you must have at least 20 observed data values;
▶ the **expected frequency** of each category must exceed 4.

Why use the Chi Square test?

Suppose you want to compare the frequency of data distributed across different categories. For example, the categories could be pebbles of different shapes. Or, the categories could be responses to a questionnaire which have been sorted according to people from different groups (such as younger/older, male/female, or residents/non-residents). The Chi Square test compares the frequency of data between the categories. It involves making a judgement about whether the observed (investigated) data is similar or different from the expected (theoretical) data that would be collected if data was distributed randomly between the categories.

Calculating Chi Square

One Chi Square test starts with an assumption that the data is divided between the categories in a random way so you begin by stating the null hypothesis.

Two You use the formula

$$X^2 = \sum \frac{(O - E)^2}{E}$$

to calculate X^2.

Three You check your result against a set of significance tables (see Appendix 2).

- If the value of X^2 is greater than the critical value in the significance table (at a significance level of 5%) you can reject the null hypothesis.
- If the value of X^2 is less than the critical value in the significance table (at a significance level of 5%) the null hypothesis must be accepted.

> You must have at least 20 observed data values or the test is meaningless.

Application of Chi Square test

Chi Square can be used to test:

- data with a single variable that has been collected in categories such as pebble shape, orientation of a geographical feature, type of soil, type of land use;
- data with two or more variables that has been collected in categories such as different groups of people who have responded in different ways to a questionnaire or Likert Survey.

Worked example with one variable

Imagine a student is investigating the orientation of large blocks of stone in an area that was subject to periglacial conditions at the end of the ice age. The orientation of the stones apparently forms patterns. Chi Square can be used to determine the probability that apparent patterns in the sample data represent actual patterns in all of the stones.

The first task is to rank the orientation data using a spreadsheet (see Figure 12.49) so that the sample can be organised into categories (see Figure 12.50). In this case, four equal sized classes of data have been created based on the orientation of the stones.

Figure 12.48 A student has collected data on the orientation of these large blocks.

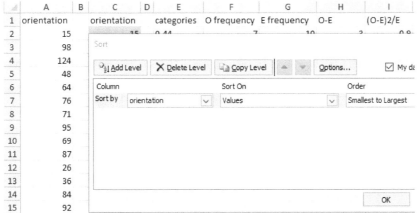

Figure 12.49 Use a spreadsheet to rank (ratio) data. This data shows the orientation of blocks of stone at the Stiperstones.

	A	B	C	D
1	orientation		orientation	
2	15		15	
3	98		22	
4	124		24	
5	48		26	
6	64		36	
7	76		42	
8	71		44	
9	95		48	
10	69		54	
11	87		56	
12	26		63	
13	36		64	
14	84		68	
15	92		69	
16	112		70	
17	116		71	
18	78		72	
19	84		73	
20	42		76	
21	44		77	
22	63		78	
23	54		79	
24	24		82	
25	106		84	
26	72		84	
27	85		85	
28	92		87	
29	138		92	
30	22		92	
31	82		94	
32	140		95	
33	70		98	
34	56		102	
35	68		106	
36	73		108	
37	77		112	
38	79		116	
39	102		124	
40	108		138	
41	94		140	

Figure 12.50 Once the data has been ranked (ratio) categories can be created. In column C the data has been ranked. The range of this data is from 0 degrees to 180 degrees. This range has been divided into four equal classes (or categories): 0 - 44.9, 45 - 89.9 etc. Each category has been tinted so that the frequency in each category can be counted.

Always consider the significance of any statistical test you have carried out by checking your result in a table of critical values.

One State the null hypothesis (H_0).

> H_0: **There is no significant alignment of the stones.**

Two State the alternative hypothesis (H_1)

> H_1: **The stones show a preferred orientation.**

Three Organise the data into suitable categories. A spreadsheet has been used to sort the data (see Figure 12.50). The range (180 degrees) has then been divided into four categories of 45 degrees each. This gives the observed frequency (O).

Four Calculate the expected frequency (E). In this example the student had observed 40 stones and has 4 categories. If the null hypothesis is correct you would expect there to be $40 \div 4 = 10$ stones in each category.

Five The observed frequencies and expected frequencies are then fed into a table, like Figure 12.51, to calculate the value of Chi Square. This makes the equation easy to calculate:

Categories	Observed frequency (O)	Expected frequency (E)	O-E	$(O-E)^2 \div E$
0 – 44 degrees	7	10	-3	0.9
45 – 89 degrees	20	10	10	10
90 – 134 degrees	11	10	1	0.1
135 – 180 degrees	2	10	-8	6.4
	$\Sigma = 40$	$\Sigma = 40$		$X^2 = 17.4$

Figure 12.51 Calculating the value of Chi Square for the sample of stones at the Stiperstones.

Six Calculate the degrees of freedom (df) for test. This is equal to the number of categories minus one, so, in this case $df = 4 - 1 = 3$.

Seven Decide on a level of significance. For geography fieldwork a level of 5% is considered to be satisfactory i.e. you can be 95% certain of your result.

Eight Using the critical values table we can check the 0.05 value at 3df. See Figure12.52. In this case the value of X^2 is greater than the critical value on the table (at a significance level of 5%) so the null hypothesis can be rejected.

This is the column for 5%

Degrees of freedom (df)	Significance level	
	0.05	0.01
1	3.84	6.64
2	5.99	9.21
3	7.82	11.34
4	9.49	13.28
5	11.08	15.09
6	12.59	16.81

Figure 12.52 Use a critical values table to check whether your Chi Square result is significant or not.

Worked example with two variables

Chi Square test can also be used to investigate the differences between categories where there are two or more variables. This makes it particularly useful in human geography investigations to test whether the behaviour or perception of different groups of people is following a random pattern or not.

Suppose a researcher has used participant observation (see page 70) to count the number of teenagers and older people who spend time in an area that has recently undergone regeneration. They have also observed the number of teenagers and older people spending time in an adjacent area that was not part of the regeneration scheme. Chi Square test could be used to test whether the observed frequency of teenagers and older people in each area is what could be expected if the two demographic groups were distributed at random. In this example, the test could be used to prove that one age group is more likely to be found in a particular part of the city.

Imagine a student is investigating the socio-economic impacts of a rural festival. During the weekend of the festival, the high street is closed to traffic to allow a procession to take place.

Figure 12.53 A weekend festival in Bishop's Castle, Shropshire.

The student notices that the road closure enables a lot of visitors to come into the town but it prevents local people from parking near their homes. The student is interested to see whether residents and visitors have a similar perception of the road closure. They conduct a Likert survey in which people have to respond to the following statement: '*The closure of the high street has more benefits than drawbacks*.'

To use Chi Square test in this investigation:

One State the null hypothesis (H_0).

> H_0: There is no difference between the attitudes of residents and visitors.

Two State the alternative hypothesis (H_1)

> H_1: There is a difference between the attitudes of residents and visitors.

Three The observed frequencies are organised in a table like Figure 12.54.

	Agree	Disagree	TOTAL
Residents	15	25	40
Visitors	27	5	32
TOTAL	42	30	72

Figure 12.54 The observed frequencies collected by the student.

Four The expected frequencies are calculated by completing a table like Figure 12.55. Notice that the expected frequencies for the residents (23.33 and 16.67) still add up to 40, which is the same as the number of observed total for residents. The same is true of each column and each row.

Figure 12.55 The expected frequencies

	Agree	Disagree	Total
Residents	(42 x 40) ÷ 72 = 23.33	(30 x 40) ÷ 72 = 16.67	40
Visitors	(32 x 42) ÷ 72 = 18.67	(32 x 30) ÷ 72 = 13.33	32
Total	42	30	72

32 is the total number of visitors who were interviewed.

72 is the total number of people who were interviewed.

This cell shows you how to calculate the expected frequency of **visitors who agreed**.

42 is the total number of people who **agreed** that the street closure was a good idea.

Five The observed frequencies and expected frequencies $(O-E)^2 / E$ are calculated for each row and column in the observed/expected frequency table. This is demonstrated in Figure 12.56.

15 is the observed number of residents who agreed.

23.33 is the expected number of residents who agreed.

Figure 12.56 How to calculate $(O-E)^2 / E$ for each row and column in the observed/expected frequency table.

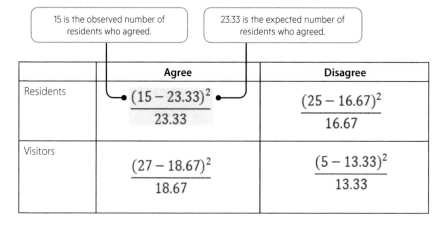

	Agree	Disagree
Residents	$\dfrac{(15 - 23.33)^2}{23.33}$	$\dfrac{(25 - 16.67)^2}{16.67}$
Visitors	$\dfrac{(27 - 18.67)^2}{18.67}$	$\dfrac{(5 - 13.33)^2}{13.33}$

Six The sum of the four (O-E)^2 / E equations are calculated:

$$\frac{(15-23.33)^2}{23.33} + \frac{(25-16.67)^2}{16.67} + \frac{(27-18.67)^2}{18.67} + \frac{(5-13.33)^2}{13.33}$$

So to calculate Chi Square: $X^2 = \sum \frac{(O-E)^2}{E}$

In this case: $X^2 = 2.97 + 4.16 + 3.72 + 5.21 = 16.05$

Seven The degrees of freedom (df) are calculated. This is equal to the number of rows minus one in the observed frequency table (Figure 12.54) multiplied by the number of columns minus one. In this case df = (2-1) x (2-1) = 1

Eight Using the table of critical values we can check the 0.05 value at 1df (this means 19 out of 20 likelihood that we can accept the hypothesis).

In this example, we have one degree of freedom so the critical value is the one with a ring around it.

Degrees of freedom (df)	Significance level	
	0.05	0.01
1	3.84	6.64
2	5.99	9.21
3	7.82	11.34
4	9.49	13.28
5	11.08	15.09
6	12.59	16.81

Figure 12.57 Use a critical values table to check whether your Chi Square result is significant or not.

As the value of X^2 (16.05) is **greater than** the critical value at 0.05 significance level, the null hypothesis can be rejected.

Nine It is important to complete the analysis by interpreting the results. In this case, the null hypothesis has been rejected, so we can accept that the pattern observed in the sample, in all probability, reflects an actual pattern in the population, i.e. there is a significant difference in attitudes between residents and visitors about the temporary closure of the high street.

Mann-Whitney U test

The Mann-Whitney U test allows you to make comparisons between two sets of data that are measured on an ordinal scale or ratio/interval scale and put into rank order. For example, you could use it to compare noise levels in one urban location with noise levels in a contrasting location. This test starts with an assumption that there is no significant difference between the two samples. The formula needs to be applied twice, once for each set of data:

$$U_A = N_A . N_B + \frac{N_A . (N_A+1)}{2} - \sum r_A$$
$$U_B = N_A . N_B + \frac{N_B . (N_B+1)}{2} - \sum r_B$$

Where N_A = the number of sample points in Sample A
N_B = the number of sample points in Sample B
$\sum r_A$ = the sum of all rankings in Sample A.

To conduct the Mann-Whitney U test follow these steps.

One State the null hypothesis.

Two Use the formula to calculate U for each sample and select the lower of the two U values.

Three Check your result against a set of significance tables (see Appendix 2). If the value of U is equal to or smaller than the critical value in the significance table (at a significance level of 5%) you can reject the null hypothesis.

When to use Mann-Whitney U test

The Mann-Whitney U test is used with ordinal data – data that is in rank order. Interval and ratio data (data that has been measured on a continuous scale such as temperature, height, wind speed, or noise) **can** also be analysed using the Mann-Whitney U test as long as you put the data into rank order first before applying the test.

To conduct a Mann-Whitney U test you **must** satisfy the following criteria:

▶ you must be able to put the data in rank order;
▶ the data must be grouped into two categories;
▶ you must have at least 5 observed data values;
▶ you must have less than 20 observed data values.

Note that you do **not** need to have an equal amount of data in each data set. The Mann-Whitney U test is testing whether or not there is a significant difference between the two medians of the two data sets – in effect, whether an apparent difference that you have spotted could have occurred by chance.

Why use Mann-Whitney U test

The Mann-Whitney U test is the ideal test to use with data collected in perception surveys where people have responded to a scale such as a bipolar or Likert scale. It can also be used with EQI data. For example, you could use it to make comparisons between:

▶ the responses to a bipolar survey given by two different groups of people – such as teenagers and retirees;
▶ the values given in a Cleanliness/Graffiti Index in two different locations.

Worked example 1: investigating two urban locations

Imagine a student is investigating two urban locations, A and B. Location A has recently undergone regeneration whereas Location B has not. The student has selected seven sample points within each location and conducted an Environmental Quality Index (EQI) at each. The EQI scores range from 2 (for the poorest quality environment) to 12 (the highest).

To use the Mann-Whitney U test in this investigation follow these steps.

One State the null hypothesis (H_0).

H_0: There is no significant difference between the median EQI score at each location.

Two State the alternative hypothesis (H_1)

H_1: There is a significant difference between the median EQI score at each location.

Three Organise the observed EQI score in a table like Figure 12.58.

EQI scores in location A	Rank (r_A)	EQI scores in location B	Rank (r_B)
12		10	
8		5	
7		8	
9		4	
5		3	
8		7	
6		2	
ΣR_A		ΣR_B	

Figure 12.58 Observed EQI scores at Location A and Location B.

Four Rank the EQI scores from lowest to highest. This process must be done across the total set of data. The student took EQI scores from 7 sample points in Location A and another 7 in Location B so the ranking is across all 14 values. This can be done by hand and the results recorded in columns two and four of a table like the one shown in Figure 12.58. However, it is possible to make rank order errors. To avoid this, the data can be put into a spreadsheet and ranked using the sort function. This is shown in Figure 12.59. The completed table is shown in Figure 12.60.

Figure 12.59 Using a spreadsheet to rank order the data avoids errors.

	A	B	C	D	E	F
		unsorted			all data	overall
1	Location	data		Location	sorted	rank
2	A	12		B	2	1
3	A	8		B	3	2
4	A	7		B	4	3
5	A	9		A	5	4.5
6	A	5		B	5	4.5
7	A	8		A	6	6
8	A	6		A	7	7.5
9	B	10		B	7	7.5
10	B	5		A	8	10
11	B	8		A	8	10
12	B	4		B	8	10
13	B	3		A	9	12
14	B	7		B	10	13
15	B	2		A	12	14

Data is ranked from low to high.

Notice that these two sample sites have the same EQI score so they have an equal rank. They would have been ranked fourth and fifth but as they are equal a mean has been calculated, hence the rank is 4.5

EQI scores in location A	Rank (R_A)	EQI scores in location B	Rank (R_B)
12	14	10	13
8	10	5	4.5
7	7.5	8	10
9	12	4	3
5	4.5	3	2
8	10	7	7.5
6	6	2	1
ΣR_A	64	ΣR_B	41

Figure 12.60 The completed rank order table.

The Mann-Whitney U test requires the sum of the rankings within each set of data.
ΣR_B means sum of all rankings in Location B.

Five The Mann-Whitney U statistic is calculated by applying the data from each Location to the equation as follows:

In Location A

$$U_A = N_A \cdot N_B + \frac{N_A \cdot (N_A+1)}{2} - \sum r_A$$

Where N_A = the number of sample points at Location A

N_B = the number of sample points at Location B

$\sum r_A$ = the sum of all rankings in Location A.

$$U_A = 7 \times 7 + \frac{7 \times 8}{2} - 64$$

$$= 49 + 28 - 64 = 13$$

In Location B

$$U_B = N_A \cdot N_B + \frac{N_B \cdot (N_B+1)}{2} - \sum r_B$$

$$= 7 \times 7 + \frac{7 \times 8}{2} - 41$$

$$= 49 + 28 - 41 = 36$$

Six A quick check of the arithmetic should be made. The value of $U_A + U_B$ must equal the value of N_A multiplied by N_B. If they do not, there is a mistake somewhere. In this example, 13 + 36 = 49 and 7 x 7 = 49.

Seven The lower of the two values of U is the one that must be used to test the significance of the result. In this case it is U_A and the value is 13. Check the value for U against a set of significance tables. The number in the header for the rows and columns is the same as the number of sample points in each set of data (in this case, 7 and 7). If the value of U is equal to or **smaller** than the critical value in the significance table (at a significance level of 5%) the null hypothesis can be rejected. In this case, the value of U=13 is higher than the critical value in the table. We must, therefore, accept the null hypothesis.

Eight It is important to complete the analysis by interpreting the results. In this case, the null hypothesis has been accepted. Based on this evidence:

There is no significant difference between the median EQI score at each location.

This means that the apparent difference between the EQI scores collected at the two sites is not significant – we cannot assume that there is any measurable difference in EQI between the two locations. As a researcher, this may be an example of messy geography – it isn't necessarily what we expected but we have to accept the result. It would be wrong, at this stage, to conduct a second statistical test on this data in the hope that we might get a different result.

Spearman's Rank Correlation Coefficient

Spearman's Rank Correlation Coefficient is a statistical test that you can use to test the relationship (or correlation) between paired sets of data.

The value of Spearman's Rank Correlation Coefficient (r_s) is found by applying the following equation.

$$r_s = 1 - \frac{6\sum d^2}{n(n^2 - 1)}$$

Where: Σ = the sum of
        d = the difference between pairs of ranks
        n = the number of pairs of data.

When to use Spearman's Rank Correlation Coefficient

Spearman's Rank Correlation Coefficient is used with data measured on the ordinal, interval, or ratio scale.

To conduct Spearman's Rank Correlation Coefficient test your data **must** satisfy the following criteria:

▶ you need paired variables (bivariate data) that you suspect show a correlation;
▶ the data must be capable of being expressed in rank order;
▶ you must have at least 10 observed data values but the more the better. However, more than 30 pairs of data is hard to manage.

Spearman's Rank Correlation Coefficient starts with an assumption that the two sets of data are not related.

One You state a null hypothesis.

Two You use the formula to calculate the value of rs.

Three You check your result against a set of critical values tables. If the value of rs is greater than the critical value in the table (at a significance level of 5%) you can reject the null hypothesis. Tables of critical values for Spearman's Rank Correlation Coefficient are printed in Appendix 2.

Why use Spearman's Rank Correlation Coefficient

Spearman's Rank Correlation Coefficient test will allow you to identify the direction of the relationship (positive or negative) between two variables and, if the data set is large enough, it gives some indication of the strength of the relationship too.

The value of Spearman's Rank Correlation Coefficient (known as rs) is always a number between +1 and -1. Figure 12.61 suggests how the value of rs may be interpreted. Having a value is more useful than having a line of best fit on a scatter graph if you want to compare the strength of correlation of more than one set of bivariate data. However, apparent relationships between data can be deceptive and it is possible to get a result that appears in one of the green zones of Figure 12.61 purely by chance.

Figure 12.7 on page 183 shows how sampling too few pairs of data can lead to spurious correlations. To avoid any uncertainty, the probability that the value of rs could have been generated by chance should always be tested using the significance test described on page 218.

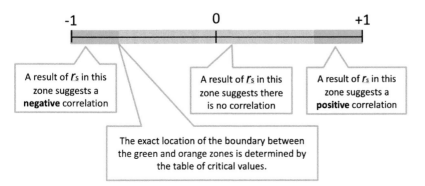

Figure 12.61 The range of values of rs and what the values mean.

Worked example: potential correlation between educational achievement and occupation

The student wants to test the correlation between educational achievement and occupation. He has selected data for various wards in Cardiff from the National Census.

One State the null hypothesis (H_0).

H_0 = There is no rank correlation between the percentage of residents with a degree and the percentage of residents in professional occupations in the wards.

Two State the alternative hypothesis (H_1).

H_1 = There is a correlation between the percentage of residents with a degree and the percentage of residents in a professional occupation in the wards.

> It is easy to make a mistake when ranking the data. To avoid this error use a spreadsheet such as Excel. Then use the sort function to do the ranking for you.

Three Use a table to find Σd^2. Figure 12.62 shows the sequence for completing the table. This can be done as a paper and pen exercise or by putting data into a spreadsheet (such as Excel) and ranking the first variable. This makes the process quicker. The data should always be ranked from highest to lowest.

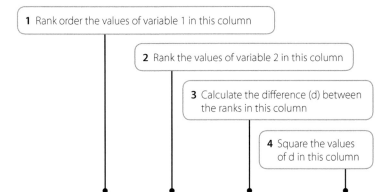

1 Rank order the values of variable 1 in this column

2 Rank the values of variable 2 in this column

3 Calculate the difference (d) between the ranks in this column

4 Square the values of d in this column

	Variable 1	Variable 2	Rank variable 1	Rank variable 2	Difference (d)	d^2
Canton	50	32.8				
Pontprennau	38	23.8				
Whitchurch	37	26.8				
Rhiwbina	35	27.9				
					Σd^2	

5 Calculate the sum of d^2 and record the value in this cell.

Figure 12.62 How to complete a table to find the Σd^2.

Four To find Σd^2:
- rank order the values of variable 1;
- rank order the values of variable 2;
- calculate the difference (d) between the ranks;
- square the values of difference (d).

Five Calculate the coefficient (rs) by applying the formula.

$$r_s = 1 - \frac{6\Sigma d^2}{n(n^2 - 1)}$$

Using the data from all of the wards from Figure 12.63.

$$r_s = 1 - \frac{6 \times 13}{14(14^2 - 1)}$$

$$r_s = 1 - \frac{78}{2,730} = 1 - 0.03 = 0.97$$

Figure 12.63 How to complete a table to find the Σd^2.

Comparing the value of +0.97 to Figure 12.63 you can see that this result suggests a positive correlation. However, we will check the significance of this result later by comparing the result to a table of critical values.

Figure 12.63 shows a completed table. It contains the same data that was used to draw the scatter graph shown on page 165 in Figure 11.28. Notice that the values for variable 1 in Cathays and Grangetown are the same so they should have the same rank order. They occupy the rank positions 10 and 11 so the mean of these ranks (10.5) has been entered for each of these wards.

Ward	% of residents with a degree	% of residents in professional occupations	Rank variable 1	Rank variable 2	Difference (d)	d2
Canton	50	32.8	1	1	0	0
Pontprennau	38	23.8	2	4	2	4
Whitchurch	37	26.8	3	3	0	0
Rhiwbina	35	27.9	4	2	2	4
Butetown	33	20.1	5	5.5	0.5	0.25
Riverside	32	20.1	6	5.5	0.5	0.25
Llanishen	31	19.5	7	7	0	0
Adamsdown	28	14.5	8	9	1	1
Splott	26	17	9	8	1	1
Cathays	22	13.4	10.5	10	0.5	0.25
Grangetown	22	13	10.5	10	0.5	0.25
Rumney	13	9.2	12	12	0	0
Caerau	10	5.4	13	14	1	1
Ely	9	6.1	14	13	1	1
Σd^2						13

Figure 12.63 An example of a completed table.

Six Once you have calculated the value of rs, its significance should be tested. This is a statistical test to find the probability of whether or not the value of rs could have been generated by chance. Compare the value for r_s with the critical values in a table. An annotated example of a table is given in Figure 12.64. If the result of r_s that you have calculated is **lower** than the values in the appropriate row of this table, then the null hypothesis must be accepted. If the result of r_s that you have calculated is **greater** than the values in the appropriate row of this table, then the null hypothesis can be rejected.

To do this you need to:

1 Calculate your value for n, where n = the number of paired values – 2. In this example, n = 14 - 2 = 12.
2 Read off the critical values in the appropriate row.

First, check the critical value for the column with a 0.05 probability. In this example, our value of +0.97 is greater than the critical value of 0.503 so we can be 95% confident that the null hypothesis can be rejected. Next, check the critical value for the column with a 0.01 probability. In this example, our value of +0.97 is greater than the critical value of 0.678 so we can be 99% confident that the null hypothesis can be rejected.

Seven It is important to complete the analysis by interpreting the results. In this case, the null hypothesis has been rejected. Based on this evidence we can accept the probability that:

There is a correlation between the percentage of residents with a degree and the percentage of residents in a professional occupation in the wards. We can infer that wards that have higher percentages of residents with a degree have a higher percentage of people in professional jobs.

There is a 5% probability that your value of r_s was generated by chance.

there is a 1% probability that your value of r_s was generated by chance.

There is a 0.1% probability that your value of r_s was generated by chance.

Figure 12.64 Critical values of Spearman's Rank.

n	0.10	0.05	0.025	0.01	0.005	0.001
4	1.000	1.000	-	-	-	-
5	0.800	0.900	1.000	1.000	-	-
6	0.657	0.829	0.866	0.943	1.000	-
7	0.571	0.714	0.786	0.893	0.929	1.000
8	0.524	0.643	0.738	0.833	0.881	0.952
9	0.483	0.600	0.700	0.783	0.833	0.917
10	0.455	0.564	0.648	0.745	0.794	0.879
11	0.427	0.536	0.618	0.709	0.755	0.845
12	0.406	(0.503)	0.587	0.678	0.727	0.818
13	0.385	0.484	0.560	0.648	0.703	0.791
14	0.367	0.464	0.538	0.626	0.679	0.771
15	0.354	0.446	0.521	0.604	0.654	0.750

Write up your analysis in your report. Interpret your findings and integrate the written analysis with your data presentation.

So far we have explored various techniques of analysis and, hopefully, you have selected the ones that are appropriate to your own data. Now you should be ready to make sense of your findings and write up your report.

Structuring your write-up

Steps 11 and 12 show that there is cross-over between data presentation and data analysis. Patterns, trends, and correlations that are visible on a map or graph can be number crunched, annotated, and described in a written analysis. Consequently, the most effective way to analyse each dataset is to integrate the data presentation and analytical methods so that they occur on the same page of the report. This will enable you to make straightforward references to the data presentation in your written work.

The data presentation and analysis section of your report may run over several pages. The most effective way to structure these pages is to mirror the structure used by your investigation. In other words, sequence the presentation and analysis of data under sub-headings that reflect the natural sequence of the research questions that you have investigated. Figure 12.65 gives an indication of how this structure might work.

Figure 12.65 How to structure the presentation and analysis sections of the report.

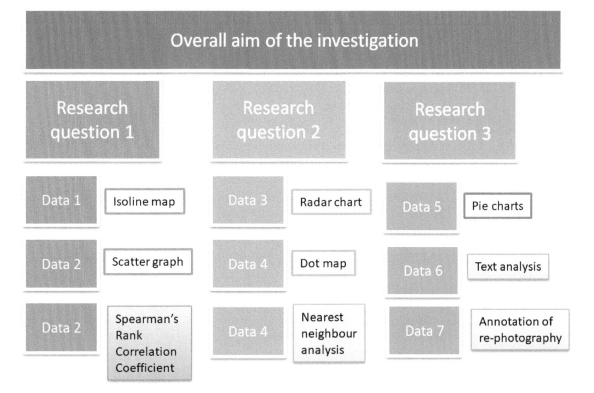

Interpreting your findings

The exam board (Awarding Body) mark schemes refer to this as either explaining or **interpreting** the data. This means to give clarity and meaning to geographical evidence that could be complex or difficult to read if you were not a geographer. Think of yourself as an interpreter – giving expert advice about geographical evidence just like a language interpreter would help you understand documents in a foreign language.

As you begin to interpret your data it might be helpful to ask yourself some questions. For example:
- Do I have any evidence for …?
- Why do I think that…?
- How clear is the pattern or trend?
- How strong is the connection between this variable and that…?
- What may be causing this variation in the data?
- What effect does this variable seem to have?

Make connections between the evidence

To make sense of your data you also need to make connections between the evidence. Looking for evidence of cause and effect will help you to explain the evidence. For example, imagine an investigation of the regeneration of a shopping centre. You might investigate the patterns of pedestrian flows. Why are some parts of the town centre busier than others? You could collect evidence such as:

> Well-written analysis will systematically break down complex evidence into individual components. You should be trying to use the evidence to make logical connections between (for example) causes and effects.

- pedestrian surveys at different times of day;
- interviews with shoppers about the features of the town centre that they like and dislike;
- the rateable value of shops could be found on the internet.

To make sense of this evidence you might look for connections such as whether:
- the busiest streets also have a lot of features that the shoppers like;
- Rateable values are higher in the busiest streets. If so, this might explain why national chain stores are located on busy high streets but local shops are on quieter side streets.

Link your findings to the literature review

It is important to link your findings to the geographical theories or concepts that you researched in Step 2 when you did your literature review. An effective analysis will:
- compare findings (real data) to predicted outcomes (what you expected having read the academic literature);
- use your understanding of the geographical literature to explain your findings;
- refer to factors, processes, concepts, models, or theories that might explain the patterns, trends, and correlations in the data that you have observed;
- provide accurate references (see page 233) to the documents you read in the literature review;
- make inferences about the wider population based on the analysis of your sample data.

Messy geography

What if your data reveals things you didn't expect? Many investigations turn up evidence that does not support the geographical theory that you read in the literature or which even contradicts it. This is sometimes described as **messy geography** because, in the real world, data is untidy and chaotic. It does not necessarily follow the neat patterns that were predicted by the book or academic article that you read during your literature review.

For example, in an urban investigation of the factors that affect house prices, you might have been influenced by (out-dated) urban land use models and predict that your fieldwork will show that property values rise steadily as you move out towards the suburbs. If so, a map of house prices would show a regular (or systematic) pattern. In reality, such a map is likely to be much more complex. It is likely to show clusters of higher house prices in inner urban areas – probably connected to positive features of the environment such as urban parks.

QUESTION I don't think I can really do a statistical test with any of my data? Does it matter?

ANSWER No, it's not essential to do a statistical test as part of your data processing. What is important is to use the most suitable ways to analyse and present your data and to be aware of any limitations of any techniques you have used.

Before you move on to Step 13 you should complete the review points below.

Review Points

Tick off each review point before moving on to Step 13.

I am aware of the need to check the significance of any statistical test by comparing the outcome of my test to a table of critical values. ☐

I have interpreted my findings, written up my analysis and integrated this text with the data presentation in my written report. ☐

Action points

1 Evaluate your research. Identify strengths and weaknesses of your investigation. Evaluate the validity of your research, the accuracy and reliability of your evidence.

2 Draw together the individual pieces of evidence to write a conclusion that addresses the initial aim of your investigation.

3 Suggest how the investigation could be improved.

You've collected data, processed, presented, and analysed it. It's time to complete your report by making your conclusions and writing an evaluation of the whole investigation. These are two very important elements of any independent investigation. All of the exam boards reward this part of the report with a large proportion of the marks (see Figure 13.1 and Appendix 1 for more details). Consequently, if your report is 4,000 words in total you should allocate about 1,000 words of this to writing about your conclusions and evaluation.

Your conclusions must be based on the data collected in your investigation so if there are problems with the data, or faults in the way that data has been collected, then the conclusions could be wrong. Consequently, there is logic in writing your evaluation first. In that way you can refer to any limitations in the data when you are writing your conclusions.

Whether you write your evaluation before your conclusions, or vice versa, always use clear subheadings to separate these two important parts of your write-up.

Figure 13.1 Marks allocated.

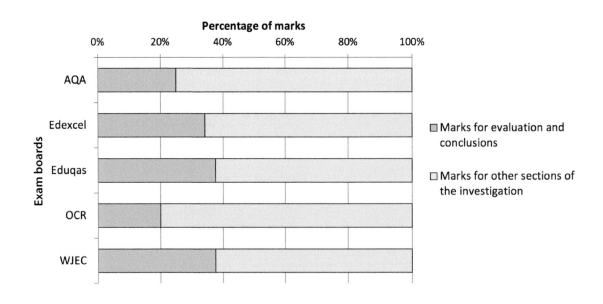

Action Point I

Evaluate your research. Identify strengths and weaknesses of your investigation. Evaluate the validity of your research, the accuracy and reliability of your evidence.

A good evaluation should be balanced – it should weigh up the strengths of an investigation against its limitations. A great evaluation uses specific evidence to support the statements that it makes.

You can evaluate any of the steps in your investigation. A great evaluation will reflect on all stages in the investigation and consider:

▶ whether the research questions were valid;
▶ the accuracy and reliability of the primary and secondary data;
▶ whether or not you gave sufficient consideration to the ethical dimension of your research;
▶ whether the sampling strategy gave you a representative sample. In particular, the frequency and timing of your sample;
▶ the suitability of the methods you used to collect, present, and analyse the data;
▶ whether the evidence supports your conclusions.

Limitations of research

Research relies on data so it is important to think critically about whether the data contained in your research can be trusted. Research is subject to four main types of limitation. These are summarised in Figure 13.2.

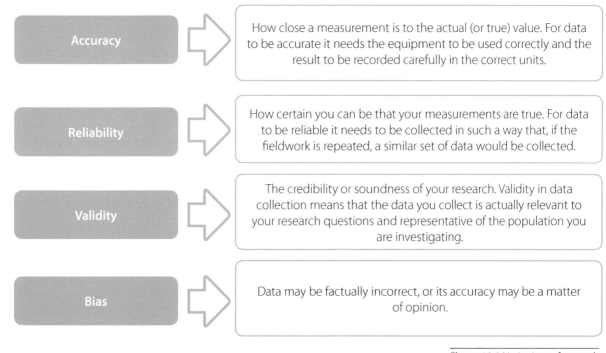

Figure 13.2 Limitations of research

Accuracy is largely controlled by your data collection methods. For example:

▶ was the most suitable data collection used?
▶ was fieldwork equipment used correctly?
▶ were there errors in recording the data or presenting and analysing it?

Validity

Validity in research means that your findings are factually sound.

Figure 13.3 The features of a great evaluation.

Reliability and **validity** are largely controlled by wider issues of research design.

▶ Did you choose the most effective research questions?
▶ Were you able to successfully control the variables?
▶ Did you design an effective sampling strategy?
▶ Was the sample representative?

Consequently, a good evaluation will consider a variety of factors that may have had an influence on accuracy, reliability, validity, and bias, as shown in Figure 13.3.

A mediocre evaluation	A great evaluation
• Fails to consider the validity of the research questions. • Focuses on what you enjoyed and didn't enjoy on the fieldtrip. That's not evaluation. • Blames bad weather for a poor set of results. • Provides generic evaluation of data collection methods. • Identifies limitations or strengths but not both. • Identifies issues relating to data collection but not sampling strategy.	• Starts by evaluating the aims of the investigation and considers the validity of the research questions. • Recognises that findings are often tenuous or uncertain. • Uses specialist terms, such as validity, reliability, and accuracy, in the correct context. • Identifies limitations and strengths and provides specific evidence in support. • Carefully considers the design of the sampling strategy, including the frequency and timing of samples. • Provides specific evidence of evaluation that relates to the actual investigation. • Discusses whether or not the ethical dimension was given sufficient consideration.

Evaluate the sampling strategy

You must evaluate the design of your sampling strategy. A consideration of the **frequency** and **timing** of your sampling should help you to decide whether or not your strategy provided a **representative sample**.

You should consider:

▶ the frequency of your sample:

Representative sample

A representative sample reflects the features/characteristics of the whole population.

  • this is partly about **sample size**. Was your sample large enough? Ten questionnaires is unlikely to be enough to be representative. Reflecting on your investigation you may now realise that you should have selected a larger sample from a homogeneous population, i.e. people who share something in common;

  • frequency is also about the **density of sample points**. For example, if you used a systematic point sampling strategy along a transect, were the points close enough together to represent the actual variations along the transect? Systematic sampling may have missed sudden changes in an environmental gradient. See Figure 13.4. In this example, the systematic sample points miss the sea rocket which only grows in the embryo dunes. In this example, the systematic sampling needs a greater frequency of sample points.

▶ the **timing** of your sample:

Diurnal

A diurnal variation is one that takes place on a daily basis.

  • data may be affected by **diurnal**, weekly, or seasonal variations in the data. The data from some investigations can be affected by predictable daily changes such as the tide or flows of commuter traffic. Did your sampling strategy take this into account?

Antecedent

A condition or event that existed immediately before.

  • data collected on a particular day may also be affected by **antecedent** conditions. A beach profile may have been affected by a recent storm. Infiltration will almost certainly be affected by recent rainfall. Did you take these factors into account?

  • data may be affected by variables that cause it to fluctuate repeatedly over short periods. Wind speed and noise levels vary constantly. In these circumstances you get more reliable data if you take several readings and then calculate the mean.

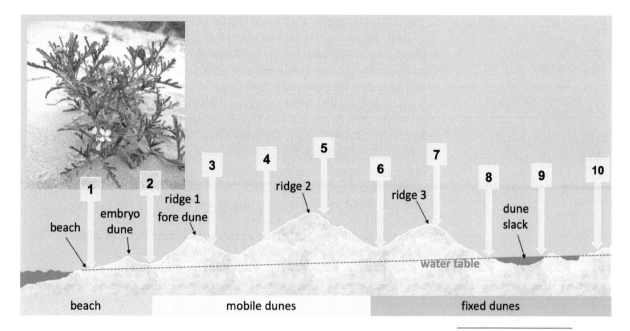

Limitations in primary data

The accuracy of primary data can be affected by a number of factors, including:

▶ **use of suitable equipment**. For example, if you use a ruler to measure the length of a pebble you are relying on your eye to judge where the measurement starts and ends. The use of callipers (shown in Figure 13.5) makes the data more accurate because they allow you to measure the true value exactly without any guesswork;

▶ **units of measurement**. For example, when recording the length of pebbles, measuring in millimetres is more accurate than measuring to the nearest centimetre;

▶ **inconsistency when estimating**. For example, recording orientation of a corrie requires you to estimate the direction in which an irregular shape is facing;

▶ **inconsistency when applying criteria such as an EQI or Cleanliness Index**. This issue can be resolved by photographing examples that match each criteria;

▶ **errors when apparatus is read**. For example, you weighed some sediment samples but forgot to zero the scales;

▶ **carelessness when results are recorded**. Data errors can be caused by reversing numbers when you write them down. Untidy handwriting can also cause data errors.

Evaluation

The accuracy of your primary data will affect the accuracy of your conclusions. For each of the bullet points opposite, reflect on the strengths and weaknesses of your primary data.

Figure 13.5 Use the correct equipment to improve accuracy of data.

Evaluate qualitative primary data

It is a mistake to automatically label qualitative data as biased.

Qualitative data is really important to the outcome of many investigations, especially if you are interested in people's perceptions or points of view. Qualitative data is subjective rather than objective but that is its strength rather than a limitation. It allows you to collect opinions rather than facts and, if your aim was to investigate opinions, then your qualitative data is valid. Subjective data isn't necessarily less accurate than quantitative data either. If the research has been conducted carefully then you will have photos or interviews that accurately reflect the thoughts and opinions of your respondents.

You should consider the methods you used to collect your qualitative data. For example, if you used a questionnaire:

▶ **did you avoid writing leading questions?** Questions that lead people to agree with your own point of view will give you unreliable data;

▶ **was the sample large enough to be representative of the wider population?** You really need at least 50 questionnaires;

▶ **did you use an appropriate sampling strategy** to try to increase sample size and reduce bias such as using snowball sampling or expert sampling.

Consider limitations in secondary data

Some sources of secondary data, including some websites, are more reliable than others. We can trust that data collected by a UK government department, or academic organisation, will be reliable because it will have used a suitable sampling strategy. Consequently, the data found in academic papers and UK government websites should be reliable and, in most cases, accurate too. However, even trustworthy secondary sources may report data that is not completely accurate. This is because data goes out of date. A classic example is the census which only collects data every 10 years.

Another problem you may face is that secondary data may have been collected at a resolution that cannot be compared to your primary data. For example, you may be trying to compare secondary data that has been collated at a county or regional level with primary data that you collected from a specific postcode area.

Unreliable secondary data

You need to consider whether the evidence found in a secondary source is unreliable. This applies to both quantitative and qualitative data. Data on some websites may be unreliable because:

▶ we do not know who collected the data or how large the sample was;

▶ the sampling strategy was flawed so that the data is not representative.

In addition, there may be **bias** because the author or website is representing a certain point of view. For example, many news organisations support a particular political view – they are described as left-leaning or right-leaning, see Figure 13.6.

Bias in a source can be a limitation of your research. If your investigation relies on what you assume is **impartial** evidence from sources that are actually **partial** then bias in the data will limit the validity of your research and is likely to make your conclusions unreliable.

On the other hand, if the aim of the investigation is to explore people's values and attitudes then the analysis of bias is a valid method of research. If we analyse the evidence presented to us in the media (on TV, in newspapers, or in blogs), we can identify that some data is presented as fact but is actually biased because it is someone's opinion. Identifying this bias is useful – it should be regarded as a strength in your evaluation. An impartial view helps us describe the opinions of certain groups of people. By considering this bias we may also begin to understand why certain groups of people have strong opinions.

> Bias in a secondary source isn't necessarily a limitation in your evaluation.

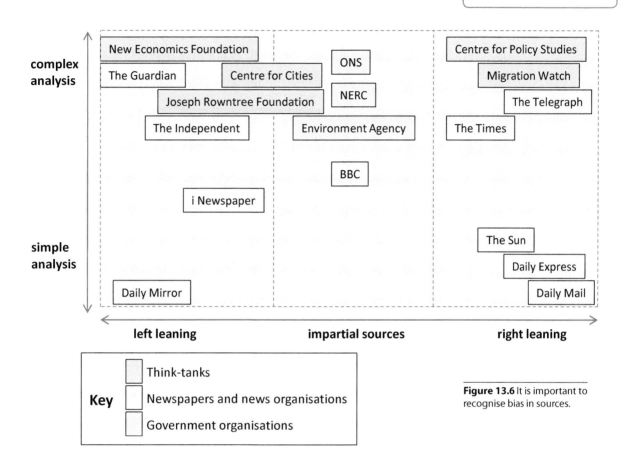

Figure 13.6 It is important to recognise bias in sources.

Factual	Biased	Not genuine
Fair	One-sided	Fake
Impartial	Partial	False
Unbiased	Partisan	Misinformation
Objective	Prejudiced	Misrepresented
	Opinionated	

Figure 13.7 Useful words to describe data.

Consider the ethical dimension

It is important to comment on the **ethical dimension** in your evaluation. Evaluate whether or not the ethical dimension was given sufficient consideration when you designed your data collection. Did you consider issues such as access? Did you respect the integrity of the site and the dignity of your subject? For example, if you conducted a questionnaire, consider whether people would have been more open in their responses if you had:

▶ been more explicit about the purpose of the investigation;
▶ assured respondents that their data would be made anonymous and treated with confidentiality.

Ethical dimension

Research should be conducted with respect for people and the environment. This is the ethical dimension of research.

Draw together the individual pieces of evidence to write a conclusion that addresses the initial aim of your investigation.

Address the aims of the research

Perhaps the most important role of your conclusion is that it presents answers to the original aim of your investigation. To do this, your conclusion must:

▶ refer directly to your initial aims;
▶ be structured around your research questions or hypotheses;
▶ summarise your key findings;
▶ be based on the evidence you have collected;
▶ draw on your literature research by using geographical theories, concepts, and processes to help explain your observations.

Synthesise key findings

A good conclusion demonstrates **synthesis** – in other words, it concisely summarises all of the findings from your investigation and explains them using your wider geographical understanding. You may think this sounds like you have to repeat all of the analysis again. Don't do this! A typical analysis looks at one piece of evidence at a time. Each separate table, graph, or map you have drawn told a small part of the story. The conclusion takes an overview of this evidence to tell the whole story. It is rather like making a jigsaw puzzle. The analysis only looks at one piece of the puzzle at a time. You need to bring the pieces of the puzzle together so that you can see the whole picture – that's what the conclusion does.

> **Synthesis**
>
> Synthesis weaves together separate lines of evidence to present the whole picture.

> A well-written conclusion is concise. It synthesises your findings and clearly relates back to the original aim of the investigation.

Things to do	Things to avoid
• Link your findings to the aims and sub-questions of your investigation. • Link your findings to the literature. • Your conclusion must be evidence based.	• Do not introduce any new data. • Don't introduce models or theories that weren't part of your literature review. • Do not make 'leaps of faith'. Conclusions must be based on the data you collected.

Figure 13.8 Things to do (and things to avoid) in your conclusion.

Base your conclusion on evidence

Your conclusion should present a well-argued case. There is a certain logic to building a strong case when you present any kind of argument.

One You start with a clear aim.

Two You build a case on hard evidence – in this case, data that can be trusted to be a representative sample of the whole population.

Three Next, you analyse the data using suitable methods of analysis.

Four You use your understanding to pull together a conclusion that is supported by the evidence.

You need to provide evidence that is based on the data you have collected and analysed to support a successful conclusion. Figure 13.9 describes some dos and don'ts of using evidence to support your conclusion.

Dos of using evidence	Don'ts of using evidence
• Do refer to key pieces of evidence that have emerged in your data analysis. • Do consider whether your data is accurate and reliable. • Do acknowledge that conclusions may be tentative or uncertain because of a lack of evidence.	• Don't jump to conclusions that cannot be supported by the data. • Don't refer to data that hasn't been presented or analysed earlier in the report. • Don't ignore data because it doesn't fit the pattern that you predicted.

Figure 13.9 Dos and don'ts of using evidence in your conclusion.

Recognise the limitations of the evidence

This part of your report must provide a link between the data you collected and the conclusions you are making. However, what happens if:

▶ your data is incomplete; or

▶ your sample is not representative of the whole population; or

▶ you selected methods of presentation and analysis that were not effective?

If your evidence is not clear or convincing then your conclusions should be tentative rather than certain. You need to be realistic about your conclusions – as we saw on page 182, the data you have collected provides probabilities rather than certainties. Figure 13.10 provides some helpful adjectives you could use when describing your evidence and the consequent conclusions. The green columns could be used with the strongest evidence, whereas the orange columns should be used when the validity of the data is questionable.

Evidence could be:			Conclusions could be:		
Definitive Clear-cut Explicit Unambiguous	Implicit Ambiguous Limited Imperfect incomplete	Contested Debated Challenged Questioned	Certain Convinced Definite Unequivocal	Tentative Provisional Speculative Conjectural	Uncertain Unresolved Doubtful Unconvinced Equivocal

Figure 13.10 Be realistic about your conclusions.

Signposting your answer

In order to write a well-argued case you can use signposting to structure your Conclusion or your Evaluation. Signposting is a technique that tells the reader what is coming next – like a signpost tells you where you are going. Some useful signposts are suggested in Figure 13.11.

Adding points	Contrasting and comparing	Adding emphasis	Linking cause and effect
Moreover Furthermore In addition What is more	Although Similarly Likewise However On the other hand Whereas	Especially Predominantly Chiefly Uniquely Most significantly	As a result Consequently Ergo Hence Thus Therefore

Figure 13.11 Useful signposts.

Refer to geographical literature

An investigation is all about comparing the reality of actual fieldwork data to what is theoretically understood about geography. Your conclusion must:

▶ demonstrate that you understand the factors, processes, theories, models, or concepts that underpin your investigation;

▶ make direct reference to the literature review that you described in the introduction of your report.

Atypical

To conclude that somewhere or something is atypical means that your investigation has found that your field study area does not follow the 'normal' pattern that is theoretically expected.

It is possible that the evidence from your research will confirm a particular geographical theory. However, it is also possible that your research is at odds with your literature research and your own expectations. This isn't really that surprising and there may be a good reason for it. It may be that the geographical model you are investigating is a general one – in reality, individual places deviate from this model. If so, try to explain the local factors that might make your place different from the norm. Why is your place **atypical**?

By comparing the evidence collected in your investigation to the evidence in the literature you should be able to come to conclude that:
▶ the place you have studied matches the literature – it is typical;
▶ the place you have studied does not match the literature – it is atypical;
▶ your findings are inconclusive because the evidence was incomplete or your data collections methods were flawed.

Messy geography

The results of your fieldwork will not always be what you expected. When you review the evidence it may be that your graphs show no real trend and that your maps show no clear pattern. You may even find that the evidence you have collected contradicts what you had predicted. In reality, the results of geography fieldwork are often messy rather than neat and tidy. Don't be surprised if your results don't exactly match your predictions. It would be a mistake to automatically blame your data collection methods.

Summary

Figure 13.12 Features of a great conclusion

Your conclusion is an important part of your report – so write it carefully. Figure 13.12 summarises the key features of a great conclusion.

A Mediocre Conclusion	A Great Conclusion
• Is over-long. • Only vaguely relates the findings to the original aims of the investigation or the research questions/hypotheses. • Fails to relate the findings to any geographical literature. • Makes claims without supporting them with any evidence. • Is repetitive. It repeats some of the analysis without drawing it together.	• Is concise. • Addresses the aims that were set out in the introduction. • Uses research questions and/or hypotheses to provide structure. • Makes clear links between the findings of the investigation and the literature review that was described earlier in the report. • Is based firmly on the evidence. • Provides synthesis. It effectively combines the evidence to reach a summative conclusion.

Action Point 3

Suggest how the investigation could be improved.

As part of your evaluation you should think carefully about whether there is anything else you could have done. A lot of students write that they could have collected more data. This may be true, especially if you only did 10 questionnaires! However, this is a very basic level of response and you should aim to do better than state you could have done 'more of the same'. More of the same data might not have told you anything else. It is better to think about whether other kinds of data would have given you greater insight during your investigation.

Suggest realistic improvements

There are five main areas to consider when you suggest improvements. These all relate to steps in the investigation where you were making key decisions. With the benefit of hindsight did you:

▶ **word your research questions carefully?** Perhaps other research questions would have been more suitable;

▶ **select suitable primary data sources?** Perhaps the data you collected didn't really answer your research questions. This will have affected the validity of your research. It either means you collected the wrong data, or asked the wrong research questions;

▶ **design a suitable sampling strategy?** Think about how you could improve the frequency and timing of your sample. Perhaps you could have:
  • collected data at a different time of day?
  • collected data at the same time but on another day?

▶ **select the right data collection methods?** Perhaps you needed a wider variety of data and therefore needed to select additional methods of data collection;

▶ **select suitable methods to analyse the data?** Perhaps you needed to use a statistical test or coding to give a more thorough analysis of the data.

Whatever you suggest by way of an improvement, make sure the suggestion is realistic. Your A level investigation shouldn't take more than 40 hours so it would be unrealistic to suggest a form of research that is very time-consuming or involves the use of expensive equipment that is not available to you. On the other hand, there are lots of ways that technology can be used, cheaply and efficiently, to improve an investigation. For example, the use of an online survey to increase the sample size of a questionnaire, or the use of GIS to create maps of your data.

QUESTION Can I write the conclusion first and finish with an evaluation?

ANSWER Yes, of course, you can. There is no set order to these two parts, although, because the conclusions may be affected by the reliability of your data it may seem sensible to write the evaluation first. Whichever order you choose, it is important to give each part (conclusion and evaluation) a clear sub-title.

Review Points

Tick off each review point before moving on to Step 14.

I have written an Evaluation of my investigation that:
- considers the validity of my research; ☐
- weighs the strengths and limitations of my research; ☐
- considers my sampling strategy. ☐

I have written a Conclusion to my investigation that:
- provides answers to my original aims ☐
- is supported by evidence from my data analysis; ☐
- refers to theoretical geography and the literature review; ☐

I have suggested how the investigation could be improved. ☐

STEP 14 Complete the write-up

It's time to complete the write-up of your report. This step is all about checking that everything is finished to a high standard. You are almost certainly working to meet a deadline set by your teacher. Don't leave this step to the last minute! You will only be putting yourself under a lot of pressure.

Action Point 1

Give your report a logical structure.

By this stage your report should already be completed in draft form. You should have:
1 described your aims and methodology/sampling strategy (Step 9);
2 presented and analysed your data (Steps 11 and 12);
3 written the conclusions and evaluation (Step 13).

The three point list above gives you a sensible structure for the draft report into any investigation. It's a very good idea to complete the report by giving each significant section a heading. Then use sub-headings to signpost the important elements within each section so the reader (and moderator) can find their way around. Figure 14.1 suggests a logical structure that you might use. On the right is a checklist of the things that should be covered in each of these sections of the report. Use this checklist to make suitable sub-headings.

Figure 14.1 A logical structure.

Significant sections	How many words?	Checklist	
Aims	500-750	Location of the fieldwork. Research aims and research questions. Geographical theory. Literature review.	☐ ☐ ☐ ☐
Methodology	750-1000	Justification of data collection methods. Sampling strategy (sampling framework). Ethical dimension.	☐ ☐ ☐
Data presentation and analysis	1000-1250	Range of data presentation methods. Analysis of data by research question/hypothesis. Interpretation of findings.	☐ ☐ ☐
Conclusions and evaluation	750-1000	Synthesis of research findings. Use of evidence to answer research questions. Reference to geographical theory. Strengths and limitations of the research. Areas for improvement.	☐ ☐ ☐ ☐ ☐
Bibliography		An alphabetical list of your sources.	☐

If you are taking WJEC or Eduqas A level Geography the specification requires you to submit a report that has a set structure. See Appendix 1.

See Appendix 1.

Action Point 2

Make sure that all sources are referenced.

Good geographical fieldwork reports make frequent references to geographical theory. For example, you can:

▶ refer to relevant geographical literature in your introduction when you explain and justify the aims of your fieldwork;

▶ use this theoretical understanding to interpret the primary and secondary data in your analysis section;

▶ refer back to your aims, and the geographical literature, when you are writing your conclusions to the report. Did the data collected during your fieldwork provide evidence that supported the theoretical understanding?

Now that your report is more or less complete it is time to check that you have made **enough** references to relevant geographical literature. Weaker reports only make reference to theoretical geography and literature in the introduction. Sometimes the introduction of a report reads like a mini essay that has been bolted onto the beginning of the fieldwork report. Better reports integrate the theoretical geography and literature with the fieldwork and make frequent references to the literature throughout the report – as shown in Figure 14.2.

Figure 14.2 How geographical literature should be used in your report.

A mediocre report	A great report
• Only refers to geographical literature during the introduction of the report. • Only uses one source for the literature review – usually the text book. • Uses websites such as Wikipedia to provide a geographical context to the fieldwork location. • Provides a bibliography at the end of the report but does not give accurate references to sources at the point the source is used within the report.	• Makes references to geographical literature throughout the report with correct attribution. • Uses three or four different geographical sources for the literature review. • Uses a variety of websites to provide geographical context to the aims of the fieldwork and its location. • Uses footnotes to refer to each source at the point that it is used within the report.

How to reference a source

It is very important to acknowledge any sources of information or theoretical understanding you have used while writing your report. You may have used a text book, an online journal, a website, or a geographical magazine for some of your ideas. Whatever source you used, you must provide an accurate reference for it so that the people who read your report can go back to the original source if they want to. Providing accurate references is what all good researchers do. Failure to provide a reference could be very serious. You might be accused of copying someone else's ideas and passing them off as your own – something known as plagiarism.

To provide a reference for a book, or an article in a magazine, the normal convention is to:

▶ state the author's name (surname first);

▶ then the year of publication;

▶ next, give the title of the book or article (in italic font);

▶ finally, give the name of the publisher.

This means that the correct reference for this book would be:

Owen, A. (2019) *A Level Geography Independent Investigation,* Insight and Perspective.

How to reference online sources

If you found some useful ideas online you will still need to acknowledge where these ideas came from by providing a reference to a website, a specific web page, or to an article you found online.

Online sources should be referenced in much the same way as a book or magazine article. You need to:

▶ state the name of the organisation responsible for the site and/or the name of the author who wrote the online article;

▶ in the case of an article, the date that the article was written.

You also need to do the following:

▶ state when you accessed the site (day/month/year). This is because web pages change;

▶ copy the URL. Put this between <pointed brackets>.

For example, imagine you accessed an online article, the way to reference it is as follows:

Woodland Trust (2012), *Urban Air Quality*. Accessed 15 July 2019. <https://www.woodlandtrust.org.uk/publications/2012/04/urban-air-quality/>

Or, you used the Royal Geographical Society (RGS) website to find some advice about fieldwork. The way to reference the site would be as follows:

Royal Geographical Society (RGS), accessed 15 July 2019. <https://www.rgs.org/schools/teaching-resources/sketching-and-photography/>

How to reference at point of use

The minimum requirement for your geography investigation is to list all of the sources you have used in a **bibliography** at the end of your report. The titles in your bibliography should be listed in alphabetical order. However, an even better approach is to provide a reference for each source at the point at which it has been used. There are two ways you can do this:

▶ by abbreviating the reference to the name and year of publication – so this book would be (Owen, A 2019) and adding this to a suitable point of your report. You should then give the full reference in a bibliography at the end of your report. This method is illustrated in Figure 14.3;

▶ by indicating the point in the report where you are referring to a source with a superscript number and then adding a footnote at the bottom of the page. The footnote should give a full reference for the source. This method is illustrated in Figure 14.4.

Bibliography

A bibliography is a list of sources used during research. It is placed at the end of the report.

Figure 14.3 How to reference at point of use.

The aim of my fieldwork is to investigate how planners are attempting to make the town centre more accessible and desirable to shoppers. It is argued that tree planting reduces traffic noise and helps to improve air quality (Woodland Trust, 2012). I will map sound levels throughout the town centre and also use questionnaires to investigate the possible impacts of tree planting.

The aim of my fieldwork is to investigate how planners are attempting to conserve the place identity of the shopping centre of this market town whilst making the environment more accessible. Historical façades of Georgian buildings have been conserved while the building behind the façade has been completely replaced. Façadism, however, has a history of controversy[1] in town planning as it prevents the development of contemporary designs. I will ask shoppers how important the conservation of historic buildings is as a factor of place identity.

1. Richards, J. (1994), *Facadism*, Routledge.

Figure 14.4 How to reference with footnotes.

> In Figures 14.3 and 14.4 the sources have been used to help justify the students' fieldwork investigations. This is good use of a source.

Tips for referencing

Referencing is quite a skill. Here are a few tips to help you.

1 **Be consistent.** Whatever method you use: stick to it. For example, if you decide to use numbered footnotes with a full reference at the bottom of the page, use this method throughout the report.
2 **Use your word processing package to insert footnotes.** In Microsoft Word you use the tab marked 'References' to open the relevant menu. You can also use 'Insert Citation'.
3 **Keep a full record of your references throughout the research period.**
4 **Always make it clear if you are quoting another author directly.** When you are researching, use a highlighter to indicate when text has been copied directly from a source so that you will remember that it is not your own words.

Action Point 3

Proof read your report.

Having got your report into a logical structure it is time to proof read your report. This means reading the report carefully from start to end. As you do this you should:

▶ check each page has the correct page number;
▶ check each figure has a caption;
▶ correct spelling mistakes;
▶ correct grammatical issues;
▶ check that passages make sense;
▶ remove any repetition.

As you will appreciate, proof reading is about a lot more than checking the spelling, punctuation, and grammar (although these are important). It is about presenting the story of the data in a way that is clear, concise, and coherent.

Each A level specification makes it clear that they expect the independent investigation to be between 3000 and 4000 words long and, every year, many students write a lot more than this. These longer reports are often descriptive rather than analytical and they usually contain repetitive passages that should have been edited out by the student at the proof reading stage. If your draft report is over 4000 words you should be asking yourself the following questions when you are proof reading.

> Descriptions should be pithy. A great report is concise and analytical.

▶ Do I need this description?
▶ Am I repeating myself?
▶ Can I reduce the length of some of these sentences?

Section of the report	What could be edited down or removed	What to keep
• Introduction	• Unnecessary contexts that describe historical geography of the fieldwork location. • Unnecessary lists of key terms and their definitions. • Lengthy essays about theory that have little relevance to the actual fieldwork.	• Short passages that justify your choice of fieldwork and its aims. • Concise reference to wider geographical contexts through the use of a small number of relevant sources. • A succinct introduction to the place context and why it was chosen.
• Methodology	• Lengthy descriptions of how data was collected. • General descriptions of sampling strategies that could be used in any fieldwork.	• Pithy descriptions of the sampling strategy/framework that focus on the specifics of **your** fieldwork. Clear justification of your sample location, frequency, and timing.
• Analysis and interpretation	• Lengthy descriptions of each chart, graph, or map.	• Analysis of significant patterns or trends in the data and/or spatial patterns. **Understanding** of the significance of any statistical tests you have used. • Concise links to theoretical understanding in the literature.
• Evaluation and conclusions	• Repetition of the descriptions you used in the analysis section. Remove any text that fails to summarise/synthesise your findings. • Remove generic statements that could be used to evaluate any fieldwork investigation such as 'I could have collected more data.' or 'I should have spent more time collecting data'.	• Overarching statements that link your main findings to the original aims of your research. • Judicial use of selected primary or secondary evidence that supports your conclusions. • Pithy evaluative statements about **your** investigation that are supported by relevant evidence – focus on validity, accuracy, and reliability of the data.

Figure 14.5 What to look for if you need to edit your report.

Action Point 4

Use a check list to ensure that you have included all of the important details in your report.

With the report written and the proof reading complete it is time to check the fine details. If you have used the Review Points at the end of each Step in this book your report should include all of the relevant details. However, here are two final check lists. They include some of the things that students sometimes forget about. They don't necessarily include everything that your exam board will be looking for – so the other useful thing to do at this stage is to read your report with a copy of the mark scheme in front of you. Don't try to give a mark to your report – use the mark scheme as another check list of items that should be included.

Review Points of Style

I have checked the following in my report:

My report is paginated. ☐

My name is printed on the first page. ☐

Every table, chart, graph, or map has a suitable title or figure number. ☐

Every graph has labels on each axis and suitable units of measurement. ☐

Every map has a north arrow and scale line or statement of scale. ☐

My report has an accurate bibliography. ☐

Review Points of Content

I have included the following in my report.

An introduction that explains my aims and makes links to geographical literature. ☐

A brief context to the location of my fieldwork that includes maps at different scales. ☐

An explanation of my sampling strategy/framework that refers to location, frequency, and timing of my sample. ☐

A consideration of the ethics of my fieldwork. ☐

A variety of different data presentation methods that includes some that are more sophisticated. ☐

Methods of quantitative/qualitative analysis that are relevant to the data that I collected. ☐

An interpretation of my data that links to the geographical theory. ☐

Conclusions that use evidence and which pull my research together. ☐

An evaluation that considers specific issues of validity, accuracy, and reliability. ☐

Realistic suggestions for how the investigation could be improved. ☐

Action Point 5

Submit your report to your teacher.

The time has come to submit your report to your teacher. Some students submit their report electronically but the majority of students submit a hard copy of their report. If you intend to submit a hard copy here are a final few tips.

1 **Give the report a cover sheet.** Take a bit of pride in this task – it's nice to use one of your own photos of the fieldwork location. The cover must include:
   ▶ the title of your investigation;
   ▶ your full name;
   ▶ the name of your school/college.
2 **Do an electronic word count of the full report and add this information to the front cover**.
3 **Paginate the report.** This is really helpful because your teacher will be able to refer to specific page when they are marking your work. This evidence will then help the process of moderation.
4 **Add your name to every page in a header.** If the pages of your report get separated, the page numbers and your name will help the moderator piece your work back together again.
5 **Print the report – preferably in colour.** If you have created maps and graphs by hand, add them into the report in suitable places.
6 **Secure the pages of your report.** The simplest way to do this is with a hole punch and two treasury tags. This is essential. If your report is fastened with a paper clip and your teacher or moderator drop it – you can imagine how difficult it could be to put your report back together again.
7 **Submit your report to your teacher.** Relax! You've done all you can.

Appendix 1 Exam board information

Your independent investigation report will be marked by your teacher using a mark scheme provided by your exam board. It is printed in the specification which can be downloaded from the website of your exam board. It is important that you understand how the mark scheme works and keep this in mind while you are writing the report of your investigation.

During the Spring term before you take your geography exams, a sample of work (which may or may not include your own investigation) will be sent from your school/college to a moderator. The moderator will check that the mark scheme has been applied accurately and consistently.

> Get a copy of the mark scheme as early as you can – preferably while you are writing your research plan and definitely before you write up your report.

Your independent investigation will be marked out of 60, 70, or 80 marks, depending on which exam board's specification you are following. Even though these marks vary, the actual value of the independent investigation is always 20% of the marks of your entire A level geography.

Refer to the mark scheme while you write your report to make sure you don't miss anything important. Teachers sometimes talk about an investigation that 'ticks all the right boxes' because the report covers everything that it should. However, don't assume that, just because you have included all the elements you will automatically get top marks! The report needs to include many elements but it is assessed on its quality.

NEA mark schemes

Each exam board uses a slightly different mark scheme for the NEA. Each mark scheme is organised into sections that broadly mirror the structure of the report you have written. The mark scheme for each exam board is summarised over the next few pages. Use these summaries to check what the examiner and moderator are looking for when they read your report. These mark schemes are constructed around one or more Assessment Objectives (AOs) that also underpin the questions that are set in the A level Geography examinations. The same AOs are used by each exam board – although they use them in different proportions to assess the NEA. Here is a description of each Assessment Objective.

AO1 Demonstrate knowledge and understanding of places, environments, concepts, processes, interactions and change, at a variety of scales.

AO2 Apply knowledge and understanding in different contexts to interpret, analyse and evaluate geographical information and issues.

AO3 Use a variety of relevant quantitative, qualitative and fieldwork skills to:
- investigate geographical questions and issues (strand 1);
- interpret, analyse and evaluate data and evidence (strand 2);
- construct arguments and draw conclusions (strand 3).

AQA A level Independent Investigation

The independent investigation is marked out of 60. The AQA mark scheme is organised under four section headings. These sections broadly reflect the stages of the investigative process. The key elements of each of these sections are shown in Figure 1.

Area	Marks	AO	Elements that the examiner is looking for
1 Introduction and preliminary research.	10	AO3 Strand 1 (10 marks)	Research questions are used to create an aim for the investigation. Research of relevant literature sources. The investigation is set within the context of broader geographical theories or comparisons.
2 Methods of field investigation.	15	AO3 Strand 2 (15 marks)	Observation and recording of primary data. A sampling strategy that considers frequency (of sample points) and timing of observations. Selection of appropriate fieldwork methodologies. Justification of the sampling strategy and data collection methods. Use of chosen methodologies to collect quality data (data that is accurate and reliable) and relevant to meet the aims of the investigation (in other words, data that is valid).
3 Methods of critical analysis.	20	AO2 (6 marks) AO3 Strand 2 (14 marks)	Selection of appropriate techniques to represent data and the justification of their use. Selection of appropriate techniques to analyse data and the justification of their use. Use of suitable quantitative or qualitative approaches for the analysis of data. Comments on the accuracy of field data and/or the extent to which data is representative. Links to appropriate geographical knowledge, theory, or concepts to help explain findings of the investigation.
4 Conclusions, evaluation and presentation.	15	AO3 Strand 2 (5 marks) AO3 Strand 3 (10 marks)	A written report of the investigation that is clear and logical. Use of a range of suitable presentation methods. An evaluation of the investigation. An understanding of the ethical dimensions of research. Analysis that is supported by evidence collected during the investigation. Connections between the investigation and wider geographical understanding (comparative links or reference to concepts, models or theories). The presentation of a well-argued case.

AO2 Apply knowledge and understanding in different contexts to interpret, analyse and evaluate geographical information and issues.

Figure 1 Elements of the independent investigation that are assessed in the AQA mark scheme.

AO3 Use a variety of relevant quantitative, qualitative and fieldwork skills to:
▶ investigate geographical questions and issues (strand 1);
▶ interpret, analyse and evaluate data and evidence (strand 2);
▶ construct arguments and draw conclusions (strand 3).

Edexcel A level Independent Investigation

The independent investigation is marked out of 70. The Edexcel mark scheme is organised under four section headings. These sections broadly reflect the stages of the investigative process. The key elements of each of these sections are shown in Figure 2.

Figure 2 Elements of independent investigation that are assessed in the Edexcel mark scheme.

Section	Marks	AO	Elements that the examiner is looking for
1 Purpose of the independent investigation.	12	AO1 (4 marks) AO2 (4 marks) AO3 (4 marks)	Knowledge of the location of the investigation and understanding of geographical theories that are relevant to the investigation. Connections between the investigation and its wider geographical context. Investigation of relevant geographical sources to obtain information and data. An investigation that has an aim and which uses questions or hypotheses. A justification of the aim using research. Evidence that the scale of the investigation was manageable. Planned enquiry process that has a logical structure.
2 Field methodologies and data collection.	10	AO3 (10 marks)	The selection of appropriate methods to collect data that is relevant to the aim. The design of a valid and appropriate sampling strategy/framework that links to the geographical focus of the investigation and considers frequency (of sample points) and timing of observations. Consideration of ethical dimensions of the research methods. The ability to collect data using consistent methods and that is reliable and accurate.
3 Data presentation, analysis, interpretation, and evaluation of techniques and methodologies used	24	AO3 (24 marks)	Selection and use of appropriate analysis techniques to explain the (quantitative or qualitative) data and show evidenced connections. Where statistical techniques are used (if appropriate to the investigation) their significance is discussed. An evaluation of techniques and methodologies considers: • ethical dimensions of field research • the usefulness and validity of the methods. Conclusions that: • are supported by evidence shown in data presentation methods (maps and graphs) • draw together (and link) the different strands of research.
4 Conclusions and critical evaluation of the overall investigation	24	AO1 (4 marks) AO2 (4 marks) AO3 (16 marks)	Knowledge of the location of the investigation and understanding of geographical theories that are relevant to the investigation. Connections between the conclusions of the investigation and its wider geographical context. Conclusions that: • summarise research findings • draw together the different findings of the investigation and that are linked to the investigation's aim • are supported by evidence. An evaluation of the overall success of the investigation to include: • reliability of the evidence • validity of the conclusions. The presentation of a balanced and concise argument. A clear structure to the report that reflects the enquiry process. Accurate use of geographical terminology.

AO1 **Demonstrate knowledge and understanding of places, environments, concepts, processes, interactions and change, at a variety of scales.**

AO2 **Apply knowledge and understanding in different contexts to interpret, analyse and evaluate geographical information and issues.**

AO3 **Use a variety of relevant quantitative, qualitative and fieldwork skills to:**
  ▶ investigate geographical questions and issues (strand 1);
  ▶ interpret, analyse and evaluate data and evidence (strand 2);
  ▶ construct arguments and draw conclusions (strand 3).

Eduqas A level Independent Investigation

The independent investigation is marked out of 80. The Eduqas mark scheme is organised under six section headings. These headings reflect the structure that should be used when writing your report. The key elements of each of these sections are shown in Figure 3.

Section	Marks	AO	Elements that the examiner is looking for
1 Context	10	AO1 (10 marks)	The use of literature sources to set a theoretical context for the investigation. An understanding of risk in the field and ethical issues of research.
2 Methods of field investigation	15	AO3 strand 1 (15 marks)	A well-defined research question. Use of a range of appropriate data collection techniques (quantitative and/or qualitative). An explanation and justification of data collection methods. The use, explanation and justification of an appropriate sampling strategy.
3 Data presentation of findings	10	AO3 strand 3 (10 marks)	Accurate use of a range of appropriate presentation methods (including maps and graphs) to present quantitative and/or qualitative data.
4 Analysis and interpretation of findings	15	AO3 strand 2 (15 marks)	The use of appropriate analysis techniques to interpret the data. Provides own insights into how the investigation links with wider aspects of geography.
5 Conclusions and presentation requirements	10	AO3 strand 3 (10 marks)	A summary of the investigation which includes conclusions that: • address the research question • are supported by the analysis of evidence A written report that is concise and logically structured. Accurate references to secondary information.
6 Evaluation	20	AO2 (20 marks)	An evaluation of the overall success of the investigation to include: • an appraisal of how well the investigation added to knowledge and understanding of the aims • an appraisal of each stage of the investigation, including the ethical dimension of research • consideration of possible further research • consideration of possible improvements to the investigation

AO1 **Demonstrate knowledge and understanding of places, environments, concepts, processes, interactions and change, at a variety of scales.**

Figure 3 Elements of independent investigation that are assessed in the Eduqas mark scheme.

AO2 **Apply knowledge and understanding in different contexts to interpret, analyse and evaluate geographical information and issues.**

AO3 **Use a variety of relevant quantitative, qualitative and fieldwork skills to:**
▶ investigate geographical questions and issues (strand 1);
▶ interpret, analyse and evaluate data and evidence (strand 2);
▶ construct arguments and draw conclusions (strand 3).

Eduqas insist that students **must** write their report using sub-headings that match the structure of the mark scheme. This structure is shown in Figure 4. The exam board also insists that every report **must**:

▶ be word processed in Arial, Calibri, or Times New Roman;
▶ be font size 11 point;
▶ have text set out in 1.5 spacing;
▶ have all pages numbered;
▶ have candidate number and centre number in either the header of footer on all pages;
▶ have headings and labels for such items as photographs, tables and maps, with scales and keys/legends on maps;
▶ use a conventional in-text referencing system, such as that described on pages 233–234;
▶ provide URL addresses and time/date accessed for information sourced from the internet.

Figure 4 The written report for Eduqas must use this structure.

Section	Contents
Abstract	A summary (up to 250 words) of the investigation which must include how the research is linked to the specification.
1 Context.	A statement of the location of the investigation. Discussion of the wider geographical context (concepts, theories, models or comparisons) that provide background for your investigation. Reference to your literature review. Risk assessment. Consideration of ethical dimensions of your research.
2 Methods of field investigation.	A description and justification of the sampling strategies and data collection methods that you used.
3 Data presentation of findings.	The use of appropriate techniques to represent primary and secondary data that has been collected during the investigation. These techniques should allow the use of suitable quantitative and/or qualitative forms of analysis.
4 Analysis and interpretation of findings.	The analysis and interpretation of the data that has been collected and presented in the report. Justification of the findings you have made.
5 Conclusions.	Well-evidenced conclusions that draw together the separate lines of the investigation. The conclusions should refer to the wider geographical context (concepts, theories, models, or comparisons) that underpin the investigation.
6 Evaluation.	A concise appraisal of each stage of the investigation to include data collection, data presentation, analysis, and conclusions. A consideration of the strengths and limitations of the data (primary and secondary) – its accuracy, reliability, potential errors and bias. Where appropriate, an appreciation that stakeholders (who may have provided qualitative data) will have views and interests. Ideas on how the investigation could be improved or further research that would provide further insight.
References and Appendices.	Your report must include a bibliography. You must reference your secondary sources. This can be done by in-text referencing or footnotes – see pages 233–234. You may also include an Appendix which includes further details that may help clarify your data, such as examples of data collection sheets. It may also include transcripts of interviews (where appropriate).

OCR A level Independent Investigation

The independent investigation is marked out of 60. The OCR mark scheme is organised under six section headings. These sections reflect the stages of the investigative process. The key elements of each of these sections are shown in Figure 5 .

Figure 5 Elements of independent investigation that are assessed in the OCR mark scheme.

Section	Marks	AO	Elements that the examiner is looking for
1 Planning, purpose and introduction.	8	AO3 (8 marks)	A well-focused plan that has an aim and which uses questions or hypotheses. A focus on a geographical topic or issue defined within a research framework. Justification for the investigation. Precise description of the location and scale of the investigation using geo-spatial techniques. Reference to literature research that gives the investigation context within broader geographical models, theories, or comparisons.
2 Data, information collection methods and sampling framework.	7	AO3 (7 marks)	Knowledge and understanding of suitable data collection methodologies for the collection of quantitative **and/or** qualitative data. These methodologies are personalised to suit the actual research. A justification of data collection methods. Observation and recording of primary data **and** secondary data. Collection and use of digital, geo-located data. A sampling strategy/framework that considers frequency, range, and location of data. A justification of the sampling strategy. A consideration of ethical and socio-political dimensions of the chosen methodologies.
3 Data presentation techniques.	9	AO3 (9 marks)	Data that is most relevant to the investigation is selected for presentation. The selection of suitable techniques to represent each dataset. A balance of simple and more sophisticated data presentation methods are used.
4 Data analysis and explanation.	14	AO3 (14 marks)	The use of appropriate techniques to analyse and explain the data. Where the investigation requires it: • statistical techniques are used and their significance is discussed • appropriate techniques are used for analysing qualitative data Analysis that is clearly linked to the aims of the investigation. The use of appropriate geographical knowledge, theory, or concepts to help explain findings of the investigation.
5 Conclusions and investigation evaluation.	12	AO3 (12 marks)	Conclusions that are: • linked to the investigation's aim and its questions or hypotheses • supported by primary and secondary evidence. Evidence that the investigation relates to wider geographical understanding (e.g. comparisons, concepts, models or theories). An evaluation of the overall success of the investigation to include: • reliability of data sources • accuracy of data • sampling strategies • validity of the analysis and conclusions. Understanding of ethical and socio-political dimensions of research and data presentation.
6 Overall quality and communication of written work.	10	AO3 (10 marks)	The standard of writing and communication of ideas, findings. The use of geographical terms. Few errors of spelling, punctuation, or grammar. Presentation of a clear line of argument. A written report that is well-structured and concise. Selection and creation of maps, graphs, photos that are integrated into the text. Sources of data and literature that are accurately referenced throughout the investigation's report.

AO3 Use a variety of relevant quantitative, qualitative and fieldwork skills to:
▶ investigate geographical questions and issues;
▶ interpret, analyse and evaluate data and evidence;
▶ construct arguments and draw conclusions.

WJEC A level Independent Investigation

The independent investigation is marked out of 80. The WJEC mark scheme is organised under six section headings. These headings reflect the structure that should be used when writing your report. The key elements of each of these sections are shown in Figure 6.

Figure 6 Elements of independent investigation that are assessed in theWJEC mark scheme.

Section	Marks	AO	Elements that the examiner is looking for
1 Context.	10	AO1 (10 marks)	The use of literature sources to set a theoretical context for the investigation. An understanding of risk in the field and ethical issues of research.
2 Methods of field investigation.	15	AO3 strand 1 (15 marks)	A well-defined research question. Use of a range of appropriate data collection techniques (quantitative and/or qualitative). An explanation and justification of data collection methods. The use, explanation and justification of an appropriate sampling strategy.
3 Data presentation of findings.	10	AO3 strand 3 (10 marks)	Accurate use of a range of appropriate presentation methods (including maps **and** graphs) to present quantitative **and/or** qualitative data.
4 Analysis and interpretation of findings.	15	AO3 strand 2 (15 marks)	The use of appropriate analysis techniques to interpret the data. Provides own insights into how the investigation links with wider aspects of geography.
5 Conclusions and presentation requirements, .	10	AO3 strand 3 (10 marks)	A summary of the investigation which includes conclusions that: • address the research question • are supported by the analysis of evidence A written report that is concise and logically structured. Accurate references to secondary information.
6 Evaluation.	20	AO2 (20 marks)	An evaluation of the overall success of the investigation to include: • an appraisal of how well the investigation added to knowledge and understanding of the aims • an appraisal of each stage of the investigation, including the ethical dimension of research • consideration of possible further research • consideration of possible improvements to the investigation

AO1 Demonstrate knowledge and understanding of places, environments, concepts, processes, interactions and change, at a variety of scales.

AO2 Apply knowledge and understanding in different contexts to interpret, analyse and evaluate geographical information and issues.

AO3 Use a variety of relevant quantitative, qualitative and fieldwork skills to:
  ▶ investigate geographical questions and issues (strand 1);
  ▶ interpret, analyse and evaluate data and evidence (strand 2);
  ▶ construct arguments and draw conclusions (strand 3).

WJEC insist that students must write their report using sub-headings that match the structure of the mark scheme. This structure is shown in Figure 7. The exam board also insists that every report must:
▶ be word processed in Arial, Calibri, or Times New Roman;
▶ be font size 11 point;
▶ have text set out in 1.5 spacing;
▶ have all pages numbered;
▶ have candidate number and centre number in either the header of footer on all pages;

- have headings and labels for such items as photographs, tables and maps, with scales and keys / legends on maps;
- use a conventional in-text referencing system, such as that described on pages 233–234;
- provide URL addresses and time/date accessed for information sourced from the internet.

Figure 7 The written report for WJEC must use this structure.

Section	Contents
Abstract.	A summary (up to 250 words) of the investigation which must include how the research is linked to the specification.
1 Context	A statement of the location of the investigation. Discussion of the wider geographical context (concepts, theories, models or comparisons) that provide background for your investigation. Reference to your literature review. Risk assessment. Consideration of ethical dimensions of your research.
2 Methods of field investigation	A description and justification of the sampling strategies and data collection methods that you used.
3 Data presentation of findings	The use of appropriate techniques to represent primary and secondary data that has been collected during the investigation. These techniques should allow the use of suitable quantitative and/or qualitative forms of analysis.
4 Analysis and interpretation of findings	The analysis and interpretation of the data that has been collected and presented in the report. Justification of the findings you have made.
5 Conclusions	Well-evidenced conclusions that draw together the separate lines of the investigation. The conclusions should refer to the wider geographical context (concepts, theories, models, or comparisons) that underpin the investigation.
6 Evaluation	A concise appraisal of each stage of the investigation to include data collection, data presentation, analysis, and conclusions. A consideration of the strengths and limitations of the data (primary and secondary) – its accuracy, reliability, potential errors, and bias. Where appropriate, an appreciation that stakeholders (who may have provided qualitative data) will have views and interests. Ideas on how the investigation could be improved or further research that would provide further insight.
References and Appendices	Your report must include a bibliography. You must reference your secondary sources. This can be done by in-text referencing or footnotes – see pages 233–234. You may also include an Appendix which includes further details that may help clarify your data, such as examples of data collection sheets. It may also include transcripts of interviews (where appropriate).

Appendix 2 Significance tables

The following tables provide reference tables for use with statistical tests that you can complete as part of the analysis of your data. For how and when to use these tables see the cross references below.

1 Random numbers (range 01-99)

80	57	35	10	76	72	01	06	60	88
87	82	89	15	27	44	75	52	21	95
48	98	33	06	55	44	23	76	81	41
33	09	96	52	65	12	20	05	90	44
22	78	81	08	73	87	56	78	15	97
30	33	22	98	85	23	28	63	30	50
88	63	35	03	04	19	34	53	43	67
54	33	73	43	62	45	39	99	22	26
11	83	60	72	89	22	40	52	36	31
44	76	43	68	65	99	38	18	14	12

2 Critical values for Spearman's Rank Correlation Coefficient

Reject the null hypothesis if the value of the Spearman's Rank Correlation Coefficient is **greater than** the critical value at the chosen significance level.

Degrees of freedom	Significance level		
	0.05	0.01	0.001
4	1.000	-	-
5	0.900	1.000	-
6	0.829	0.943	-
7	0.714	0.893	1.000
8	0.643	0.833	0.952
9	0.600	0.783	0.917
10	0.564	0.745	0.879
11	0.536	0.709	0.845
12	0.503	0.678	0.818
13	0.484	0.648	0.791
14	0.464	0.626	0.771
15	0.446	0.604	0.750
16	0.429	0.582	0.729
17	0.414	0.566	0.711
18	0.401	0.550	0.692
19	0.391	0.535	0.675
20	0.380	0.522	0.662
21	0.370	0.509	0.647
22	0.361	0.497	0.633
23	0.353	0.486	0.621
24	0.344	0.476	0.609
25	0.337	0.466	0.597
26	0.331	0.457	0.586
27	0.324	0.449	0.576
28	0.318	0.441	0.567
29	0.312	0.433	0.558

3 Critical values of Mann-Whitney U at the 0.05 significance level

Reject the null hypothesis if the value of U is **less than or equal to** the critical value at the chosen significance level.

nx \ ny	1	2	3	4	5	6	7	8	9	10	11	12	13	14	15	16	17	18	19	20
1																				
2					0	0	0	1	1	1	1	2	2	2	3	3	3	4	4	4
3					1	2	2	3	3	4	5	5	6	7	7	8	9	9	10	11
4				1	2	3	4	5	6	7	8	9	10	11	12	14	15	16	17	18
5		0	1	2	4	5	6	8	9	11	12	13	15	16	18	19	20	22	23	25
6		0	2	3	5	7	8	10	12	14	16	17	19	21	23	25	26	28	30	32
7		0	2	4	6	8	11	13	15	17	19	21	24	26	28	30	33	35	37	39
8		1	3	5	8	10	13	15	18	20	23	26	28	31	33	36	39	41	44	47
9		1	3	6	9	12	15	18	21	24	27	30	33	36	39	42	45	48	51	54
10		1	4	7	11	14	17	20	24	27	31	34	37	41	44	48	51	55	58	62
11		1	5	8	12	16	19	23	27	31	34	38	42	46	50	54	57	61	65	69
12		2	5	9	13	17	21	26	30	34	38	42	47	51	55	60	64	68	72	77
13		2	6	10	15	19	24	28	33	37	42	47	51	56	61	65	70	75	80	84
14		2	7	11	16	21	26	31	36	41	46	51	56	61	66	71	77	82	87	92
15		3	7	12	18	23	28	33	39	44	50	55	61	66	72	77	83	88	94	100
16		3	8	14	19	25	30	36	42	48	54	60	65	71	77	83	89	95	101	107
17		3	9	15	20	26	33	39	45	51	57	64	70	77	83	89	96	102	109	115
18		4	9	16	22	28	35	41	48	55	61	68	75	82	88	95	102	109	116	123
19	0	4	10	17	23	30	37	44	51	58	65	72	80	87	94	101	109	116	123	130
20	0	4	11	18	25	32	39	47	54	62	69	77	84	92	100	107	115	123	130	138

4 Critical values of Chi Square

Reject the null hypothesis if the value of Chi Square is **greater than** the critical value at the chosen significance level.

Degrees of freedom	Significance level		
	0.05	0.01	0.001
1	3.84	6.64	10.83
2	5.99	9.21	13.82
3	7.82	11.34	16.27
4	9.49	13.28	18.46
5	11.07	15.09	20.52
6	12.59	16.81	22.46
7	14.07	18.48	24.32
8	15.51	20.09	26.12
9	16.92	21.67	27.88
10	18.31	23.21	29.59
11	19.68	24.72	31.26
12	21.03	26.22	32.91
13	22.36	27.69	34.53
14	23.68	29.14	36.12
15	25.00	30.58	37.70
16	26.30	32.00	39.29
17	27.59	33.41	40.75
18	28.87	34.80	42.31
19	30.14	36.19	43.82
20	31.41	37.57	45.32

Index

Insight & Perspective Titles

GCSE Geography Fieldwork for AQA	Andy Owen	ISBN 9781912190034
GCSE Geography Fieldwork for EDUQAS	Andy Owen	ISBN 9781912190027
GCSE Geography Fieldwork for OCR	Andy Owen	ISBN 9781912190058
GCSE Geography Fieldwork for WJEC	Andy Owen	ISBN 9781912190010
A Level Geography Independent Investigation	Andy Owen	ISBN 9781912190065
Environmental Science A Level AQA	Richard Genn	ISBN 9781912190072

For more information and to keep up to date with new titles and downloads
please visit our website at

www.insightandperspective.co.uk

Insight and Perspective Ltd, 701 Stonehouse Park, Sperry Way, Stonehouse, Glos, GL10 3UT
www.insightandperspective.co.uk

First published 2019
10 9 8 7 6 5 4
ISBN 13: 978-1-912190-06-5

Designed and typeset by Wooden Ark
Printed by TJ Books Limited, Padstow, Cornwall, UK

Acknowledgements
The author and publishers would like to thank Sam Rudd and Rachel Atkins for their advice and contributions to the development of this book.

The author and publishers would like to thank the following for permission to use the following photographs/copyright material:
Front cover and p93 Salmon Lane in the Rain (1987) Doreen Fletcher; p10 Ink sketch by Jenny A Hall, shows Shelton Bar Steel Works in Etruria, Stoke-on-Trent. Private collection; p10 Stephen Davies/Geopix; p53 Check my flood risk; p99 & p111 OS Mapping of Roundton Hill © Crown copyright 2019 OS 100059646 Blackwell's Mapping Online; p108 Signage at Roundton Nature Reserve, Montgomeryshire Wildlife Trust; p117 Industrial Ruin I (copper works Swansea) by George Little (1927-2017). Private collection; p114 Google Street view; p117 postcard of Queen Street in Cardiff (1947); p119 Extrium England Noise Viewer; p120 www.police.uk; pp123, 124 parallel.co.uk; p130 what3words; p131 NoteCam; p131 National Library of Scotland https://mapsnls/geo/explore; p139 Ordnance Survey OpenData basemaps available from parallel.co.uk; p177 hydrograph www.riverlevels.uk/esk; p190 Woodland Trust (2012), Urban Air Quality. All other photographs Andy Owen.

The publishers have made every effort to trace the copyright holders. If they have inadvertently overlooked any they will be pleased to acknowledge these at the first available opportunity.